METHODS OF GEOGRAPHIC INSTRUCTION

A BLAISDELL BOOK IN GEOGRAPHY

Methods of
Geographic Instruction

John W. Morris · EDITOR
UNIVERSITY OF OKLAHOMA

National Council for Geographic Education

Blaisdell Publishing Company
A Division of Ginn and Company

WALTHAM, MASSACHUSETTS · TORONTO · LONDON

Preface

IT IS THE BELIEF of the National Council for Geographic Education that geography, when properly taught, can make a distinct contribution to the advancement of a better understanding between peoples and countries. This book has been developed to help student and teacher in the preparation of geography lessons, and it is also hoped that it will aid the administrator or supervisor.

The book is divided into six parts: I. The Dynamics of Geography, II. Instructional Aids, III. Geographic Methodology, IV. Geographic Methodology: The Regional Approach, V. Geographic Methodology: The Topical Approach, and VI. Geography: Its Contribution to Education. Each part includes several chapters written by different authors. Although these contributions represent many points of view, there is unity in the whole. The variety of approaches and topics provides the reader with a broad geographical base on which to build as his studies in this area progress.

In addition to the authors themselves, many persons from the fields of geography and education have contributed their services to the preparation of this book by reading certain portions and offering constructive criticism. These people, together with the authors of this book, are constantly seeking ways to improve the teaching of geography and the social studies, and their work is a labor of love. The hope and desire of each is that their combined efforts will benefit students and aid them in developing a greater respect for the country in which they live and a better understanding of mankind. The authors believe that this book will allow teachers to present the student with concepts which he may develop and enlarge on himself as he continues his education.

JOHN W. MORRIS

Contents

PART I
The dynamics of geography

GEOGRAPHY, BECAUSE of the very nature of its material, must be a dynamic subject for the modern world itself is dynamic, a place of rapid change. All parts of the world are now within a few hours travel time of each other; most are only minutes apart in communication time. The activities of any one group of people may greatly affect the work and life of any or all other groups.

Modern geography is *not* just a description of the earth; it is *not* just the accumulation of facts about an area of the world; it is *not* a series of locational exercises for a student to put on a map; it is *not* a set of definitions of such words as urban, mountain, or strait; it is *not* a division of the world by physical or political boundaries. Geography includes some material from all these, but it is much more than any one of these and much more than all combined. Dr. Neville V. Scarfe states:[1]

> Geography is selective; it is explanatory; it is reasonable; it is discipline; it is a way of thinking. . . . Geography is a sequence of ideas or concepts which develop into a coherent subject looking at the world from a point of view.
>
> It has a great deal to do with associative and relational thinking. It is an attempt to see the relatedness of physical facts and cultural facts over the *earth* for the precise purpose of throwing intelligent light on the problems of society. It is an attempt to see some sense of pattern or guiding principle in the apparently haphazard distribution of human life and activity over the globe.

---

[1] *Geography in School* (Normal, Illinois: National Council for Geographic Education, 1965), p. 1.

1

One of the most important concepts in teaching modern geography is that of "perpetual transformation."[1] Certainly the geography of today is not the geography of yesterday, nor should it be considered the geography of the coming tomorrows. The teacher of geography must be as able to progress with the present rapidly changing technology as is the physicist or chemist; at the same time he must be conscious of man's changing role in these environmental adjustments as is the historian or the economist.

---

[1] Wilhelmina Hill (ed.), *Curriculum Guide for Geographic Education* (Normal, Illinois: National Council for Geographic Education, 1964), p. 21.

1

History and philosophy of geography

I am a part of all that I have met:
Yet all experience is an arch wherethro'
Gleams that untraveled world whose margin fades
For ever and for ever when I move. ALFRED, LORD TENNYSON

GEOGRAPHY HAS BEEN called many things, and many things have been called geography. In a literal sense, of course, the word geography means the description, or perhaps more precisely, the portrayal of the earth. In an effort to clarify its scope and responsibility as an academic discipline, modern geographers have referred to it as earth science, landscape morphology, human ecology, regional science, the analysis of differences from place to place, the science of the spatial arrangement on the earth, or the study of the earth as the home of man.

It is clear that geography traditionally has been concerned with both the physical (that is, natural) condition of the earth's surface and man's imprint on it. People who have called themselves geographers have studied and written about such disparate subjects as the erosion of beaches and sea cliffs, the behavior of winds and storms, the types of grasslands and forests, the quality of soils and drinking water, rural and urban patterns of settlement, ethnic groups and their distribution, natural resources and their utilization, international trade and the conditions which influence it, political forms, and boundary functions. Recent volumes of our standard academic journals have even included articles by well-known geographers on "The Finnish Sauna," "The Geography of Manure," "Land for the Dead in Chicago," "Geography and Baseball," and " 'Mountain Moonshining' in East Tennessee." Geography as a research discipline has included any landscape element or pattern which shows significant spatial variation in distribution or density and which can be meaningfully related to any other landscape element or pattern. In an effort to explain some of the apparent conflicts in definitions and philosophies of geography, William

D. Pattison recently proposed that geographers frankly acknowledge the role of four different traditions in the history of their discipline and learn to live with them.[1] Pattison identifies these four traditions as the spatial tradition, concerned with the where of things and related to the development of cartography since the days of Claudius Ptolemy's *Geographia* in the second century A.D.; the area studies or chorographic tradition, which since Strabo's time or earlier, has undertaken to portray the content of areas in what is now called regional geography; the man–land tradition, which has asserted with varying degrees of insistence a causal or influential role of the environment in relation to human characteristics and activities; and the earth science tradition which presents a meaningful analysis of physical landscape patterns either for their inherent interest or as a background for understanding the social scene. All of these traditions seem to be legitimate and deserve to be encouraged, although their variety sometimes confuses even the educated layman and makes him quite understandably ask "What is geography?" or "What is a geographer?"

DEVELOPMENT OF GEOGRAPHY

The first geographer was probably some unnamed and unknown Paleolithic hunter concerned with the migratory habits of game animals, birds, and fish who asked himself questions about his daily problems of food supply. For many thousands of years, however, geographic knowledge was not cumulative and had to be learned over again as each generation explored its habitat and recognized its advantages and limitations.

Even though many of their manuscripts have been lost or exist in only fragmentary form, the ancient Greeks, beginning in the sixth or seventh century B.C., developed a body of theoretical concepts concerning the nature of the earth and its behavior in space. Thales of Miletus, famous for his uncanny ability to predict a solar eclipse, is known in the history of geography for his assertion that water was the dominant or primordial substance, in contrast to Anaximenes, who held that air was the more important. Hipparchus divided the earth into zones with a system of meridians and parallels, and several Greek thinkers agreed that a second habitable zone, for reasons of symmetry, must lie between the equator and the southern limits of the earth. Unfortunately, they reasoned man would never be able to verify the existence of this second habitable zone because of the boiling oceans and impossibly hot land which intervened. The Pythagorean school of philosophic thought was convinced that the earth was a sphere, but the arguments of the Pythagoreans were ignored for

---

[1] "The Four Traditions of Geography," *Journal of Geography*, vol. 63 (1964), pp. 211–216.

centuries, even though one of their followers, Eratosthenes of Alexandria, calculated the approximate size of the sphere by estimating the distance and comparing sun angles between two points along the Nile Valley meridian.

Descriptive accounts of the earth's surface in the early area studies tradition were written by many travelers or recorded by scribes from the reports of travelers. Whether Necho, one of the Egyptian Pharaohs, actually circumnavigated Africa about 600 B.C., as Herodotus asserts, we cannot prove with certainty, but we do have the fifth century B.C. writings of Herodotus, which contain personal observations of peoples and places from Italy on the west to Persia on the east. About 300 B.C., Pytheas sailed from Massilia (Marseilles) through the Gates of Hercules (Gibraltar) to the cold, foggy islands and rocky coasts of northwestern Europe. His journal has been lost — indeed may never have been written — but the reports of Pytheas' trip in the writings of Dicaearchus and others are sufficiently vivid that from his time on at least something was known of that side of the continent. Alexander the Great's conquests, from Asia Minor and Egypt to the Indus Valley and Samarkand, are recorded in some detail by the historian Arrian, and we have in the *Geography* of Strabo, written about the time of Christ, a truly remarkable regional description of the known world.

Imperial Rome, absorbed in building and developing an empire reaching from the western limits of Europe and North Africa to the lower Danube and the valleys of Mesopotamia, somehow failed to build systematically on the geographic competence of the Greeks. Pomponius Mela's little book *De Situ Orbis,* written in the first century A.D. shortly after the appearance of Strabo's opus, has the distinction of being the earliest known purely geographical work written in Latin, but it adds only a few minor corrections to the existing knowledge of northern Europe. Pliny the Elder's *Historia Naturalis* includes three books and part of another on geography, but they are considered poorly done, and the author was tragically killed in the eruption of Vesuvius. The brilliantly designed aqueducts and baths, the stone highways and monuments, and the far-ranging campaigns of the Roman legions were not accompanied by much accurate cartography or vivid descriptive accounts. However, Roman strip maps of the Peutinger Table type were better than no maps at all, and useful bits of geographic knowledge can be sifted from such writings as Julius Caesar's *Commentaries* and Cornelius Tacitus' *Germany.*

The decline of commerce following the disintegration of the Roman Empire and the absorption of many of the best minds in theology and religious affairs retarded for a period of centuries any major advances in geographic knowledge. Modern students find little but amusement in the so-called "T-O maps" of the early Christian period which commonly arranged the world outline so as to fit the city of Jerusalem into its very center. The Moslem Arabs contributed the next significant advances in geographic knowledge over the legacy of the Greeks.

The remarkable extension of Islam throughout the Middle East, across North Africa, and into western Europe beginning in the seventh century brought with it the need for better finding of direction and distance and more accurate descriptions of people and places. The texts of Aristotle and Ptolemy were translated into Arabic and studied with great care at centers of learning all the way from Baghdad to Cordoba and Toledo. While generally respecting Ptolemy's position for the prime meridian, a line through the Fortunate (Canary) Islands, Al-Khwarizmi and other Arabic astronomers substantially corrected Ptolemy's exaggerated estimate of the length of the Mediterranean Sea. The widespread travels of commercially minded Arab "geographers," such as Al-Istakhri, Ibn Haukal, and Al-Masudi in the tenth century, made it possible to include places as far away as Madagascar, India, Ceylon, China, Korea, and Japan in the gazetteers of the period. While Christians and Moslems were generally hostile and learned little from each other for hundreds of years, Roger II, a Christian king of Sicily in the tenth century, adopted the Moslem geographer Edrisi (or Idrisi) as a member of his court and commissioned him to prepare a celestial sphere, a map of the world in silver, and a description of peoples and cultures based on travel records and new reports of contemporary observers.

The greatest traveler of all in the pre-Columbus period was no doubt Ibn Batuta of Tangiers (1304–1378) who in the course of thirty years of wandering covered 75,000 miles and visited the shores of the Black and Caspian Seas, East Africa, and even Timbuktu — for reasons not clear from his journal except that he seems to have been curious to see what was there. The travels of Ibn Batuta became known to the Western world only in the nineteenth century, however, and it is perhaps Christian travelers of the thirteenth century who should be given credit for finally awakening Europe to the wider world to the east.

Incursions by mounted Mongol invaders from East Central Asia into the Middle East, Russia, and Central Europe stirred Pope Innocent IV and Louis IX of France to send John de Plano Carpini and William of Rubruck on the long trip to make contact with the Mongol Khan at Karakorum and hopefully to make a Christian of him. While their Christianizing missions essentially failed, their journals incorporate much new description of lands and people until then virtually unknown to Europeans. More widely circulated and hence even more influential was the *Travels of Marco Polo*, dictated in a Genoese prison by a Venetian merchant's son who had had years of travel in China and Southern Asia after ingratiating himself to Kublai Khan.

Modern scholarship has brilliantly illuminated the adventures of the largely illiterate Norsemen who roamed the North Atlantic and bordering seas in the ninth and tenth centuries, and who should no doubt be given credit for discovering the New World from the east. Continuous contact between Europe, the Americas, and the Orient, however, came only with the Portuguese explorations along the West African coast, followed by the successful voyages of Columbus, the Cabots, Vasco da Gama, Amerigo Vespucci, and Magellan. By the time of Columbus, long-distance sea travel had become safer through the development of better designed ships, an improved astrolabe for measuring latitudes, and a growing confidence in the magnetic compass. More than a century before Columbus, major corrections were being made in the Ptolemaic map, as for instance in the Catalan World Map of about 1375 which boldly showed India as a peninsula rather than an island, and in the remarkably accurate *Portolani* sailing charts of the Mediterranean basin.

Many of us learned in early grade school of the intrepid boldness of Christopher Columbus pleading with European monarchs to support his search for a westward route to the Indies, but we were not always reminded that the Florentine doctor-mathematician-astronomer Toscanelli suggested this line of approach to both Columbus and the king of Portugal. By 1510, several western European cartographers (Juan de la Cosa, Alberto Cantino, Nicolay de Caneiro, Martin Waldseemüller, and others) had incorporated segments of the American coastline into their charts, and with other map makers were beginning to fill in the detail.

An important aspect of the history of geography, then, is the filling in of the map and the compilation and evaluation of travelers' tales concerning faraway places. A well-trained geographer will have some awareness of the geographic contributions of the Spanish *conquistadores,* of the bold English and Dutch navigators who drove their ships into the Arctic ice in search of a northwestern or a northeastern route to the Indies, of the spice traders of Portugal and the Netherlands who roamed the islands of the western Pacific, of the French Jesuit missionaries who helped open the interior of North America and China, and of the adventurers, slavers, gold seekers, religious zealots, scientists, and empire builders of many countries who pushed their way into the African tropics, the Australian desert, the bleak plateau of Tibet, and the polar ice of the Arctic and Antarctic. Full credit should be given to such technical developments as the printing press, the sextant, the thermometer, the barometer, and the chronometer without which accurate longitudes were most elusive; to the conquest of scurvy with fresh fruits and vegetables; to the systems for classifying plants, animals, and rocks; to precision surveying and the use of contours, improved map projections, schooners, and steamships; and to dogsleds and snow tractors, aircraft, and electronic communications. A student who does not enjoy reading about the exploits of Cortes and Pizarro, of Sir Francis Drake and Captain Cook, of Lewis and Clark, of Heinrich Barth and Francois Garnier, of Nikolai Przhevalsky and David Livingstone, or of Sven Hedin and Sir Vivian Fuchs is clearly not a good prospect for becoming a geographer.

MAPS AND ATLASES

Explorations and surveys, however motivated, have made possible a gradual improvement of map accuracy, an enlargement of map scales, and an increase in the number and kinds of data shown on maps. Most of the sixteenth and seventeenth century atlases portrayed little but coast-lines, rivers, political boundaries, and towns, with presumed mountain ranges added where space was available, and with decorative sea mon-sters, land animals, icebergs, and exotic natives included in the margins. By the eighteenth century, it had become permissible for map makers to leave blank spaces on unexplored areas of the map, and cartographers like M. S. Cruquius and Philip Buache were starting to experiment with the contour method of portraying relief. The Cassini Survey of France (1669–1818), using geometric techniques and hachured relief, culminated in a complete map of the country on a scale of 1 : 86,400. Governments of many nations have instituted official mapping agencies, among them the Ordnance Survey in Great Britain (1791) and the Coast and Geodetic Survey (1807) and Geological Survey (1879) in the United States.

Several countries have now been mapped in their entirety at scales of at least one inch to the mile (1 : 63,360), but there is no uniform map of the world at a scale larger than 1 : 1,000,000. Although most of the area of the United States has been mapped at scales of 1 : 125,000, 1 : 62,500, or larger, the 1 : 250,000 series of the United States Geological Survey is still incomplete. A 1 : 500,000 series as the largest scale map of uniform basis of the entire country remains to be done. The United States Army Map Service and the United States Aeronautical Chart and Information Service, both established during World War II, have compiled and pub-lished maps on various scales of many parts of the world.

Atlases — organized collections of maps of special topics or areas — have been flowing from governmental and commercial publishing houses in an ever-widening stream. Heinrich Berghaus' *Physikalischer Atlas,* first pub-lished in Gotha in 1837–1848, was a leader in the inclusion of climatic and other physical maps along with general reference maps of the familiar type. Modern school atlases now commonly include numerous maps of physical features along with plates showing distributions of population, languages, livestock, crops, mineral resources, industrial districts, and other phenomena. Beautiful national atlases showing a wide range of distributional data have been published by Canada, France, Sweden, Finland, Czechoslovakia, Australia, and other countries.

GEOGRAPHIC SOCIETIES

Scholarly societies, established to promote research, publication, and popular education, have existed for several centuries, but they have greatly proliferated in the past 150 years. The oldest of the geographical societies still in existence in the Société de Géographie de Paris formed in 1821. Similar societies were founded in Berlin (1828), London (1831), Mexico City (1833), Frankfurt-am-Main (1836), Rio de Janeiro (1838), St. Petersburg (1845), and New York City (1852). Eighteen geographical societies were in existence by 1866 — eleven in Europe, three in Asia, three in Latin America, and one in the United States.[1]

Since geography as a profession has really emerged only in the last century, all of these early geographical societies should be regarded as laymen's societies established and directed by men primarily interested in travel, exploration, colonization, or overseas trade. The majority of their members were armchair geographers, but most of the programs and some of the organizational leadership were provided by men of action with experience in exotic faraway places. Journals were established on shoestring budgets and maintained, often as a labor of love, by one individual or a small voluntary staff. Popular lectures were a favorite type of program, and the development of photography and the lantern slide added greatly to the general interest. Travel lectures as a form of public entertainment have declined in popularity with the coming of movies and television, and perhaps also with the general affluence of society which permits more individuals to go and see distant places for themselves. The number of geographical societies and journals continues to increase, however, and the number of amateur geographers who travel in response to their curiosity about other lands and people, and amass vast collections of colored slides to prove they have "really been there," is legion.

Modern geographical societies, of which there are hundreds, tend to fall into four general types of classes in relation to their areal focus and the predominant concern of their membership. These can be identified as: local societies, centered mostly in large cities or at major educational centers, which encourage research and publication on the local area and frequently sponsor popular lectures and excursions; national laymen's societies with a broad range of interests and a large circulation journal, typified best by the National Geographic Society of Washington, D. C.,

---

[1] Griffith Taylor (ed.), *Geography in the Twentieth Century, A Study of Growth, Fields, Techniques, Aims and Trends* (New York: Philosophical Library, 1951), p. 548.

whose familiar yellow-bordered monthly magazine reaches more than five million homes and libraries; societies for the improvement of teaching and teaching materials in geography, illustrated by the Geographical Association in the United Kingdom and The National Council for Geographic Education in the United States; and the professional research societies, with a few hundred or, at most, a few thousand members, supported predominantly by university and government scientists, which arrange meetings for the reading of scholarly papers and support publication outlets for research monographs, articles, and book reviews. The last of the four types of societies would include the Association of American Geographers, organized in 1904 under the strong leadership of Professor William Morris Davis of Harvard University, and the *Association de Géographes Français,* the Institute of British Geographers, and the Canadian Association of Geographers, all formed since World War I. Some of the strongest of the societies, such as the Royal Geographical Society and the American Geographical Society, have multiple functions, maintaining large research libraries and their own research programs, while participating vigorously at the same time in popular education efforts.

An International Geographical Congress was convened in 1871 at Antwerp under the local sponsorship of individuals wanting to give proper recognition to Gerhard Kremer (Mercator) on the occasion of the unveiling of a statue of the famous cartographer in his hometown. About twenty subsequent international congresses have been held, at intervals of approximately four years. Professor Emmanuel de Martonne of the University of Paris assumed leadership after World War I in formalizing an International Geographical Union which now coordinates national memberships, arranges the international congresses, and somewhat directs the activities of a number of commissions concerned with such disparate interests as erosion surfaces, historical maps, land use mapping, regional planning, and arid zone research.

GEOGRAPHIC PUBLICATIONS

It is impossible in a chapter of this length to comment with any degree of fairness and balance on all the range of geographical publications. While there is still a dearth of monograph-length studies on smaller regions and systematic coverage of topics by professional geographers, especially in the English language, the number and quality of textbooks are improving, and the number of outlets for geographic articles seems adequate. Limiting their enumeration to strictly professional and other predominantly geographical journals, Chauncy D. Harris and Jerome D. Fellman in 1960 identified 1,651 such geographical journals as having been published and 559 as being published currently in fifty-one different countries.[1] The *Research Catalog of the American Geographical Society*, published in 1962, provides a short route to the identification of much of this journal material, as well as to relevant books and maps. Keeping abreast of the current literature is facilitated by the American Geographical Society's monthly list of *Current Geographical Publications*, the Royal Geographical Society's semiannual *New Geographical Literature and Maps*, and the International Geographical Union's *Bibliographie Géographique Internationale*. The *Geographisches Jahrbuch*, supported for nearly a century by the geographical publishing house of Justus Perthes in Gotha, has been suspended, but its bibliographical efforts are being replaced by other agencies in Germany and elsewhere. The Library of Congress in Washington, D. C., has prepared many special bibliographies, and excellent bibliographical compilations by other sponsors are now available on such topics as the Soviet Union and the Arctic.

GEOGRAPHIC POINTS OF VIEW

The increasing professionalization of geography is evident in the training programs in colleges and universities leading to the bachelor's, master's, and doctor's degrees. While occasional lecture series in geography were offered much earlier, as for instance the lectures on physical geography by the philosopher Immanuel Kant at the University of Koenigsberg starting in 1765, the appointment of Karl Ritter to the chair of geography at the University of Berlin in 1820 is regarded as a major milestone, marking the beginning of continuous attention to the field in higher academic circles. Chairs of geography were established at major universities in several European countries during the nineteenth century, and in 1901 the first Doctor of Philosophy degree was granted in the United States, that by the University of Pennsylvania to J. Paul Goode. While still a comparatively small and little-known field in American higher education, the latest *Directory of College Geography of the United States* shows that 635,181 students in 1,332 different colleges and universities were enrolled in geography courses, and that graduate training is available at 126 of these institutions.[2] More than a thousand doctoral degrees in geography have been granted by universities and colleges in the United States to date, and the number of new master's and doctor's degrees approximates 300 annually.

The field of teaching continues to attract the largest number of persons

---

[1] *International List of Geographical Serials* (Chicago: University of Chicago, Department of Geography Research Paper No. 63, June 1960). A summary of this compilation was published in *Geographical Review*, vol. 51 (1961), pp. 284–289.

[2] *Directory of College Geography of the United States, Academic Year 1966–1967*, XIX, No. 1, J. R. Schwendeman (ed.), Association of American Geographers, Southeastern Division (Richmond: Eastern Kentucky University, 1968).

holding graduate degrees in geography, although since World War II opportunities in government employment, business research, and editorial work have expanded more rapidly than the number of trained personnel available for such positions.[1] Outside of academic circles, there is still little familiarity with geography as a professional field, although the inclusion of "Geographers" as a heading in the U. S. Department of Labor's *Occupational Outlook Handbook,* starting in 1961, may in time help to correct this situation.

Geographers themselves seem to spend an unconscionable amount of time and energy worrying about the nature of their discipline and trying to define its functions. Perhaps this is unavoidable, given the fact that the study of geography is not confined to a special category of phenomena or to any particular point in time. While it usually emphasizes the more stable, visible aspects of the landscape, geography as a discipline may include analysis of such invisible or ephemeral phenomena as air temperatures, voting habits, linguistic patterns, commodity flows, and tourist registrations. Although it is commonly focused on the contemporary scene rather than the historical one, well-known geographers have studied and written about the prehistoric dispersal of cereal grains and domestic livestock, the seaports of ancient Greece and Rome, population distribution in medieval England, the Atlantic seaboard of the United States in 1810, and the migration of plants, animals, and people to New Zealand. What seems to provide an element of unity in geographical studies is the concern for finding place relationships or rational sequences in space-taking phenomena — the search for *Zusammenhang* in the words of Alexander von Humboldt and Karl Ritter, or of a *principe de connexité* as expressed by Jean Brunhes. As history and philosophy are synoptic disciplines dealing, at least in a theoretical sense, with the totality and meaning of past events, geography is also synoptic, encompassing the total content of space.

Alfred Hettner (1859–1941) attempted to put the field of geography in its broadest possible philosophical framework and reasoned as follows:

> Reality is simultaneously a three-dimensional space which we must examine from three different points of view in order to comprehend the whole; examination from but one of these points of view alone is one sided and does not exhaust the whole. From one point of view we see the relation of similar things, from the second the development in time, from the third the arrangement and division in space.[2]

---

[1] *American Geography 1960–1963: Education, Employment, and Other Trends* (Washington: Association of American Geographers, 1964).

[2] A. Hettner, *Die Geographie, ihre Geschichte, irh Wesen und ihre Methoden* (Breslau: Ferdinand Hirt, 1927), as quoted in R. Hartshorne, *The Nature of Geography* (Washington: Association of American Geographers, 1951), p. 140.

The difficulties inherent in trying to deal in unitary fashion with the realities of spatial arrangements have long been recognized. Bernard Varenius, in his *Geographia Generalis* published in 1650, divided geography into two divisions, general or universal geography, which would deal topically with aspects of the earth as a whole, and special geography or chorography, which would deal descriptively and analytically with the "terrestrial properties" and "human properties" of particular locations. The modern terms usually employed for these two approaches are systematic geography, which can be either systematic physical or systematic human geography, and regional geography, whose basis can be found in either the physical or the cultural landscape or, ideally, in both.

Many of the major guidelines to the content and approach of systematic physical geography derive from Alexander von Humboldt (1769–1859) whose five volume *Kosmos,* published 1845–1863, summarized the major facts and relationships which support the "earth science tradition." Emmanuel de Martonne's *Traité de Géographie Physique,* first published in 1909, and modern textbooks by such authors as V. C. Finch and Glenn T. Trewartha, Philip Lake, Francis J. Monkhouse, and Arthur N. Strahler are in line of succession to Von Humboldt's classic statement. Earth–sun relations and the behavior of the earth in space; weather phenomena and world climates; landform processes and types; oceans, seas, and waters of the land; soil zones and their distribution; and major plant and animal associations and their occurrences — these are the themes of modern physical geography.

Systematic human geography, the study of man himself and the imprint of man on the earth, derives in part from the masterful nineteen-volume *Erdkunde* of Karl Ritter (1779–1859), published between 1822 and 1859, but perhaps even more from later European scholars like Friedrich Ratzel (1844–1904), Paul Vidal de la Blache (1845–1918), Jean Brunhes (1869–1930), and Max Sorre (1880–1965). The geography of population and of rural and urban settlement patterns; the production, movements, modifications, and consumption of economic commodities; and the spatial forms and functions of political organization in their relation to earth conditions — these are the major concerns of systematic human geography.

Regional geography has no clear beginning and no widely accepted definition of either scope or methodology. If the early roots are in Herodotus and Strabo, some of the most impressive multivolume examples of the modern period are Ritter's *Die Erdkunde;* Elisée Réclus' *Nouvelle Géographie Universelle: La Terre et les Hommes* (Paris: Hachette, 1878–1894); the somewhat more scholarly *Géographie Universelle* edited by Paul Vidal de la Blache and Lucien Gallois (Paris: Armand Colin, 1927–1946); and the beautifully illustrated *Handbuch der Geographisches Wissenschaft* edited by Fritz Klute (Potsdam: Athenaion, 1930–1940). Regional geography is widely taught at all levels from the elementary school to the university, and textbooks, monographs, and journal articles are available on regions large and small, from the world as a whole to units no larger than a thumbprint on a wall map of a single country. If the writers of this regional material are not steeped in the sophisticated philosophy of "The Regional Concept and the Regional Method," as presented in Chapter 2 of *American Geography: Inventory and Prospect* (1954) prepared by Derwent Whittlesey and a committee of the Association of American Geographers, they at least are making an effort to present a coherent and interesting account of some place worth knowing about — if for no other reason — because it is there.

Environmentalism, the concept that things are as they are on the surface of the earth because Nature's guidelines are compelling, has long since been discarded by most professional geographers. Both safer and more scientific is the idea that cultural inheritance and human choice have shared with the physical environment in the shaping of our man-made landscapes. Possibilism, the opportunity for varied responses to Nature's challenges, is surely a more defensible position than environmentalism. Many geographers would prefer to regard the man–land relationship as a kind of mutually interacting one, with the degree of dominance by one side of the equation or the other varying with time and circumstances. Still others have argued that geography as a discipline should do little searching for paths of causation because there is more than enough to do in identifying the spatial phenomena of concern, in grouping these phenomena into meaningful patterns with cartographic and other techniques, and in recognizing significant secular trends or changes in the coincidences or discontinuities of the patterns. New developments in statistical and cartographic techniques are supplementing the traditional methodologies of observation, interview, and compilation. There is ample reason for optimism that geographers in the future will contribute even more than they do now, either as individuals or as members of interdisciplinary research teams, to the shaping of insights into the meaning of the past and present, and to the formulation of projects for the creation of a more interesting and socially satisfying future.

CONCLUSION

Teachers of geography can take pride in the long history of their discipline and in its present achievements. In leading young children and older students to be more aware of the earth's surface and to see some meaning and organization in its intricate variety of forms, these teachers are performing an immensely valuable service. The further enrichment of geographic knowledge and the widening of geographic horizons can surely make students and teachers alike more interesting people and more understanding citizens of their country and the world.

2

General objectives of geography

*Out of the fact, or truism, that natural and man-made phenomena
are unequally distributed over the face of the earth comes a series of
basic concepts.* CLYDE F. KOHN

SEVERAL DECADES have now passed since John W. Studebaker, erstwhile United States Commissioner of Education, issued what many have regarded as a major pronouncement related to geography's role in the curriculum. Studebaker said, "Apart from rather backward nations, we are more illiterate geographically than any civilized nation I know." Geographers have been fondly quoting this statement for years. Obviously, Studebaker seems to call for more geography in the curricula of the American schools, and this can only mean more geography classrooms, more geography students, more geography materials, and, of course, more geographers.

The statement also has a distinctly sobering aspect. Every American citizen who acquired his formal education in the schools of this country did study something called geography as a part of his social studies program. In fact, he probably spent several years in the elementary grades studying a school subject called geography. Why, then, did he remain so geographically illiterate?

What kinds of images, for example, does the man in the street conjure up when a news broadcast mentions a Vietnamese village in the Mekong Delta, or when a friend talks of an impending holiday trip to Tahiti? Is one a misty and terribly vague impression of a jungle scene, while the other leaps full-blown out of an old South Seas movie? Are not his views based on improvised and frequently distorted notions stemming more from television programs and romantic novels than from substantial concepts developed out of a sound acquaintance with the academic discipline of geography?

Whatever Dr. Studebaker may have meant, to geographers "geographic illiteracy" certainly means more than the fact that children cannot locate Afghanistan. Geographic understanding requires more than an ability to recite the name, capital, and population of each new African nation, to complete blank outline maps, or to commit to memory the names of the capes and bays of the British Isles. It means more, too, than the reading of adventure stories about what some have characterized as "the geography of strange lands and funny people." It is not a dull recitation of facts about places and products coupled with tedious preaching to children that they must learn to "tolerate" people from other lands whose color, language, religion, food, or clothing is different from their own. Rather boys and girls must be granted new opportunities to become acquainted with the concepts and methodology of the modern discipline of geography. This statement raises fundamental questions about the objectives and concepts of this discipline as it is practiced by the professional geographers, for it is through the discipline from which the school subject has been derived that the substance of geography comes alive.

A SEARCH FOR MEANING IN TODAY'S WORLD

When one interested in the teaching of geography in the schools considers the seemingly inexplicable problems of our stage in the sweep of time, one wonders how the varied patterns of distribution and flow over the face of the earth, as interpreted by professional geographers, can be explained in a meaningful fashion to children. Nevertheless, if our children are to understand the world in which they live, and geography is surely a fundamental strand to this understanding, geography educators are obligated to find efficient, realistic approaches to the study of this field for school purposes.

It is little wonder we have difficulty in adjusting our thinking to the realities of the second half of the twentieth century. The basic organizing themes of western culture, and of the nonwestern cultural regions as well, developed gradually over thousands of years on a planet where distance through these years kept a fairly constant meaning. Then, in the short period of one century, distance abruptly lost all its former meaning. Within the lifespan of persons still living, distance as a meaningful concept has been abolished. It is not surprising, then, that we have difficulty in organizing earth-space for instructional purposes in a fashion that has relevance to the extraordinary circumstances of our time.

Throughout most of the time that the human species has occupied this earth, distance had been reckoned in terms of "walking men,"[1] that is, men who have had to do all of their traveling over the earth's 57,230,000 square

---

[1] The concept of walking man and the changes in the scale of thinking required by new views of the meaning of distance were derived from the stimulating concluding chapter of M. Bates, *Where Winter Never Comes, A Study of Man and Nature in the Tropics* (New York: Scribner's, 1952), pp. 261–275.

miles of land surface by foot. Within this walking frame of reference our diverse cultures and civilizations, our races, and our languages have all slowly evolved.

In the millennia of the human occupancy of this planet man, by walking, has covered a vast territory. He spread over all the continents except Antarctica very early in his evolutionary history. Thousands of years ago, much earlier than we believed a short time ago, man probably also walked to the Americas over land connecting between Eurasia and North America.

At some period in the unwritten past, man came upon the idea of a boat, and with it he was able to extend the range of his movement over the earth to the islands of the world ocean. With all of the developments in seamanship and navigational techniques, however, land movement continued to be locked to the speed of a walking man.

Man on land ultimately learned to get off his own feet and made use of the feet of horses and camels. He found ways of constructing roads, and then laid out stage routes and systems of post relays. Significant as such discoveries were, they brought little progressive change in the speed of communication. Indeed, travelers in the time of the Pharoahs, Alexander, the Incas, the Romans, and Napoleon all moved with approximately the same speed and facility. These rates of travel and communication formed the framework within which our systems of social organization and cultural diversity were established and embellished.

A little more than one hundred years ago the age-old conception of distances began to shatter. Into the life of walking man came railways, automobiles, airplanes, the telegraph, marine cables, telephones, radios, television, space ships, and the communications satellites.

Many of us may have come to dislike the term *neighborhood* because of the too cozy way in which it has been used in elementary social studies programs. Nevertheless, the planet on which we live has become a neighborhood in an areal-time sense. Travel time has converted the great oceans to small lakes and the continental landmasses to easily spanned islands. Those age-old physical barriers that so long blocked the movement of men and the spread of ideas, have in a sense, been wiped off the face of the earth. Nations, cultures, and political systems have all lost the context in which they were conceived and nurtured — the context of distance in terms of a walking man.

THE TEACHER'S PERSPECTIVE

Fundamental to this discussion is the fact that we, as educators, are essentially concerned with the present. This is, after all, our time in the scheme of things. Furthermore, the education that we received, supposedly designed to prepare us for effective teaching of social studies, was one that dealt principally with the past. Somehow there was an almost mystical assumption that we could take the ideas of the past, put them into the frame of the present, and have them make sense to children who will live in the future. The children and youth we teach are deeply concerned with neither the past nor the present, but with a future that we will certainly never know and find difficult even to imagine.

In spite of these apparent difficulties, we surely have the potential for upgrading the teaching of geography. Indeed, we must if our children are to be equipped with both the knowledge and the ways of knowing that are necessary to understand and to deal with the challenges of the future. Nonetheless, new and creative thinking must be added to our past experience in curriculum development for geography. We cannot possibly teach our children what they will need to know for the years ahead if we stubbornly persist in passing along only the information with which we are familiar, using only the tools, materials, and techniques of instruction with which we feel secure and comfortable. We must not, then, use objectives and concepts created by those who think as walking men; instead we must turn directly to the scholar who operates within the framework of his discipline.[1]

STRUCTURE AND DISCIPLINE

During the current period of curriculum reform, most of the debate has hinged on two rather obvious questions: what is knowledge, and how should it be studied and taught. At different times in the history of education, schoolmen concerned with the various social sciences have presented widely differing answers to these questions. Early in the century the traditionalists taught the time-honored subjects as anthologies of topics in the vague hope that somehow the bits and pieces of factual information would turn out to be useful. As a result history became as Toynbee points out, "one damned thing after another." Civics turned out to be a dull recital of miscellanea about state and local governments. Geography was nothing more than a compendium of facts about places and products.

The unhappy days of the 1930's convinced some curriculum planners that this kind of teaching would never prepare students to face the complex realities of their world. This period, then, became the heyday of the so-called progressive reformers. From their efforts did come a new cur-

---

[1] P. Bacon, "Challenge to Curriculum Change: A Geographer's View," *The 1963 Jennings Scholar Lectures* (Cleveland: The Educational Research Council of Greater Cleveland, 1964), pp. 219–234.

riculum — one centering on the personal and social problems of children and youth. Such a curriculum drew on the academic disciplines only as they became relevant to the problems under study. The disciplines were viewed as storage vaults from which facts and ideas might be drawn as required. The central focus, however, was on the practical ordering of knowledge as it had reference to the particular problem under examination. This meant, of course, that curriculum decisions were based largely on knowledge of society and of the child. Relegated to a minor role were the disciplines of organized knowledge out of which man's knowledge is made. Geography was particularly set aside for it did not clearly fit the neat, compartmentalized structure of social or natural science.

Today, the pendulum of curriculum decision making has now swung solidly toward the disciplines — to the logical order inherent in knowledge itself; or, putting it another way, to the structure of concepts and principles that characterize the disciplines. Jerome Bruner, largely responsible for introducing the idea of structure to educational discourse, writes:

> Knowledge is a model we construct to give meaning and structure to regularities in experience, the organizing ideas of any body of knowledge are inventions for rendering experience economical and connected. We invent concepts such as force in physics, the bond in chemistry, motives in psychology, style in literature as means to the end of comprehension. . . . The power of great organizing concepts is in large part that they permit us to understand and sometimes to predict or change the world in which we live. But their power lies also in the fact that ideas provide instruments for experience.[1]

Bruner concludes, "The structure of knowledge is the proper emphasis in education. For it is structure, the great conceptual inventions that bring order to the categories of disconnected observations, that gives meaning to what we may learn and makes possible the opening up of new realms of experience."[2]

The suggestion, simply stated, is that each discipline has certain key ideas and theories. These ideas and theories characterize and are fundamental to understanding a particular discipline. The ideas serve as the logical, and indeed essential, means of introducing a given discipline to its students.[3]

It is important to recall, too, that conceptual schemes have a dynamic quality. As they are tested in the course of inquiry, they are modified and sometimes replaced by more fruitful larger concepts. It is through this

---

[1] *The Process of Education* (Cambridge: Harvard University Press, 1960), p. 33.
[2] *Ibid.*
[3] For an excellent review of this topic, see P. Phenix, "Key Concepts and the Crisis in Learning," *Teachers College Record,* vol. 58 (1956), pp. 137–143.

process that the great explosion of knowledge has come to so many fields, including geography. Today, with a dynamically evolving discipline such as geography we can expect an extensive reorganization of a given body of scientific knowledge to occur at intervals of five to fifteen years rather than every century as in the past.[1]

Fundamental, too, to an understanding of a given discipline is its *way* of making new knowledge, that is, the procedures and methods by which it uses its conceptions to attain its goals. Within the methodology of a given field, of greatest significance is the process of evaluating the outcome of inquiry. With reference to geography, what methods does the geographer use to certify the validity or truth of his findings? For instructional purposes the methodological aspect of the discipline seems of most urgent concern, for here is the way in which the learner is inducted into the fraternity of scholars. This is the way in which he may become an active participant in the making of knowledge rather than being the pedantic regurgitator of the knowledge made by someone else.

AN OVERVIEW OF GEOGRAPHIC OBJECTIVES

"The single most characteristic thing about human beings is that they learn. Learning is so deeply ingrained in man that it is almost involuntary. . . ."[2] Our objective, then, is to capitalize on this will to learn, so that geographic knowledge becomes a part of "everyman's" knowledge. This goal seems so essential to our survival in this world of conflict that to argue it would be anachronistic. In a sense, the winning of geographic knowledge becomes primary to any overview of attitudes and objectives related specifically to the discipline of geography.

The central objective for the learner is learning; the central goal for the teacher is creating an environment particularly conducive to learning. These two concepts apply to any discipline; how, specifically, do they apply in geography?

The great eighteenth century philosopher, Immanuel Kant, demonstrated that there are but three essentially different ways of organizing human knowledge into manageable segments. Kant describes these categories as grouping things and events together that are alike because they have a common origin; grouping things and events in the order of occurrence; and groupings things and events together because they occur in the same part of the earth's surface.

---

[1] J. Schwab, "The Concept of Structure of a Discipline," *Educational Record*, vol. 43 (1962), p. 200.

[2] J. Bruner, *Toward a Theory of Instruction* (Cambridge: Harvard University Press, 1966), p. 113.

Kant's three organizing principles, referred to as substantive, chronological, and chorological, provide the conceptual structure for any field of learning. Geography, of course, is that field of learning that organizes its concepts on the chorological principle. It is geography that focuses attention on the areal association of things and events of unlike origin, and on the interconnections among things and events that are areally associated. No other field of learning accepts this basis as its fundamental concern. The study of geography is certainly not a substitute for other approaches to learning, but it does present a unique perspective regarding the significance of position on the planet Earth, and this perspective is basic to general education.

ATTITUDE AND APPRECIATION AS OBJECTIVES IN GEOGRAPHY

Social studies educators have long been given to proliferation in the development of those objectives that might be entitled "attitudes and appreciations." Certainly high flown and glittering generalities can readily be developed for the geographic part of the curriculum as well; however, the attitudes and appreciations sketched below are specifically related to the content of the discipline of geography rather than to the broader objectives of education in general:[1]

1. Foremost in relating a school subject to its parent discipline is the role of the testing of hypotheses. A major goal should be the development of an attitude of objectivity, which would include learning to formulate, to test, and to determine the validity of hypotheses in geography.

2. In addition to the above, and also fundamental to the ties between geography as a research discipline and geography as a school subject, is the development of an appreciation for the realm of geographic scholarship. For the beginning geography student this appreciation will be at a fairly specific rather than abstract level. Nonetheless, it is useful in helping the young geographer see that geography as a professional field ranges far beyond descriptions of Japanese tea gardens and that a host of exciting and rewarding careers await the individual who follows this pursuit. Of special functional value to the teacher is an appreciation of the possibilities of applying the methodology of geographic scholarship to problems that can be solved directly in the school classroom. The utilization of such methodologies can move geography far from the passive, parroting back of ready-made information about places to the discovery of new views of thinking about places.

---

[1] For a particularly helpful examination of objectives in geography, one that was intensely used in this review, see W. D. Pattison, *Advisory Paper for Teachers Associated with the High School Geography Project* (Bozeman, Montana: High School Geography Project, 1962, reissued, 1965).

3. Related to an appreciation for the realm of geographic scholarship is the development of an appreciation for the role of the field, library, and map in the making of geographic knowledge and in the testing of hypotheses. This appreciation is an essential part in understanding geographic methodology.

4. Through the winning of new knowledge, a fourth objective is realized — that of a deeper appreciation for the physical, biotic, and cultural diversity of our planet. This appreciation, then, relates to both ecosystems (the areal associations of interconnected physical and biotic processes without interference by man) and habitats (an ecosystem that has been modified by man). This objective obviously includes an appreciation for the need of human society, if it is to survive, to work out an acceptable connection with the earth's resources. It is the habitat, after all, that is the resource base of human societies.

5. A fifth attitude and appreciation is directed toward the heart of modern cultural geography. It is the antithesis of "environmental determinism" which accepted the concept that the nature of man's physical and biotic environments (habitats) either determines, or at least sets limits to, man's ways of living. The concept now generally accepted by geographers for the interconnection between man and his habitat can be stated as follows, "The significance to man of the physical and biotic features of his habitat is a function of the attitudes, objectives, and technical skills of man himself."[1] This appreciation involves the development of an attitude toward the habitat that allows man to be the decision maker. It also permits a functional attitude toward natural resources — an attitude that would see resources coming into being and dynamically evolving as a reflection of man's attitudes, objectives, and technical skills.

GEOGRAPHIC KNOWLEDGE AS AN OBJECTIVE

The acquisition of geographic knowledge is fundamental to the general education of every citizen. Objectives under this category relate directly to the winning of this knowledge:

1. To relate the school subject of geography to the discipline, a central objective is to develop a knowledge and understanding of geography as a scholarly discipline and to build a working knowledge of its basic methodology.

2. Geographic knowledge includes an understanding of the meaning and utility of the regional concept. This understanding would include recognition of both formal and functional regions.

---

[1] P. E. James, "A Conceptual Structure for Geography," *Journal of Geography*, vol. 64 (1965), pp. 292–298.

3. Geographic knowledge would be incomplete indeed without the gaining of an understanding of spatial relations. This objective would include a recognition of the significance of such critical spatial factors as location, distribution, association, and movement of things over the surface of the earth.

4. Another basic objective is the gaining of a fundamental knowledge of the essential qualities of a persistent theme in geographic literature: man-land relations. We could interpret this relationship to mean an understanding of man's adjustments to and modification of his physical and biotic habitats.

5. A fifth objective relates to the acquisition of pertinent factual information about places. This would include a knowledge of basic locational schemes and a grasp of general world distribution patterns.

6. Perhaps as a capstone to an acquisition of geographic knowledge one could call for the passing of what Preston E. James has so often referred to as the "thumb test." Such a test would require the student to "know sufficient about the processes which shape the spatial distribution of selected landscape features so that with a minimum memorization of basic facts and anomalous relationships he can state with a fair degree of accuracy the complex of landscape feature he would expect to find on any given part of the earth's surface, expressly noting the amount of diversity present at any given scale, and the changes he would expect to result from any given shift in conditions affecting the processes."[1]

THE ACQUISITION OF GEOGRAPHIC SKILLS

Certainly a major objective in the teaching of geography is to help the learner acquire a working understanding of the essential geographic skills. Having a grasp of these skills will enable the learner to continue to gain in geographic knowledge long after his formal education has ended. Educators can only provide a beginning, and the very best of beginnings is the acquisition of those skills that make possible the continued growth of knowledge:

1. A skill fundamental to any discipline is the increasing acquaintance with the sources of factual information. Geography has its own especially valued sources; consequently, a realistic objective of geographic education is to help the learner know *where* to search out appropriate data and *what* data are appropriate for the task at hand.

2. A skill especially pertinent to geography is facility in map reading, which would include an ability to visualize terrain from a variety of

---

[1] G. F. White, "Geography in Liberal Education," presented to the Association of American Geographers, Committee on Liberal Education, December 12, 1963, p. 6.

symbolic representations. Also relevant is an understanding of scale, directional coordinates, and projections.

3. Related to reading maps is facility in interpreting them. This requires the ability to analyze relationships between two or more distributions, which in many ways is the essence of geography.

4. A particularly pertinent geographic skill is that of sharpening one's powers of observation. Perhaps more than any other, this skill can add richness to life. Having learned to "read the landscape," one never again travels with blinders.

CONCLUSION

Neville Scarfe has reminded us that, "No subject can claim a place on the school curriculum unless it has a clear structure, a precise theme, and a worthwhile purpose."[1] Geography is an old and honorable discipline. Its history is clear.

In a day when time has virtually destroyed space as a barrier, "the need for men to carry on the task of supplementing ignorance with knowledge, or displacing prejudice with sympathy born of understanding, is truly great."[2] Obviously no single subject matter can accomplish this enormous objective alone, but geography may come closest to the goal. Geography does help its student to gain a perspective on the world. It focuses on the physical and cultural diversity of this planet in a way that is unique. It views the land through eyes of the men who occupy the land. It views the choices that man has made as he uses the land as a reflection of his culture. In this sense there is no right or no wrong. With this view, no one people, no one color, no one language or religion makes the *right* choices. The choices are simply a reflection of a blending of time and space, of man and land. Perhaps through such themes the learner acquires broader understanding of man's role on the face of the earth and a more generous attitude toward man himself.

---

[1] "Depth and Breadth in School Geography," *Journal of Geography,* vol. 64 (1965), p. 153.

[2] J. R. Whitaker, *Geography in School and College: Talks on Values and Problems* (Nashville: Peabody College Bureau of Publications, 1948), p. 27.

3

Geographic myths

A generalization, in any field, must be abandoned if it obscures what
teachers want to teach, for it is, then, a bad generalization.

PRESTON E. JAMES

A MYTH MAY appropriately be defined as a story believed to be true — and, make no mistake, certain myths are probably true. Nevertheless, many of the myths perpetuated by teachers on all levels are untrue or only partially true. Unfortunately, this generalization applies to geography teachers as well as to teachers in other disciplines.

At least a portion of geographic mythology is created by the nature of the educational process which requires various levels of generalization. Everyone is familiar with the necessity of establishing broad generalizations and finality in teaching students at the elementary level. For the very young student few questions are open-ended. Generalizations become less sweeping and questions are often left completely unanswered or only partially answered as students progress up the academic ladder. In spite of the fact that more sophisticated students are willing to accept the fact that knowledge is imperfect and that teachers are fallible, the teacher is often unwilling or unable to admit the fallibility. When one then adds to this educational dilemma the fact that many geography teachers are inadequately or improperly trained, conditions are ripe for the promulgation and perpetuation of geographic myths of all shades of truth or untruth at all educational levels.

The purpose of this study is to explore certain commonly accepted myths and to enumerate those facets of truth, or lack of it, pertaining to each example. Obviously such an approach will permit the examination of only a tiny fraction of active geographic myths, and these can be examined in the most perfunctory way. The author makes no claim to omniscience, and it is certainly true that the myths set forth are not espoused by all geographers. However, it seems a reasonable assumption that all of us are guilty of indulging in geographic mythology of some sort at some time.

Certainly, all generalizations (including this one) lack the capacity for complete, unvarnished, and exclusive truth. It is doubtless true, therefore, that in discussing certain geographic myths the author will allow segments of his ignorance to shine through in the form of other myths. Hopefully, however, this study will call attention to the necessity of maintaining an open (not empty) mind and the desirability of admitting to ignorance on occasion. The search for and examination of new truth must be the geographer's watchword.

EROSION

Erosion is undesirable. Erosion can be prevented. How many times have we heard these statements? Certainly either of the statements represents a partial truth at best. Erosion cannot be prevented. Geologic erosion proceeds apace, has always gone on, and will continue into the future. But what of man-induced or man-accelerated erosion, can it not be prevented? No! Land stripped of its natural vegetation for the purpose of practicing agriculture or grazing will always be susceptible to some acceleration in erosion. It is true that well known conservation techniques will reduce the most serious depredations of erosion, but even the most advanced of technologies cannot completely eliminate erosion.

Further it should be pointed out that erosion is not undesirable at all places under all circumstances at all times. Erosion, geologic or man-induced, means concomitant deposition in rich flood plains, alluvial fans, or deltas. It would be difficult to convince inhabitants of river flood plains and deltas in south and east Asia that erosion in the headwaters of major rivers was a bad thing.

Such relationships between erosion and deposition are universally understood, but we often neglect the potentially beneficial effects of erosion upon ferralitic soils of the tropics. Many of these tropical soils would benefit measurably from the removal of the A-horizon. Erosion might, in fact, make certain soils, now useless, amenable to cultivation. The relationship of erosion to soil is obvious, but our understanding of soils is imperfect.

SOILS

Soils are particularly susceptible to mythological treatment by geographers, since most geographers lack appropriate backgrounds in pedology or chemistry to allow them to appreciate the subtleties of physical and chemical characteristics related to soil fertility and tilth. To illustrate, geographers have been so anxious to dispel the common misconception that humid tropical soils are fertile that they have gone overboard in emphasizing that tropical soils are infertile. No generalization can be made for tropical soils — either that they are fertile, or infertile. The ferralitic soils are generally termed infertile, but will this assumption hold up under close scrutiny? No great soil group which can support selva or jungle over thousands of square miles can logically be termed infertile. The proliferation of vegetative growth in the rain forest is well known, and the total quantity of organic matter produced per acre is truly prodigious. To be sure, when such lands are cleared for planting to typical agricultural crops, yields are normally low and productivity decreases rapidly after a few years.

Further, of course, areas of azonal and intrazonal soils within the tropics may yield prolifically under a hot sun and abundant rains. An opposite situation, however, may occur when patches of true laterite prove to be as barren of vegetative growth as a concrete pavement.

We know, too, of the obsession by many with the notion that volcanic and alluvial soils are fertile. Here again, of course, some are and some are not. For the semisophisticated it appears to be enough to point out that simatic ejecta weathers into fertile soil and sialic materials produce infertile soils. As a crude generalization this concept has the germ of truth within it. However, a multiplicity of factors must be considered before one makes such a pronouncement. The physical and chemical characteristics of the ejecta must be considered along with time exposed to weathering, types and intensity of weathering and eroding agents, microclimatic milieu, slope and exposure, type and character of vegetative pioneers, and human involvement, if any.

Not infrequently alluvial soils are productive, since they are typically composed of topsoil removed from other areas. Nevertheless, one should consider the general lack of fertility near the apex of most alluvial fans where bouldery, gravelly, or sandy material may be mineralogically sterile and physiologically arid. Similarly, productive soils may be buried under the heterogeneous debris left by a flash flood or mud flow. Plows turning furrows four and five feet deep testify to the difficulty of dealing with such disasters.

No attempt will be made here to resurrect the ghost of soil color as an appropriate index of soil fertility. The spectre, however, still walks down the halls of many ivy-covered walls in academe. Soil color is, of course, no reliable index of soil fertility.

VEGETATION

With deference to plant geographers and ecologists many neglect man in the environmental equation in considering plant associations presumed to represent climax vegetation. In southeastern China, for example, it is ridiculous to discuss natural vegetation in terms of the usual physical environmental framework. Man has almost certainly been the most important selective agency — is the "natural vegetation" of southeastern China, then, a physical or a cultural phenomenon? Does a real natural vegetation exist at all?

In addition, most attempts at vegetative mapping on all but maps of the largest scale are so general as to obscure practically all the significant detail within an area. For example, a popular world map of natural vegetation captions one area as "grass and other herbaceous plants." The inadequacy of such a caption is perhaps best illustrated by citing an area which the author knows reasonably well. In Oklahoma the previously mentioned caption obscures significant areas of gallery forest, large sections of the "cross timbers," relict stands of eastern hardwoods, and significant areas where herbaceous plants grow to the virtual exclusion of grass. Nor does such a classification take cognizance of the vast differences in grass associations. Doubtless the author of the map is aware of its shortcomings, but his audience often is not.

Too often geographers, in examining the plant world, are prone to try to establish a relationship between plant communities and climate. This is not surprising since most of the commonly used climatic classification schemes are based on vegetation patterns. Unfortunately such attempts leave the geologic and edaphic factors in a position of secondary or tertiary importance. Frequently, of course, the geologic or edaphic factor is the critical control marking, oftentimes rather sharply, the transition between different vegetative associations.

Often, too, geographers are swept along by the comforting concept of homogeneity in vegetation associations. It is convenient, for example, to talk of the taiga as the northern coniferous forest without mentioning the large areas of deciduous forests which are interconnected and interbedded within the coniferous area.

Another example of attempted dragon slaying, where the dragon has bitten the slayer, is in the rainforest-jungle controversy. In attempting to correct the notion of the lay public that all humid tropical areas are choked with impenetrable jungle, the geographers have been successful in pointing to areas of selva with minimal underbrush, i.e., rainforest, not jungle. However, such attempts to play down jungle vegetation have probably obscured the real vegetative world. Vast areas of jungle exist because the light essential to its existence can penetrate to the forest floor in many circumstances. To illustrate, coastal and river margins, steep slopes, and man-made clearings all contribute to light penetration and concomitant jungle growth. With the dramatic expansion in human numbers and activities, few areas have not felt the shifting cultivator's machete or the woodsman's ax.

Not only do people create environments favorable to the development of jungle in tropical regions, but vast areas of savanna are clearly man-induced. Tools and fire have definitely created many of the *natural* vegetation associations which we observe today.

CLIMATE

Perhaps in no other area has empiricism beckoned so enticingly and geographers fallen so completely on their intellectual faces as in the area of climatology. It is not my purpose to attack the parameters established by various climatologists in setting forth various climatological classifications. Rather, the purpose of this discussion is to ask certain questions concerning the utilization of any climatic classification the reader comes to use.

Existing classification schemes are based largely on means, maxima, and minima of various observed climatic data. That these data are often put through complicated arithmetic and/or algebraic manipulations is really beside the point. The point is that climatic classifications are developed for mean conditions over a fixed number of years (thirty years is popular now because of the influence of the United States Weather Bureau).

How many regional climatology courses are predicated on classifying stations according to classification scheme X and then attempt to explain the pattern of climates as depicted on a world or regional climatic map? Is it more significant to know the extreme conditions a station experienced during a given period than the mean conditions? Is it perhaps of greater importance to know that a given station experiences more years of semi-arid conditions in a fixed period than any other, although the mean conditions might show the station to have a humid environment?

Caution is essential in consideration of climatic patterns — caution in data reliability, care in the selection of length of record. Wise selection of regional climatic patterns must be left to those with an adequate background in and appreciation for physical climatology.

LANDFORMS

Whether geographers attempt genetic or empirical approaches in landform classification many pitfalls await the unwary. On any world or large areal basis most empirical approaches quickly break down. The infinite variety of forms, slopes, summit levels, and shapes, for example, even in an area deemed to be essentially featureless staggers the imagination. Application of such empirical classification systems must be used only in mapping efforts in a large scale format (1 : 10,000 or larger), and even in such circumstances the cartographer and the map user must be conversant with the established parameters and margins for error.

The genetic classification of landforms which most geographers are prone to use is also fraught with peril for the naive. Stages in the erosion cycle are difficult to discern in the field by those thoroughly schooled in geology or geomorphology. Such distinctions are next to impossible for the neophyte and the geographer who are unschooled in the intricacies of structure, process, and stage. When does a stream cease to be young and become mature? Unless the diastrophic movements creating a physical environment are considered along with degradational processes of weathering and erosion as part of a continuum, the genetic study of landforms has little meaning.

Further, geographers are often guilty of explaining geomorphological phenomena in oversimplified ways. Perhaps such oversimplification is tolerable if the teacher removes the air of finality which so often accompanies a pronouncement. Some examples of geomorphological myths are set forth to illustrate this point.

For example, mountain building occurs because of isostatic imbalance, plastic deformation of the mantle, convectional currents within the mantle, radioactive decay, or other factors. Perhaps all of these factors are involved in mountain building, but to attribute diastrophic movements to any combination of these agents at this point in time is presumptuous and dangerous.

Another example may be cited in the process of atoll formation and coral disintegration. How many instructors continue to use the Darwinian subsiding volcano as the type example for atoll formation? (Doubtless a number of atolls are formed in this way.) However, the lion's share of coral atolls appear to have developed on subsiding guyots, and the generally circular plan relates to the fact that only the peripheral edges of the coral (and algae), facing waters rich in organic matter, are living.

Of course coral sand is created by the weathering and erosion of barrier reefs and atolls subjected to the pounding of waves and the surge of tropical storms. This is true in part, but only in part. Beaked fishes, such as the parrot fish and the wrasses are known to run tons of coral rock through their gut to extract organic material. Their principal defecatory product is coral sand.

In addition to misinterpretation or misunderstanding of geomorphological processes, however, the bland assumption that topographic maps are useful to analyze and explain landform orogeny is widespread and erroneous. To be sure topographic sheets are valuable tools, but beginner and expert alike are on shaky ground in trying to analyze the geomorphological·aspects of terrain without the assistance of a detailed surface and subsurface geologic map or the use of topographic sheets in conjunction with extensive field work.

STATISTICS

In the period since World War II, especially, geographers have gotten caught up in the trend toward quantification. Sophisticated employment of statistics has dispelled many of the myths formerly permeating the field of geography, but others have been created. Perhaps the most disturbing myth of all is that the quantifier cannot talk to the nonquantifier. This lack of dialogue between the two groups is the result of a two-edged sword that cuts both directions.

The quantifier has been guilty of a multitude of sins including attempts to quantify the essentially nonquantifiable, manipulation of equations and misuse of statistical processes for the sheer joy of watching numerical blocks fall into place, and failure to demonstrate convincingly results and the significance thereof. Many of the statistically oriented geographers have become so enamoured with the jargon and manipulation of such things as coefficients of correlation, regression analysis, multiple regression analysis, polynomials, permutations, skewness, point plot diagrams, balanced, and unbalanced cycles that they have lost sight of the real utility and importance of some of the functions they derive.

At the same time, many other geographers have rejected out of hand what the quantifiers have had to say because they have been unable or unwilling to learn to understand the statistician's tools and techniques. Much that is good and valuable has been discovered in the relatively recent past by the quantifiers. Contributions can be and will be made by members of both camps. The sooner proponents of both approaches come to this realization the better it will be for the entire geographic profession.

MAN IN PHYSICAL GEOGRAPHY

Geographers subscribe to a variety of definitions of the field, but most would probably accept that "geography is the study of the relationship of man to his environment." Scholars have long since abandoned the idea of geographic determinism, but many geographers continue to discuss and explore the limitations on man set by environment or they examine man's cultural creations with little apparent cognizance of his role as a modifier of the physical environment.

It could be cogently argued that man's modification of the physical landscape is human geography, but this author is inclined to the opinion that human activities modifying the physical landscape are part of physical geography. In any case, it is high time that geographers expound man's role as a geomorphological, biological, climatological, and edaphic agent; if it has existed at all such treatment has been largely shallow or perfunctory in the average classroom situation.

Obvious evidences of man's geomorphological activity are omnipresent. Open cut mines furrow the landscape around the globe, man-induced faulting and earth tremors occur regularly in abandoned mining regions, alluvial debris chokes streams in areas adjacent to placer workings, and hills of waste rock rise above surrounding areas in regions of well-established mining activities.

Effects of dam construction and the impoundments that dot the globe provide dramatic proof of man's hydrological influences. His utilization of ground water for a variety of purposes has led to an array of subtle and dramatic modifications of the landscape.

Interference with natural selection has led to a whole host of useful plants, modification of ecological succession, and development of entirely new climax associations. The eradication, domestication, or spread of a given animal species has altered nature's balance in a number of areas — sometimes to man's benefit, but more often than not to his detriment.

Climatological influences are significant, although as yet imperfectly understood. Some climatological influences are obvious. Central heating has taken much of the sting out of high latitude winters, and air conditioning has provided comfort in low latitude summers. Artificial stimulation of precipitation has met with limited success, but occasionally local results have been dramatic. Prospects of steering or dissipating dangerous storms are on the horizon. Burning millions of tons of hydrocarbons must have both short- and long-term effects. Most man-developed climatological changes are subtle, but almost certainly they are inexorable and pervading.

As an edaphic agent man has clearly influenced many of the soils of the world in a relatively short time more than natural forces have done in thousands of years. Consider some of the obvious influences. Erosion has resulted in top soil being stripped off vast areas. Heavy fertilization and soil treatment in intensively utilized areas have dramatically modified the character of preexistent soils. Deforestation, overgrazing, and mining have all produced dramatic changes in edaphic conditions.

Discussion of air and water pollution are mentioned in the press daily, but the specific, detailed, and practical influences on environment and man are left largely to study by scientists in some special field — geographers shy away. Power plants in New Zealand, Italy, the United States, and elsewhere using natural thermal areas are mentioned causally, but the ramifications of such activity on the physical environment are largely ignored. The myth that man is only a cultural agent should certainly be dispelled.

CONCLUSION

Geographic myths persist like myths in all disciplines for a variety of reasons. Among the most important of these are ignorance, resistance to change, inability to admit imperfection, credibility in accepting spurious reasoning, and conditioning based on past teaching, experience, or presumed expertise. Perhaps the most important fact for geographers to keep in mind is that essentially every facet of both the physical and cultural environment is imperfectly known. Whereas generalization is necessary, since the world is an infinitude of microcosms, no two of which are alike, it is important to point to the exceptions, focus on the incompletely understood, and to search for a more perfect understanding to the benefit of yourself, colleagues, students, and the lay public. The Greek Heraclitus left an admonition which it would behoove geographers to heed, "The only constant in the universe is change. . . ."

PART II
Instructional aids

GEOGRAPHY, AS MUCH AS any subject in the curriculum, must be visualized to be understood. The student with a vivid imagination who can "see" the earth rotating on its axis or revolving in its orbit is better able to grasp many more concepts than the student with little or no imagery perception. Therefore each teacher of geography must have available a large number of instructional aids such as maps, globes, still and moving pictures, and certain kinds of specialized equipment such as stream tables, drawing materials, and models. Thus, if the teacher is equipped to deal with geographic concepts, he must have a working knowledge of the basic principles involved in the interpretation and use of maps, globes, pictures, and the outdoor laboratory.

The two basic tools of the geography teacher are maps and globes.

> By means of maps the geographer expresses a large part of his knowledge most accurately and completely, and at the same time most clearly and simply. Maps are also to a certain extent his raw material, his sources of information. Not only for geographical work, but for intelligent life in the world, an educated person should be able to recognize and appreciate the facts that a map conveys, reading a map as easily as he reads a book.[1]

All too often globes are missing from the classroom or, if available, not used. Frequently this is a result of the teacher's inability to use the globe.[2]

Therefore, the teacher should become well informed about this instructional aid and how to use it.

---

[1] Olive Garnett, *Fundamentals in School Geography* (London: George G. Harrap, 1960), p. 44.
[2] J. B. Ray, *Materials of Geography* (Minneapolis: Burgess, 1963), p. 18.

One of the least used geographic aids is the outdoor laboratory. All students are interested in getting out of the "artificial" classroom of the school building into the "real" geographic classroom outdoors. The teacher must be well prepared not only in the textual material of his subject, but also in its application. Maps, pictures, globes, and textual materials may all be brought into reality outdoors.

Although geography is taught in a variety of classrooms, one equipped especially for the subject would make the presentation considerably easier. The situation presented in the last part of this section is worthy of careful consideration.

4

The globe and its uses

The sphericity of our earthly dwelling place provides geographers with a multitude of facts from which many understandings about location can be drawn.   HENRY J. WARMAN

ALTHOUGH A TERRESTRIAL globe was made by the Greek philosopher Crates around 150 B.C., most known globes were made after the beginning of the Age of Discovery in 1492. The Renaissance globes were generally small, often only four to six inches in diameter because of high cost of their construction, and they were more ornate than accurate. Nevertheless, they found wide use, even as technical instruments by astronomers and navigators, and by the eighteenth and nineteenth centuries the subject of globe usage had become common in academies and colleges.

More globes are now being manufactured than ever before, yet we know less of their potentials than did our ancestors. One of the reasons for this is that globes are best utilized in the teaching of mathematical geography, which treats the earth in its planetary relationships, emphasizing its shape, size, motions, and illumination. (This approach should not be confused with the current trend toward quantification of data in other branches of geography.) Although once considered to be on a par with physical and human geography, this topic suffered a decline after World War I, when the more technical branches of geography were replaced by commercial geography, or even by courses which offered no real geography at all. Fortunately, the advent of the space age is bringing a new interest in the earth as a planet and a consequent revival of interest in globes. Small globes have even been incorporated into instruments for navigation in space, a development which parallels their employment during the early days of sail.

GLOBES VERSUS MAPS

The globe has sometimes been described as "the perfect map projection." An analysis of the advantages and disadvantages of globes will show, however, that this statement is incorrect in two respects.

Globes are representations rather than projections. In projections, the round surface of the earth must be depicted upon a flat plane. This inevitably involves distortion, whether it be of shape, area, distance, or direction. The globe, which represents the nearly spherical earth upon a spherical surface, is almost free from any of these distortions. Other advantages stem from the fact that the globe is a representation. Of all of our tools, it gives the best visual illusion of the earth as seen from space, and is the most direct and versatile instrument for mathematical analysis.

The fact that the globe depicts the earth in three dimensions rather than two makes it less than perfect, however. Globes are bulky to store and handle, and they are much more expensive than maps of the equivalent scale. As the diameter of the globe is increased, its cost increases disproportionately, which explains why large globes are a rarity. Further, being an opaque, solid object, a globe cannot depict the entire earth's surface in one glance, but must limit the viewer to slightly less than one half of the total area. Hence globes should not be overemphasized. They are best for specialized uses, and must take their place alongside other established tools of the geographer.

CHOOSING A GLOBE

Globes may be classified according to their size, their surface, and their mode of mounting. To obtain the greatest utility from globes, the following recommendations for selection are made.

Concerning size, the larger the globe, the more the detail that may be portrayed upon its surface, and the more it will convey the great dimensions of the earth. These factors must be tempered by considerations of cost, space, and the setting of the globe. An inexpensive globe, 12 inches in diameter, can be used by a small group, but in the classroom lecture 16 inches would be the desirable minimum. So uncommon are larger globes that a 19- or 20-inch model conveys the impression of being big, and a 32-inch library model appears to be several feet in diameter. Anything larger than the latter, such as a spectacular 75-inch model that has been put into limited production, can only be seen in special displays.

Concerning the surface, the bright colors of the common political globe are useful for locating places, but give a poor illusion of the physical earth. Moreover, they inevitably become out of date and thus should be avoided in large, expensive globes. Physical globes, with their subdued shades of green, brown, and blue, give a more naturalistic appearance and may be used, with care, for years. Most of these are actually physical-political globes, with overprintings to indicate place names and boundaries. Other compromises are a centrally illuminated globe, in which the light may be turned on to throw shaded relief onto the political surfaces, and ones in which a three-dimensional relief is imprinted upon the states and nations.

The latter brings up the subject of *relief* globes. These vary greatly in appearance and utility. The best ones, large models which are colored to portray the earth's vegetation, are beyond our means, but a 12-inch plastic relief globe may be painted in the same manner to provide a smaller, but satisfactory, substitute. Some relief globes are divided at the equator so that they may be opened to show a cross section of the inner zones of the earth. All of these models have an exaggerated relief, as the elevations, if made on the same scale as the rest of the globe, would be almost imperceptible. Other limitations stem from their roughened surfaces, as the exposed "mountains" are liable to damage and make it harder to slide the globe within a cradle for rectification.

The usefulness of the *slated* globe, which is either totally blank or which only has outlines of the seas and continents, proves that surface detail is not always important. The instructor can provide his own markings, in white chalk upon the darkened surfaces, and these globes are the best ones for demonstrating certain geometrical principles.

The mounting is one of the least appreciated portions of the globe, but it is necessary for both the protection and the effective use of the model. The two most frequent types are the *axial* and the *cradle* mountings.

In the axial mounting, the more familiar of the two, the globe is attached so that it may be freely rotated about an axis passing through the poles. Often the attachment is not directly to the base but to a graduated meridian ring. A common practice is to have the axis rigidly inclined 23½° away from the vertical in harmony with the earth's axis, a practice which aids in certain demonstrations of rotation and illumination, but which makes rectification difficult (Figure 4.1).

In the cradle mounting, the globe lies freely within its support and may be turned to any position. This not only aids in rectification, but also in the study of hemispheres and the measurement of distance and direction upon the globe. The best cradle mountings are surmounted by a horizontal graduated circle, termed the *horizon ring*.

Compromises between the two mountings have been devised. Some cradle mountings have accessories to permit rotation at a 23½° angle, and some axially mounted globes have an adjustable meridian ring which permits rectification. A recent development is an axially mounted globe with a pivoting, rather than a horizontal, horizon ring.

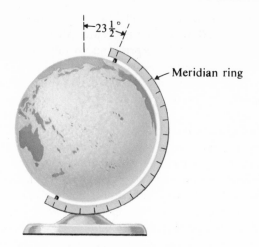

FIGURE 4.1   *Globe with axial mounting.*

MEASUREMENT WITH THE GLOBE

In the primary grades, the teacher may well have to handle both arithmetic and geography, and the globe provides an excellent tool for demonstrating principles of terrestrial measurement, particularly in the cases of linear and circular measure.

For the teaching of circular measurement, the globe is covered with a network of lines which should be called *meridians* and *parallels*. "Latitude" and "longitude" refer to angular distances, as measured from the circles of the equator and prime meridian. From these basic reference lines, the parallels are generally spaced at intervals of 10° and the meridians at intervals of 15°. Finer degree markings may be found on the horizon and meridian rings of the mountings. As the student is shown the principles underlying latitude and longitude, the practical application of circular measurements will become obvious.

Linear measurements are most easily accomplished by means of a tape measure or string stretched tautly over the globe. In this position it forms a *great circle* route, which is the shortest distance between two points on the surface of a sphere. In converting the length of the string or tape into miles, the concept of *scale* can be introduced. For example, the mean diameter of the earth is 7,918 statute miles, and by simple arithmetic we find that a 12-inch globe is constructed on a scale of 660 miles to the inch, and the 16-inch globe on a scale of 495 miles.

Some cradle mounted globes have a scale of miles laid out on their horizon rings, which can be used by moving the globe until the two points, whose distance is to be measured, lie along the ring. Since the ring is also graduated in degrees, the relationships between linear and circular measurement can be shown. One degree of a great circle of the earth will be equivalent to 69 statute miles.

Some types of linear measurement have been created in order to harmonize with the circular values. In the English-speaking nations, these will be nautical miles, which are not arbitrary in nature (as are the statute miles) but are equivalent to one minute of a great circle. In other nations the kilometer is used, and this was originally intended to be one ten thousandth of a great circle route from the pole to the equator. From the above information, the relationship between the various units of measurement may be calculated. Thus, there will be 60 nautical miles to the degree, yielding a nautical mile which is 1.15 times as long as a statute mile. Similarly, a circuit of the earth will involve 40,000 kilometers, but only about 25,000 statute miles, demonstrating that the kilometer is five eighths of a mile in length.

DIRECTION ON THE GLOBE

Besides length, lines have the property of direction, which is also of interest to the primary student. The meridians and parallels on the surface of the globe have been so laid out that they form right angles, and thus point north-south and east-west, at every intersection. Any other line on the globe will intersect these lines at an acute or obtuse angle, and from this angle the direction of the line can be obtained.

By the use of a line, tape, or horizon ring some unusual features concerning direction can be shown to the students. The great circle route, unless laid out along the equator or a meridian, will not intersect every parallel or meridian at the same constant angle. Thus great circle routes are not necessarily the same as *rhumb lines,* or lines with a constant compass direction.

The great circle route between New York and Rome does not run along the 40th parallel, but bends considerably to the north of it. As one chooses locations farther north, or farther apart, the deviation becomes more pronounced. Thus, the shortest route between Seattle and Moscow misses the North Pole by only a few degrees.

THE HEMISPHERES

A great circle route, if extended completely around the earth, would divide it into two halves. The great circle of the equator is the boundary between the northern and southern hemispheres, and that formed by the prime meridian and its extension, the 180th meridian, is the boundary between the eastern and western hemispheres. Concerning these hemispheres, the distinction between the northern and southern ones will be the most important, relating to the physical principles of illumination and climate (which are reversed for each season and hemisphere). The eastern and western hemispheres, as commonly taken, have been used as cultural divisions, but this is only an approximation. (Some have attempted to improve matters by taking the circle formed by the meridians of 20° W and 160° E as the dividing line, but this has not gained popular approval.)

Just as the commonly drawn parallels and meridians are not the only lines which could be drawn upon the globe, the hemispheres bounded by such lines are not the only ones of interest to the students. With a cradle mounting, the globe can be turned so that a maximum amount of land or water is visible to the viewer. The land hemisphere should be centered around 47° N, 1° 30′ W, near Nantes, France, and the water hemisphere in the Pacific Ocean southeast of New Zealand, at approximately 47° S, 178° 30′ E. The horizon ring and one of its vertical supports can be used as cross hairs for placing these points in the center of the visible half of the globe (Figure 4.2). These two locations are *antipodal* with

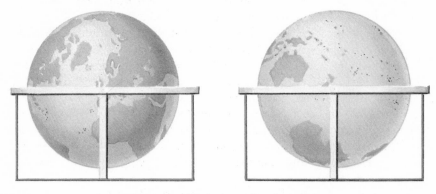

FIGURE 4.2   *Globe in cradle mounting.*

respect to each other, and it will be noted that most land areas are situated opposite water areas, a situation which has given rise to theories concerning the structure of the earth.

THE ILLUMINATION OF THE GLOBE

Once the concept of hemispheres has been grasped, the student is ready for the topic of the illumination of the earth. There are two methods that are generally used.

The most common demonstration is that of artificial illumination. The globe should be axially mounted, at the 23½° angle, within a darkened room. A spotlight (which may be improvised with a flashlight or slide projector) is directed horizontally at the center of the globe, dividing it into light and dark hemispheres. The great circle bounding these two areas is called the *circle of illumination,* or the terminator.

The globe may be oriented so that one pole or the other is pointed toward the light, indicating the illumination at one of the solstices, or so that neither pole points toward the light, indicating conditions at the equinoxes. Intermediate positions may also be shown. By rotating the globe during the demonstrations, such phenomena as midnight sun, polar night, and differing lengths of daylight and darkness may be illustrated. It will become apparent that the conditions of the northern hemisphere will always be reversed in the southern.

By moving a flashlight close enough to cast a small spot of light upon the globe, the differences in insolation by latitude and season can be shown. When the rays of light strike the globe in a nearly vertical position, as in the tropics, the spot is small and the lighting intense. The reverse will be true when the rays hit the globe obliquely, as in the polar regions.

Less well known is the demonstration of natural illumination. This requires the additional technique of *rectification,* which is one of the most important skills of globe usage.

To be rectifiable, a globe must be so mounted that it may assume any position in space. For this purpose the cradle mounting preferably with a horizon ring, is best, although axial mountings which can adjust the degree of inclination may also be used. The best procedure to follow is:

1. Rotate the globe around its axis until your local meridian is at the top.
2. Adjust the inclination of the axis until your local parallel is at the top (Figure 4.3).
3. Turn the entire globe on its stand until its north pole is pointing toward due north on the earth.

In this position, points on the globe will have the same orientation in space, or *attitude,* as corresponding points on the earth. Thus, your globe should have your own locality at its top, and its axis should parallel that of the earth.

Illumination is now accomplished by placing the globe, still properly rectified, in direct sunlight. The globe will then be illuminated in the same manner as the earth at that particular moment, particularly if care has been taken to minimize the reflection of light from other surfaces and thus preserve the sharpness of shadows (Figure 4.4).

Stevens Point, Wisconsin: $44\frac{1}{2}°$ N

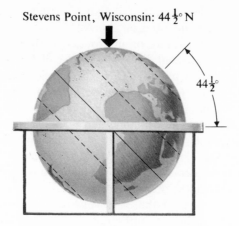

$44\frac{1}{2}°$

FIGURE 4.3   *Rectification of the globe.*

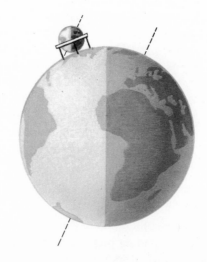

FIGURE 4.4   *Illumination of the globe.*

Thus, the globe will be divided into a sunlit and a darkened hemisphere and, if the demonstration is conducted for any length of time, the circle of illumination may be seen to change its position as the earth rotates, at the rate of 15° per hour. The line of shadow to the west of your location will move westward to put new areas under illumination; this is the line of sunrise. The corresponding line of sunset may be seen to the east, steadily moving to place formerly sunlit areas under darkness.

At the time of the equinoxes, the circle of illumination may be seen to pass through the poles, and thus every point on the surface would experience daylight and darkness during a full rotation. At other times, particularly during the summer and winter, an area around one pole will be constantly illuminated, and an area around the other pole constantly shaded, no matter how long the demonstration lasts. If the globe is carefully rectified and sharp shadows obtained, the circle of illumination will touch the polar circles at the times of the solstices.

The greatest advantage of natural illumination is its realism, as the student sees the earth's light and shadow as it would appear at that very instant to an observer in space. The problems that will arise are those of obtaining days of bright, steady sunlight, and the fact that one must take several months to obtain a complete set of demonstrations.

ADVANCED TOPICS WITH THE GLOBE

On the more advanced levels, topics of geography can be related to the informal geometry and general science of junior high school, and the formal geometry and earth science of senior high. In these demonstrations not only the common globe but also the slated variety can be brought into play. By now the students should be sufficiently familiar with basic locations to work imaginatively with lines over a partially blank surface.

One basic principle of geometry with a geographic application is the concept of *locus*. We might conceive of a parallel as the locus of all points a given angular distance from the equator, and define a meridian in similar terms with respect to the line of Greenwich. Each meridian and parallel will, like any line, contain an innumerable number of points. However, by drawing a chalked meridian and parallel upon the slated globe, it can be shown how they will intersect at only one specific point, giving a location that is unique upon the globe.

Besides the principles of plane geometry, those of solid geometry can also be used. A plane and a sphere intersect to form a circle. If the plane passes through the center of the sphere, dividing it into two equal halves, the intersection will be a *great circle*. If the plane does not pass through the center, a *small circle* will be formed. An inspection of the common lines on the globe will show that meridians are halves of great circles, the equator a full great circle, and that all other parallels are small circles.

A little more geometry will show why the great circle is the shortest route over a spherical surface. Since such a circle is the largest one that can be drawn upon a sphere, one of its arcs will be the closest possible approximation of a straight line than can be laid over the curved surface. To illustrate this, it is best to bring in the plane surface of the blackboard, plus a straight edge and compass, to supplement the globe.

THE SUBSOLAR POINT

In secondary school the illumination of the globe can be treated in more detail. To do this logically and geometrically, it is best to introduce the concept of the *subsolar point*. This point, also known as the "point of vertical ray" or "sun mark," is that location upon the earth where, at any given moment, the sun is observed to be directly overhead. The antiquity of this concept may be seen in the fact that it figured in Eratosthenes' measurement of the earth.

A little reasoning will bring to mind two principles concerning the point. First of all, it will be located in the exact center of the circle of illumination, 90° away from every point of the circle. Secondly, the subsolar point must move in harmony with the motions of the earth, latitudinally by season and longitudinally by the hour of the day.

There are two methods for locating the subsolar point. If one only wishes to locate the point for the given moment, and the sun is shining, one need but rectify the globe and place it in direct sunlight. A thin wooden stick is then kept pointed toward the center of the globe and moved about until it casts the minimum round shadow, at which location it will indicate the subsolar point. Holding the stick by a pin thrust into its side will eliminate interferences from the shadow of the hand (Figure 4.5).

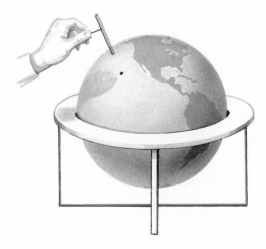

FIGURE 4.5   *The subsolar point.*

If direct sunlight is not available, or if one desires to locate the point for other hours or other days of the year, one should study the periodic motions of the point. The north-south motion is indicated by means of the *analemma,* that curious figure-eight diagram found over the eastern Pacific on many globes. It is simply a graph of the different locations of the subsolar point, by latitude, for the different days of the year.

The desired longitude may be calculated from your knowledge of standard time and the fact that the point moves westward at the rate of 15° per hour. At noon, standard time, it should be over your standard meridian. Since the meridians drawn upon a globe are usually standard meridians or "hour circles," 15° apart, the desired location can be readily determined for other hours of the day. However, for greatest accuracy, these results should be adjusted according to the equation of time, since the sun is not always exactly "on the meridian" at noon. This correction can be obtained from the analemma, which bends to the east or west of its central meridian to the exact degree that the sun is ahead, or behind, schedule for each day. If the sun is fast (or the clock slow) for a particular day, the subsolar point will be to the *west* of the expected position. If the sun is slow (or the clock is fast) the corresponding deviation will be to the *east.* This correction would be a simpler affair if some globes did not have analemmas printed in the reverse of those of other manufacturers; a standardization is clearly in order.

The subsolar point has several applications to mathematical geography. As it moves westward over the globe, it indicates the constantly moving meridian of local noon, apparent solar time. It also provides a simple method for calculating the elevation of the sun at any given place. Since this elevation would be 90° above the horizon at the subsolar point, for every degree of a great circle that one moves away from the point, the sun will sink one degree lower in the sky (Figure 4.6). This elevation is most generally calculated for the elevation of the sun at noon; one need merely find the number of degrees between his latitude and that of the point for the desired day, and subtract this figure from 90°. At other times of the day, when one is not measuring a north-south distance along a meridian (which is a great circle), the direction of a string stretched between one's location and that of the point will indicate the azimuth of the sun at that hour; the length of the string, when laid along a meridian or the equator, will give the number of degrees which must be subtracted from 90° to give the elevation.

THE LENGTH OF DAYLIGHT

Another basic topic of mathematical geography, the varying duration of daylight by latitude and season, can be clearly demonstrated with the

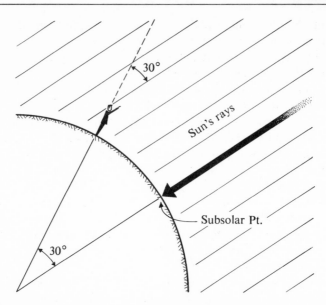

FIGURE 4.6   *Elevation of the sun.*

globe. One of the simplest exercises is to rectify the globe in direct sunlight, and then measure the distance in degrees, along a parallel, from one shadow to another. The result, when converted into hours and min- utes at the standard rate of 15° per hour, will give the interval between sunrise and sunset, at the given latitude on the day chosen for the demonstration.

This simple method has two disadvantages. Even under the best con- ditions, reflected light will blur the edge of the shadow, and the exercise is valid for only one day of the year. With a little effort, these disad- vantages can be overcome by substituting a rubber band, stretched about the globe to form a great circle, for the edge of the shadow. The position of the band can be determined by locating the subsolar point for the given time by means of the analemma, and placing the band the required 90° away. Although requiring more care in its execution, this method gives a sharp, thin boundary from which to measure, and can be made to work for any chosen day of the year.

If the globe has a horizon ring, a third method, superior to the others, may be tried. Simply rectify the globe for the desired latitude; in this position the ring and certain parallels on the globe will resemble the *armillary sphere,* an old astronomical instrument which was designed for the study of earth-space phenomena. Both the globe and the armillary sphere, in turn, will resemble a diagram of seasonal paths of the sun (Figure 4.7). The horizon ring of the globe is analogous to the earth's horizon on the diagram (from whence this ring obtained its name). Each parallel of latitude corresponds to the path of the sun on the dates when

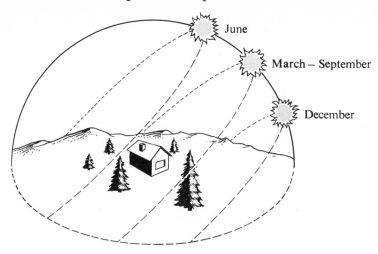

FIGURE 4.7   *The armillary sphere.*

the subsolar point is over that latitude; for example, the equator represents the path of the sun at the equinoxes, and the tropic lines the path at the solstices. For other dates, the appropriate parallel can be selected with the aid of the analemma. Further, the inclination of these parallels to the horizon ring of the globe will be the same as the inclination of the paths of the sun to the horizon at the locality of the observer, and both values, when measured from the vertical, will be equal to the latitude of the observer.

This basic model can be applied to the problem of the length of daylight by choosing a given date of the year, and the appropriate parallel of the subsolar point. The number of degrees which exist along the upper portion of this parallel, from horizon ring to horizon ring, is the number of degrees which the sun must trace from horizon to horizon on the selected day. By counting the intersecting 15° meridians as hour circles, one can readily convert this measurement into units of time.

This demonstration need not be confined to one's own latitude. By rectifying the globe for other locations, a variety of patterns of sun paths can be shown, ranging from the equatorial ones, perpendicular to the horizon ring, to those for the poles, which parallel the ring. Each position will demonstrate different seasonal patterns of daylight and darkness, from the constant twelve-hour days at the equator to the long polar days and nights. One will notice, however, that the horizon ring and the equator, being great circles, will always intersect each other at locations

180° apart, giving a geometric proof of the balance between day and night at the equinoxes.

Since the inclinations of the sun paths vary by latitude, this set of exercises will also show the variations in the length of twilight from place to place. Thus, in the tropical regions the more or less vertical paths permit the sun to pass rapidly below the horizon, resulting in short periods of dusk, and dawns that "come up like thunder." In high latitudes the reverse is true, and for locations between 60° and 66½° the "white nights" of the summer solstice can be demonstrated.

The results of all the foregoing determinations of length of daylight are theoretical values, uncorrected for the time that the sun's disk takes to cross the horizon, or for the refraction of light. Correcting for these factors can add as much as ten or fifteen minutes to the final results.

TIME AND THE GLOBE

The last two sets of demonstrations pertain to another topic of secondary school geography and earth science, the modern system of time keeping. When the subsolar point crosses any meridian on the earth, it will be noon, apparent solar time, along that line. (This must be corrected according to the equation of time to give the time of noon, mean solar time, or local time.) Because an infinite number of meridians could be drawn upon the earth, a Babel of local times plagued the transportation and communications industries prior to the advent of standard time in 1883.

Since the meridians drawn upon a common globe are hour circles, spaced 15° apart, they coincide with the standard meridians of most time zones. The instructor can point out the standard meridian for his own time zone on the globe and, by moving the pointer to the meridians to the east and west, indicate the other time zones of North America and their hourly differences from his own time or that of Greenwich. (Caution should be taken to remember that a few localities, such as Newfoundland and certain nations of southeast Asia, are on half-hourly zones based upon meridians 7½° from the standard ones.)

If one were to continue to move from one standard meridian to the next, noting the hourly change with each move, a complete circuit of the earth would result in a total change of 24 hours, or one full day. To explain how this problem has been solved, the instructor should turn the Pacific Ocean on his globe to the class and show the International Date Line. Usually shown as a prominent, dark red band, it straddles the 180th meridian in such a fashion as to avoid passing through inhabited land masses or archipelagoes. Upon crossing this line during the demonstration of time changes, the teacher should add or subtract a full day in such a manner as to counterbalance the steady loss or gain of hours, thus explaining the purpose and need for this feature of the earth's time system.

To aid in exercises of this nature, some globes have been equipped with graduated metal disks which may be spun around the North Pole. Although useful in individual work, they are hardly visible to a large classroom and will eventually wear into the surface of the globe. A better procedure is to turn the pole toward the class and use the meridians and pointer for one's reckoning.

5

The reality of maps

*A map is the beginning of adventure. Travel and treasure hunts, wars
and explorations, all open with its unrolling. Even in your armchair
a map is a magic carpet, taking the mind in a flash just where you
want to go.* DONALD C. PEATTIE

MANY PROFESSIONAL GEOGRAPHERS of today became interested
in geography through daydreaming over maps. Some of our textbooks
encourage students to indulge their fancy in poring over material on faraway places. This is a stimulating experience. To look at pictures and
find the places on a map, to travel with Alexander the Great through his
world, to be with Caesar in Gaul, to be with Daniel Boone on the Wilderness Road; all of these fantasies are learning experiences for a student.
But there comes a time when the teacher must guide the student into the
reality of the present, into the stimulating present.

The lines on a map represent real roads and railroads. They connect
real towns and cities. The area showing the distribution of corn shows
the area where real corn is grown. Real present-day problems can be
solved by these three items of information. Where is the corn grown?
Where is it consumed? What route does it take from farm to city? These
are real questions not based on fantasy. This can be as exciting as any
other mystery. It is a detective story; it is research.

With the background that most teachers have in child psychology they
must recognize when a child is enveloped in the fantasy of maps; and
then they must turn that interest, while it is still at its peak, into productive fields. However, never discourage a child from indulging in day-
dreams over maps. From these daydreamers will come our explorers, our
researchers, our geography teachers. In years to come, this student will,
if nothing more, be able to plan a logical vacation route by automobile.
If a teacher has never tried or has forgotten about this enjoyment of maps,
he may find it a pleasant way to learn new facts that will enrich teaching.

There is a danger that when one has been teaching in a given grade a long time, he will begin to act and think almost at that level. In using maps, the teacher must be above the mental level he is teaching; the concepts must be much broader and must include more facts than they can possibly convey to the student. The teacher must change mundane facts into the magic that takes the map out of the realm of fantasy and makes it real. In order for this to happen, the map must be a real teaching aid, used in the hard work of explaining locations and patterns and interpreting them so that the student can learn to make valid judgments for himself. There is no magic by which the teacher can transform the map into reality.

FRUSTRATIONS

All cartography starts with frustration. It is impossible to show or develop a sphere on a flat surface. On a globe it is possible to show four correct aspects of the earth: correct distance, correct direction, correct shape, and correct area. A map can show combinations of these, but it cannot show all four at the same time. Projections have been devised that show selected aspects in their correct relations. Some maps are developed from figures that are placed on the globe and then opened (developed) to lie flat. The common figures used are the cone and the cylinder, either tangent or secant, and the plane. Other projections are mathematical.

Certain projections are designed to take advantage of varied properties. The Mercator projection is frequently the most common projection in a school. This projection has probably been criticized more than all others. In reality, it has two strong points in its favor: it is conformal, that is, the shapes are correct; and the directions are correct. The greater distortions are in the higher latitudes while the least distortion is in the lower latitudes where most emphasis is placed in school geography. If the exaggerated polar areas distract from the information under discussion, cut these areas off. Frequently an equal-area projection will distort shapes to the point that they are no longer recognizable.

During World War II there was a concerted and commendable effort to popularize the use of more kinds of projections. No student should arrive in the upper grades without knowing about various projections and their different uses. These differences should become part of his real world, part of his real experience. He cannot acquire this experience unless the teacher exposes him to it. One projection that has been advocated strongly is the polar azimuthal equidistant. This exchanges one frustration for another. In the Mercator projection the poles are at infinity; in all cylindrical projections the pole is either a line or at infinity; in the polar projections, the pole is in the center, and the equator is a circle around it. Now the idea of north is confused. According to the standard orientation, north is to the top of the map. In the polar projections of the northern hemisphere north is toward the center from all directions. You have now changed one misconception for another.

If an interrupted projection is used, another set of misconceptions takes place. The poles are represented by points. Frequently as many as six points represent the two poles. In trying to show some correct relationships other serious distortions have been perpetrated. The area between the lobes of an interrupted projection is space and the distance from South America to Australia is increased by just this much additional space.

The only way to solve the frustration of projections is to take a course in cartography and learn how projections are designed and the uses of them. You cannot teach Greek without having studied Greek; the same is true for projections — to teach projections you must have studied projections. There is no easy method of learning about this field just as there is no easy method of learning any other field of mathematics.

Most schools do not have adequate budgets for maps. It is frustrating for the teacher to go to the map closet and pull out a map that shows the Austrian Empire with a coastline on the Adriatic Sea. This could be a good map for showing Europe before World War I, but is not a good map for showing modern boundaries of Europe. This is a real situation and there are several solutions.

The first that comes to mind is to get a larger budget for maps. This approach should not be condemned without trying it. Most officials dealing with budgets are not completely unreasonable; however, requests for maps must fit into the general plans for the organization. If the teacher can support a plea for money with concrete evidence, he will have a better chance of getting funds for maps; but if he does not make the proper effort in the proper way to the proper official, he will never get what he needs. A person who is pleading a cause must believe in the cause or his plea will fall flat.

The second way of getting maps is to find out about free copies. There are many organizations that distribute free maps. Some of these are various branches of government, federal, state, and local. Learned societies often have free maps that have appeared in their journals, or that they have published separately. Some of these can be adapted for use in the classroom. Consult the *Guide to Free and Inexpensive Material for Elementary Teachers* published by the Educators Progress Service, Randolph, Wisconsin.

The third method is to do it yourself. This can be real frustration, for teachers are busy people. A good wall map can be made by projecting a map on a 6- by 4-foot sheet of lightweight fiberboard. Paint the land with yellow ochre quick-drying wall paint and the water with a pale blue paint. The coastline can be a dark blue put on with a narrow brush. Symbols can be made out of colored paper or stencils can be cut out of cardboard and then spray paint used.

Materials already on hand may be adapted. Most elementary teachers are experienced in the use of the flannel graph. Land and water shapes may be cut from different color flannel or rough paper. Symbols also may be made from cloth or paper. Roads, railroads, and boundaries can be shown by colored floss or heavy yarn.

One should also consider the possibility of modifying that old map that hangs in the front of the room. Various methods can be used. Perhaps the art department could make suggestions as to methods. Boundaries can be updated by painting out the old boundary or by pasting opaque paper over it, and then drawing in the new boundary. A brush, wide-pointed lettering pen, or the newer felt pens can be used. Perhaps the old map is so hopeless that the only salvageable part is the roller; perhaps a new map can be glued over the old one.

Frustration coupled with imagination will solve real problems; however, there are no pat methods of solving individual difficulties. Each teacher has to know his own abilities realistically, know what resources exist in his own school system, and know the students with whom he is dealing. Every teacher faces a different set of circumstances in teaching any aspect of geography.

A GOOD MAP

The *good* map is one that has what you want to show. No matter how fancy and erudite the material may be on a map, if it does not show the combination of factors in which one is interested, it is not a good map. If the teacher does not know what he wants the map to show, no map is a *good* one. The value of the map is in what the teacher proposes to do with it.

It is erroneous thinking to suppose that a map will take the place of good preparation. This teaching aid cannot take the burden of poor lesson planning away from the teacher; in fact, it may increase the burden by no longer being an aid but by becoming a distraction.

For what can the teacher logically use a map? He can show locations and comparative locations. He can show distribution and patterns of distribution. He can show area relationships. These are the real problems that can be solved with a map. He can also point out recurring patterns that take place — the same kinds of patterns appearing in population distribution, transportation patterns, physical landscape, and land use. The teacher cannot, however, logically expect a physical map to show population distribution.

A _good_ map need not be complicated. Frequently the simpler the map the quicker the purpose of the map is understood.

THE REALITY OF TERMS

In 1947 the National Geographic Society published a monograph entitled, "The Round Earth on Flat Paper." This was a very catchy title and should have been left with the article and not detached for use with the concept of globe versus map. Geographers have been trying to use descriptive words with limited meaning. The meaning of _round_ is not limited. Webster's unabridged dictionary gives sixty-five meanings for _round_. In using the term _round_ do we mean like an apple or an orange, like a hoop or an embroidery frame, or like the trimmed ears of a dog? The relationship between a globe and a map is hard enough to explain without using a word that is subject to sixty-four misinterpretations.

Frequently, the statement is made that the earth is pear shaped. What kind of pear are you talking about, one that has a bulge at the blossom end or one that has a bulge in the middle? Are you sure that you and the student are thinking about the same pear when you discuss the earth? Geographers might do well to leave pear shaped as a term to the voice teachers where it has a real meaning. Even to use the word spheroid in describing the earth implies a serious departure from the shape of a true sphere. The shape of the earth is so close to being a sphere that at the scales teachers use the bulge cannot be measured or shown. Therefore, to become involved in a long explanation to an elementary class about the departure of the earth from true spherical shape is a needless waste of time. Reserve the explanation for a time when this bulge is important to the discussion at hand.

Latitude and longitude cannot be taught adequately until the student knows how angles are measured. Even many professional geographers have an erroneous concept of what latitude and longitude really are. Defining these phenomena, they use such expressions as "distance and direction," "imaginary lines on the earth," and "great circles." Latitude is location by means of angular measurement, expressed in degrees, minutes, and seconds measured from the plane of the equator. Longitude is the same thing measured from the plane of the prime meridian. Innumerable angles can be measured from the centers of these two planes. This center is also the center of the earth.

Contrary to popular belief, there are no imaginary lines of parallels and meridians on the earth. However, there are real parallels and meridians on globes and maps. These real lines of parallels and meridians make up the grid system. On the globe, this is a spherical grid; on the map, it is a mathematical grid. Projections can be either systematic mathematical grids or developed geometric figures.

In locating a point by means of coordinates two axes are established; from the point of intersection of these two perpendicular lines all other points are located. The quadrants are either $+$ or $-$. The equator and the prime meridian can be used for the formation of x and y axes. In order to have only positive numbers, north and south of the equator and east and west of the prime meridian are indicated instead of $+$ or $-$. By locating and connecting the intersections of latitude and longitude, a grid of intersecting parallels and meridians can be constructed.

This method is the foundation of all mathematically derived projections. By varying the mathematical properties, different intervals are obtained, making unlimited the kinds of mathematical projections.

Latitude and parallel do not refer to the same thing. Latitude gives a location; parallel describes a line on a grid having all points at the same latitude. Neither are longitude and meridian the same. Again longitude gives a location; while meridian describes a line on a grid having all points at the same longitude.

By separating the concepts latitude-longitude from parallel-meridian, one can discuss properties of both without confusion. When the two systems of terminology are combined, such statements as these occur: Latitude is an imaginary line on the earth, and lines of latitude measure lines of longitude, or rather, the interval between lines of latitude measure longitude.

Some student is sure to ask, "How do you know the distance between those two lines is 10°?" or "How many lines can you draw or get between 45° and 50°?" These questions reflect a lack of knowledge of circular measurement. Frequently students do not know the necessary vocabulary to phrase the question to indicate how deep their ignorance is. The student frequently will not know that measurement involves less than a degree. He thinks that there is some mystery in the selection of a 5°, 10°, or 20° interval on a grid. He cannot understand the arbitrary angles the teacher draws on the blackboard. At this point the teacher will have to teach angular measurement; the facts will mean more and have a greater practical use than at any other time.

When used with latitude and longitude the cardinal points of the compass are not directions but part of the system of locating in relation to the equator and the prime meridian. It is usual to orient a grid with one axis horizontal and the other vertical. *This may orient the grid, but it does not orient a map.* To be correctly oriented a map should be placed parellel to the earth and the cardinal points matched. Many experiments have been made painting a map on the floor or playground. The method is fine to teach a child east from west and how to find his way out of the schoolyard. However, a more sophisticated approach must be used when discussing a map on a polar projection with north in the center, no matter how the map is turned.

The concept of direction is learned in childhood. In the area of the country that has surveys on the section and range principle, the child learns that property lines and streets are oriented with the cardinal points of the compass. Children that are brought up in areas where the old metes and bounds system of land survey still is practiced have little concept of direction by the compass. It would be impossible to tell a stranger to go two blocks south-southwest and turn east by east. City children also have less concept of compass direction than rural children.

Another factor in the oversimplification of direction has been the use of cylindrical projections in the early grades. In these projections the parallels are parallel to the equator and the meridians are perpendicular to both the parallels and the equator. The result is that east and west are always perpendicular to north and south (Figure 5.1). The entire

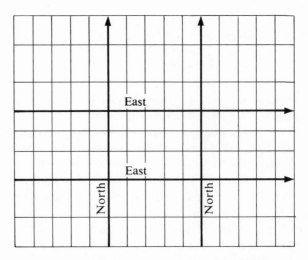

Figure 5.1 _The arrangement of parallels and meridians gives the impression that a given direction is parallel to the same direction anywhere on the map. East and West are perpendicular._

concept of direction is based on this erroneous impression that meridians are parallel to each other, and as a result any two lines that are parallel are oriented in the same direction. When other projections are used in class that show meridians and parallels similar to the arrangement on the globe,

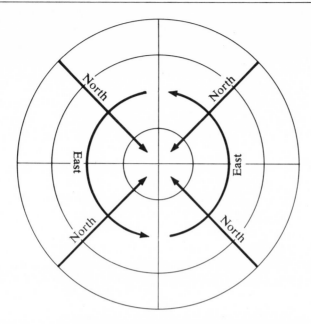

FIGURE 5.2 *A polar projection approaches the arrangement of parallels and meridians on a globe as seen from above. North is always toward the center of the globe. East circles about the pole. Moreover, the angular relation of parallels and meridians is always the same.*

the student becomes confused (Figures 5.2, 5.3, 5.4). He has assumed that the cylindrical projection is the normal, and all the others must be deviating from normal. The concept of direction should not be taught from one of the projections that has perpendicular meridians and parallels.

The American Indians had five directions, north, south, east, west, and up. They were conscious of the areas about them. They did not have a designation for down as a direction. It might be well if we employed five or six directions to avoid talking about north being at the top of the map. We all know better but we still point to the polar area of a Mercator projection and refer to it as, "up at the top of the map." This is really confusing because we frequently hear Tibet called the "Top of the World."

The concept of direction should be based on the idea that maps can be turned upside down. The north arrow on many maps gives the wrong impression. True north may be at that angle only at that location while in another part of the map, a second north arrow is almost at right angles to the first. On the north polar projection all north arrows would point to the center of the map (Figure 5.2). The polar projection would be a poor one to try to orient by putting it on the floor; it can only be truly oriented at the pole. To confuse matters still further, magnetic north and true

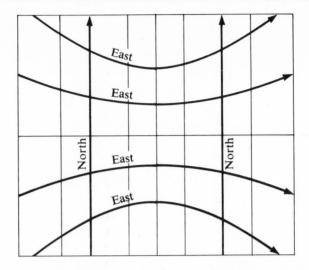

FIGURE 5.3   *The meridians are oriented in the same way as in Figure 5.1. However, the parallels are curves so that East appears to be pointing in all directions. On this projection (gnomonic) all great circles appear as straight lines; therefore all meridians are shown as straight lines. It is obvious that Figures 5.1 and 5.3 give different concepts of direction.*

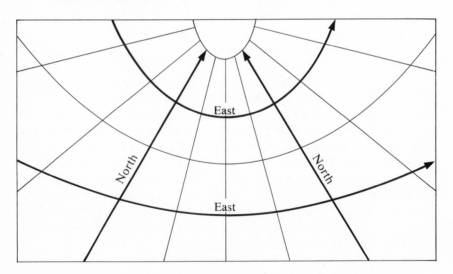

FIGURE 5.4   *In this example of a gnomonic projection, the North arrow points to the pole as in the polar projection. The meridians are still great circles shown as straight lines. The parallels are not parallel. Using this to explain direction may be confusing, for this projection can show only true distance.*

north are not often the same. Not only are they not the same, but magnetic north is constantly changing. It is only when a map is used in the field that real significance should be attached to this. Anyone using maps for field trips, or where direction is important, must explain this difference to the class concerned. Using maps in classrooms will usually not require the use of the compass.

Teachers can expect the question, "Why is Kamchatka east of New York on this map and west of New York on that map?" In this situation, the world map has the central meridian as the prime meridian. This puts Great Britain in the center of the projection. If the central meridian is selected so that the United States is in the center, then Kamchatka moves to the other side of the map. If you are using a map of the Eastern States, New Orleans will appear in the southwestern part of the map. However, if you are using a map of the Western United States, New Orleans will appear in the southeastern part. The location of New Orleans has not changed, only its relative position on the map has moved. It may be a real problem for students to understand that direction is relative and subject to change; at the same time, the direction from Chicago to New Orleans is constant and cannot change. In addition, the teacher will have to stress that direction alone will not locate a point. When direction is used to locate one town in relation to another, distance must also be considered. This is another method of location that can be used instead of using latitude and longitude. If the student can give the bearing from one point to another, and if he knows the distance, then he has located the point.

MAP SCALES

To a large extent the usefulness of a map depends upon its size. An accurate map, regardless of size or area covered, must have a definite relationship to the size of the area of the earth's surface it represents. The making of a map, then, is actually the measurement of the shape and size of an area. Since the actual size of the area cannot be shown on the map, the map is developed in proportion to the actual size. The fractional proportion is called the map scale. As the map is only a fraction of the actual size of the area mapped, it is possible to measure distance on the map only when the fraction or scale is known.

Three types of map scales are shown on many maps — fractional, verbal, graphic. The fractional scale may be shown as, for example 1/63,360 or 1 : 63,360. This simply means that one unit of measurement (inch, foot, yard, or whatever it is) on the map is equal to 63,360 of the same units on the face of the earth. Thus, if the 1 represents 1 inch on the map, the 63,360 represents the number of inches on the surface of the earth. Since there are 63,360 inches in a mile, the fraction means 1 inch on the map represents 1 mile on the earth. In like manner the fraction 1/31,680 could mean 1 inch on the map is equal to ½ mile on the earth, or 2 inches on the map is equal to 1 mile.

The verbal scale is a statement of the actual situation. Such statements could be as follows: one inch equals one mile, one inch equals 300 miles, and so on. The verbal scale is a written statement of the fractional scale.

The graphic scale is the scale most frequently used by elementary and secondary school students as well as most nongeographers. The graphic scale may be shown on the map as a line or as a double line with divisions marked thereon. This scale is divided into units which represent actual and definite distances on the surface of the earth in the area shown on the map. Making measurements by using the graphic scale is simple enough that elementary students can be taught the procedure without difficulty.

REALITY OF MAP READING

Map reading, like any other reading, is done by means of symbols that have no meaning until combined. The alphabet can be combined to make meaningful words if you know the language. Chemical symbols have meaning if you understand the language of chemistry. Map symbols are similar to those used in vocal language and to those used in science. A German, Russian, Iranian, or Turk can read a map printed in English if he can understand the legend. In the same way, an English speaking person can read a map printed in German, Russian, Persian, or Turkish if he can understand the legend.

However, there are no absolutely standard symbols, like those in chemistry. Map symbols are more like the letters making words where the word carries the meaning. *Sale* means one thing in English and another in French; a circle means a city on one map and a mine on another. A dot means a village in one case and 10,000 pigs in another. A solid black line is a railroad on some maps; on others it may be a boundary. If the solid line is a boundary, it may be a county boundary on the map we use today, but on tomorrow's map it is a country boundary.

There are some symbols that are used frequently enough to need no explanation. Some of these symbols come from a list that was standardized for use on United States Government maps. This list or sheet of symbols is sold by the United States Geological Survey, Coast and Geodetic Survey, and the Hydrographic Office. The United States Army also has a technical manual which contains the same information. Before using any map, the user should check the legend to determine the degree of standardization, if any, that has been adhered to by the maker.

Some maps are so designed that they do not need an explanation, and the legend is omitted. Explanatory notes may be stuck in corners of the map, in the margins, or even on the reverse side. There is really no correct place to put a legend. The placement of the legend box is a design by plan or compilation problem. The cartographer locates the legend some place that will not detract from the content of the map. After all, the legend is not the purpose of the map; it is more in the nature of an index and should be as inconspicuous as the index of a book.

Colored areas on a map have very little real meaning. Hypsometric, or layer-tinted, maps are almost standardized with green for the lowlands and reddish brown for the highlands. Geology has standardized the colors for geological maps. Other than these two types, color has no standardized meaning. The fact that the United Kingdom, in the past, was colored red on some political maps has no real justification for maps of today. This was a design technique to show a certain unity. Any other color could be used just as effectively. A teacher should never imply that a student should expect to find France any particular color on a map. Much of the effectiveness of a map is in the design, but the design should never be misunderstood for the real function, which is to show location, size, and spacial relationships.

Because of scale limitations size of symbol may be exaggerated. The width of a line that represents a railroad is really several miles wide on a map. Again, because of scale, a line cannot show every bend in a river or road. In order to make symbols visible at a distance, wall maps are among the most generalized of maps.

The visibility of a map to a class is highly important. "If you could see this pink line . . . ," should never be said by a teacher. If crucial parts of the map are invisible, the map is no longer an aid, but has become a distraction.

There are several problems involved in seeing a wall map. First, the type may be too fine for legibility. Second, the symbols may be too small. Third, the colors may be too pastel to carry to the back of the room. Fourth, the lighting may be too poor. Fifth, some students may be sitting at the wrong angle to get a direct view of the map; they see a highly distorted image. Sixth, some students may be so nearsighted that they cannot see the map unless they are a foot from it. Seventh, some students are color-blind. All teachers should be aware of the symptoms of myopia and color-blindness. All of the above problems can be corrected except that of color-blindness, and that is not too serious if it is understood. There are professional cartographers who are color-blind.

There has been a program in recent years to put foreign languages into the public schools, particularly French, German, and Spanish. One of the problems is common to all teaching — motivation. In this situation geography teachers can fill a real need by using foreign language maps. Since map reading is done by means of symbols, foreign words become just another symbol. The language barrier is not so great as it would be if textual material alone were used. By this method a learning situation is created wherein the student must consult the appropriate language lexicon in order to fully understand the map. The process is not a burden because a legend has only a limited number of items that must be translated. When it is completed the student has solved a real problem in both geography and language. Here also symbolic language has been used to help convey ideas. The map symbols may be pictorial or abstract; the language symbols may be in the Roman alphabet or some other. The results are reading, and concepts that were unknown become known.

THE REALITY OF MAP EDUCATION

"Americans always want everything in a nut-shell; what you get depends on the size of the shell — a peanut or a coconut."[1] Discussing maps in one chapter is putting the subject in a small size peanut shell. Most of this discussion has centered around maps that a teacher could use before a class, that is, a wall map.

There are dozens of map types. Some are suitable for use with large classes, some with small classes, and some only for desk use. The three types cannot be substituted for each other. The ideal situation is for the teacher to have a *good* wall map to use in discussion before the class, the student should have a desk map to refer to later, this can be in a text or atlas; and the student should have an outline map on which to record notes and ideas. This method gives map work a real function in the learning process.

Map work should never degenerate into busy work! The teacher should use the wall map to discuss location, extent, and areal relationships. The student should use the outline map to take notes. This entire procedure should be deliberate and not accidental. This is a method of integrating "Major Concepts in Geography"[2] of Dr. Henry J. Warman.

About a quarter of a century ago, Dr. Erwin Raisz pioneered teaching cartography in higher education. Today, many colleges and universities offer courses in cartography and map reading, most of which are designed for geographers with little mathematical background. One of these courses would be invaluable to the geography teacher. There are no mysteries in maps except those that exist in a closed mind. Many times a map is the

---

[1] Dr. Zein N. Zein, Professor of History, American University of Beirut, Lebanon.
[2] Wilhelmina Hill (ed.), *Curriculum Guide for Geographic Education*, Geographic Education Series No. 3 (Normal, Illinois: National Council for Geographic Education, 1964), pp. 9–27.

only way to show areal information. When a mapping technique is used, frequently, gaps in the information appear that were not seen when the lack of information was covered by words. In the last few years, several books have been published about teaching geography. In most of them a section is devoted to maps. Since maps are the major tool of the geographer, serious teachers of the subject are going to be forced to know more about them. While books and articles, such as those that appear in *The Journal of Geography*, may help in a general way, a good teacher of geography will increasingly be expected to take college level work in map reading or cartography. After such a course the teacher will have a real appreciation for maps.

CONCLUSION

Some of the frustrations of map problems can be solved by understanding how maps are compiled, designed, drafted, and printed. With the security that even partial understanding of these processes brings, a teacher can end the frustration of not knowing what to expect from a *good* map. Various map publishers have programs to increase the proficiency of classroom teachers in the use of maps. Dr. Clarence B. Odell has said, "The professional geographers associated with the educational publishers can only light the candle — but the classroom teacher must walk into the dark alone."[1] If the teacher uses imagination to solve the frustrations of maps, the candle which the publishers and professional geographers have supplied will be a flaming torch.

---

[1] "The Growing Responsibility of Educational Publishers in the Training of Geography Teachers," *Geography Teaching in Schools: Problems and Methods:* Final Report of the Commission on Teaching of Geography, XXth International Geographic Congress, London, 1965, p. 46.

6

The outdoor laboratory

*Learning how to study the landscape is essential in functional
geographic education because the landscape is the basic course of
all geographic knowledge. Thus every school has a ready-made
geography laboratory in the landscape of the local community.*

ZOE A. THRALLS

ALTHOUGH EACH STUDENT lives in a physical and cultural setting,
most are little aware of it and take it for granted. Travelers may come
for miles to see what the pupil barely notices. The outdoor laboratory,
then, can be used to make the pupil keenly aware of his surroundings so
that he may use the geographical setting he knows as a standard for
comparison with what he reads about other places.

The physical setting is present even in the most inner-city school
grounds. There may be neither exposed rocks nor any vegetation to be
seen, but the sun shines causing the temperature to go up and down. Relative humidity varies, rainfalls, and even the effect of distant volcanic
eruptions can be noticed in the color of the sunset. Certainly the effect of
drought is noticeable in the limited water supply of some of the larger
eastern cities.

The cultural setting is everywhere in settlement and transportation patterns, ethnic groups, and economic activities. Sometimes the cultural patterns all but obliterate the physical ones.

In the outdoors the pupil learns by using all his senses in exploring or
discovering. The teacher helps by posing questions and directing the
observing. This ancient method was used by Socrates, but is still a most
effective one that can be used even with nonreaders. The learner looks
for himself, thinks about what he has observed, and tries to put together
a reasonable answer to the teacher's questions. He is, in essence, following
the scientific way we learn anything.

The scientific method produces many solutions; however, only a few of
them may be correct. The search for the correct or most probable is the

next step. The pupils soon learn that all their proposed solutions will not be right. They learn to look again, recheck their findings, and make new proposed solutions. In this way they learn that science proceeds by eliminating errors. This contact with the scientific method can begin in the elementary grades and is easiest done in the outdoor laboratory.

Outdoor learning can also make good use of the prime tool of the geographer, the map. There is no better way to learn the values and limitations of maps than to go outdoors with a map in hand.

Any teacher who wants to teach outdoors in the local situation must first become a local expert. The beginning may be to find a geography of the state which will give an overall picture of the physical and cultural setting. He should learn the underlying rock structure and its significance, local soils (if they are important agriculturally), temperature and rainfall regimes, climate, and landforms. The settlement pattern, ethnic groups in the population, economic activities, transportation net, and other cultural factors will help explain the pattern of people locally. There is no substitute for this background preparation. The teacher who does not know what exists in his surroundings cannot point it out to his pupils.

USEFUL MAPS

The best assortment of mapping materials for use in the outdoors will include an enlargement of an aerial photo, 40 inches by 40 inches in size, scale 1 : 4,800 (1 inch equals 400 feet) of the area including the school grounds, and several of the 7½′ sheets of the school grounds and surroundings, trimmed and mounted together on the wall of the classroom (Figure 6.1). Nine contiguous sheets of the 7½′ series (three across and three down) mounted together will make a map 57 inches by 72 inches, an excellent picture of the area surrounding home base. Also useful will be as large a city map as can be found, preferably one that locates and names each street. (Figure 6.2). Gas stations and local auto clubs are sometimes the best sources of such maps, although commercially produced and sold maps are usually available for the larger cities. Pupils in rural schools will probably have to make their own local maps. The fact that the photo and the maps will be at different scales will help the pupils adjust to the use of scale in reading a map, a necessary ability if pupils are to use maps in the field.

The pupils will be plotting on base maps or making their own maps as they work outdoors. They can check the accuracy of their maps against the aerial photo, the topographic series, and the city map.[1]

---

[1] A useful reference for the teacher not well acquainted with maps is: David Greenhood, *Mapping* (Chicago: University of Chicago Press, 1951).

FIGURE 6.1   *Section of the aerial photo enlargement, 1 : 4,800 covering the campus of Towson State College.*

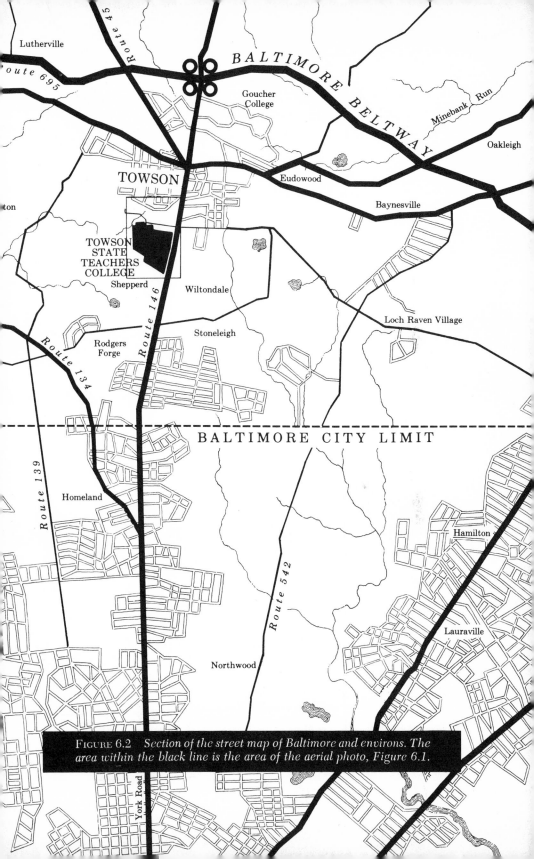

FIGURE 6.2 *Section of the street map of Baltimore and environs. The area within the black line is the area of the aerial photo, Figure 6.1.*

Detailed maps that include the school grounds may be obtainable from the United States Geological Survey. Map coverage, however, is not complete for the entire United States at all scales. A quadrange covering 1° of latitude and 1° of longitude is at the scale 1 : 250,000 (1 inch equals approximately 4 miles). These maps were made by the United States Army Map Service, but are published and distributed for civilian use by the Geologic Survey. Complete coverage is available for the entire United States at this scale. The next largest scale has a quadrangle that includes 30′ of latitude and 30′ of longitude. The scale is 1 : 125,000 (1 inch equals approximately 2 miles). It takes four quadrangles at 1 : 125,000 to cover the same area as one quadrangle at 1 : 250,000. More useful is a quanrangle covering 15′ of latitude and 15′ of longitude. The scale is 1 : 62,500 (1 inch equals approximately 1 mile). Most useful and most detailed of all is a quadrangle covering 7½′ of latitude and 7½′ of longitude. The scale is 1 : 24,000 (1 inch equals 2,000 feet). It takes sixty-four map sheets of the 7½′ series to cover the same area as one map of 1 : 250,000.[1] (Figures 6.3, 6.4, 6.5).

AERIAL PHOTOGRAPHS

Aerial photos have been made of much of the United States. Two index maps showing the status of aerial mosaics (photo maps) and aerial photography (individual prints) are issued free on application to the United States Geological Survey. Each map is accompanied by a text which gives a detailed explanation. The scale of the index map is 1 : 5,000,000 or about 80 miles to the inch.

Aerial mosaics are available showing all areas of the United States for which mosaics or photomaps have been prepared from aerial photographs, scales of negatives, dates of photography, and agencies from which copies may be obtained. Color patterns indicate the holdings of various federal and state agencies and commercial firms that have reported their coverage to date.

The most easily available air photo coverage is made by the Agricultural Stabilization and Conservation Service of the United States Department of Agriculture although not all the nation is covered by this agency. Teachers will probably find an office of the ASCS in their county complete with index maps and helpful personnel who will aid in finding which aerial photo or photos include the school grounds. Information may also be available from the county agent. Contact prints of ASCS photos are

---

[1] Teachers interested in buying 7½′ and 15′ maps can obtain a free status index map (revised semiannually) from the United States Geologic Survey, Washington, D. C. 20242.

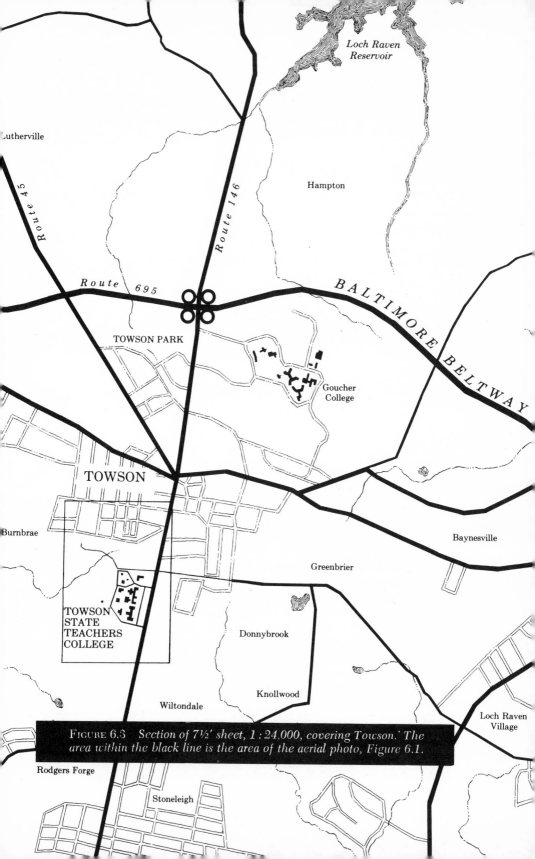

FIGURE 6.3   Section of 7½' sheet, 1 : 24,000, covering Towson.' The
area within the black line is the area of the aerial photo, Figure 6.1.

FIGURE 6.4   *Section of the 15' sheet, 1 : 62,500, covering Towson.
The area within the black line is the area of the 7½' section shown in
Figure 6.3.*

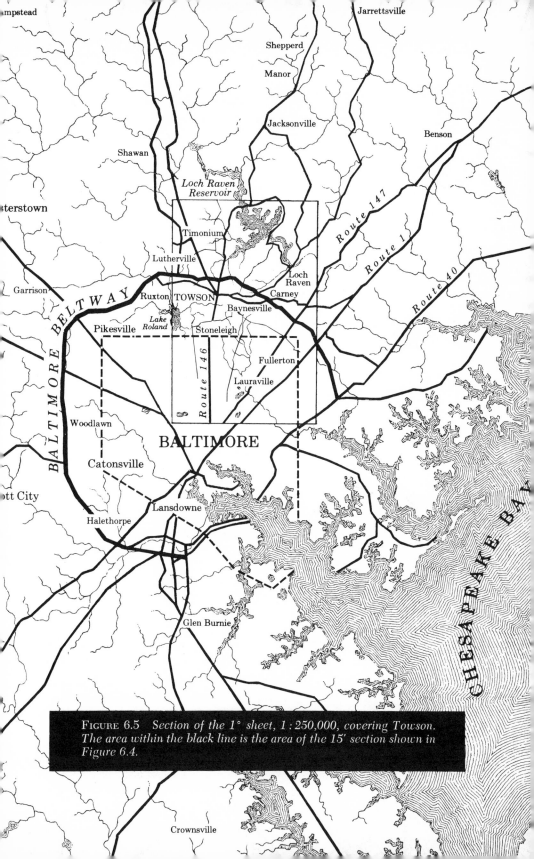

FIGURE 6.5 *Section of the 1° sheet, 1 : 250,000, covering Towson. The area within the black line is the area of the 15′ section shown in Figure 6.4.*

10 inches by 10 inches at a scale of 1 inch equaling 1,667 feet. They cost a dollar but are less expensive in quantity. Perhaps the best print for class use is an enlargement of the initial print to a size of 40 by 40 inches which makes the scale 1 inch equaling 400 feet or 1 : 4,800. The cost is $5.60 per print for single copies. The print is the most usable one the classroom teacher can have, for when it is mounted on a wall, it can be read easily without a magnifying glass.

FINDING TRUE NORTH

When the pupil goes outdoors with a map of his area in hand, the first thing he must do is orient the map — arrange it so that north on the map is aligned with true north. A compass may help, but the student must be made aware of the fact that the compass needle points to the north magnetic pole and not to the north geographic pole where all the meridians converge. In those places in the United States where the magnetic pole lines up with the geographic pole, the compass needle may point to both magnetic and true north at the same time. In most places, however, there are several degrees difference between the two norths.

It is not difficult to determine true north for any location if the time zone it is in and precise longitude of the place are known. With these two facts exact sun-time noon can be found for the locality. At that time any shadow cast will be directly north.

The United States is divided into four time zones, each taking the sun time of one meridian and using it for standard time throughout the zone. The Eastern Standard Time zone uses the 75th meridian, Central Standard Time the 90th, Mountain Standard Time the 105th, and Pacific Standard Time the 120th. It is only necessary to find the precise longitude of the place, find how far that is from the longitude line of the time zone, change the time difference from terms of space into terms of time, and then determine the precise sun time of the place.

For example, Towson, Maryland, is at 76° 36′ W longitude. It is in the Eastern Standard Time Zone, which takes its time from the 75th meridian. Towson is thus, 1° 36′ west of the meridian of the time zone. Since the earth rotates to the east, Towson has not yet had its noon when Eastern Standard Time is noon. A measure of space, 1° 36′ must be changed into units of time. The earth rotates 15° each hour, which is why the time zones are 15° apart. The earth's rotation is also

> 1° in each 4 minutes
> 30′ in each 2 minutes
> 15′ in each 1 minute
> 1′ in each 4 seconds

In changing the 1° 36′ of space into time, the 1° equals 4 minutes, the 36′ equals 2 minutes and 24 seconds of time, for a total of 6 minutes and 24 seconds of time. Since Towson has not had its sun noon at noon Eastern Standard Time, it must be having its sun noon exactly 6 minutes and 24 seconds later or 12:06 and 24 seconds Eastern Standard Time.

Drive a stake in the ground. A shadow cast at 12.06 and 24 seconds P.M. in Towson will point directly to true north. Laying a compass along side the line will show how many degrees the compass is off true north and whether it deviates west of north or east of north. As soon as the pupils have checked their compasses with the true north line, they will be able to use a compass to orient a map in the field correcting the compass for true north.

The stake in the ground can be made into a sundial by marking the location of the shadow at different times of the day. It will be more useful if it is marked according to standard time rather than according to sun time. If the time should be shifted to daylight saving time the sundial will be an hour slow.

Daylight saving time shifts are made by taking the time or the zone to the east. Eastern Standard Time becomes Eastern Daylight Saving Time by taking 60° meridian time (usually called Atlantic Time). Central Standard Time becomes Central Daylight Saving when the time is taken not from the 90° but from the 75°. Other zones shift similarly.

To determine sun time for Towson while it is on Eastern Daylight Saving Time, sun noon would be 16° 36′ west of the 60th meridian or one hour, 6 minutes, and 24 seconds after noon Eastern Daylight Saving Time, or 1 P.M. plus 6 minutes and 24 seconds.

It may be inconvenient for the teacher to have her class find true north at local sun time noon. An alternate way of determining true north is as follows: Find sun time as previously suggested. Towson's sun time in terms of Eastern Standard Time is 12:06 and 24 seconds P.M. Observations will be necessary two hours earlier and two hours later. At 10:06 and 24 seconds, see the shadow cast by the stake. Using the length of that shadow as a radius, draw an arc around the northern end of the stake. A string with a loop that slips over the stake will work nicely. Mark the place where the shadow meets the arc. Four hours later, at 2:06 and 24 seconds, the shadow of the stake will just meet the arc at another place. Mark that meeting. Now bisect the arc, using the two marked points as centers. From the point of bisection to the stake, draw a line. That line will be true north and south, and incidentally will be directly under the shadow of the sun at sun-time noon (Figure 6.6).

Pupils who have determined true north outdoors as specified can readily be introduced to the latitude and longitude system in the classroom.

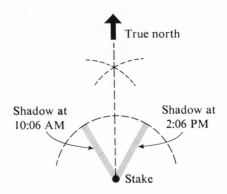

FIGURE 6.6   *Finding sun-time noon.*

UNITS OF MEASUREMENT

Few students have any first hand knowledge of units of length and units of area. Linear measurements that are most often referred to in pupil reading are the *kilometer* and the *mile*. The dictionary defines a kilometer as 0.621 of a mile, but is commonly thought of as 0.6 mile. Both a kilometer and a mile can be laid out by the teacher if his car odometer is accurate. Almost every school is on a main highway or street. The teacher could start from an established point on that highway, the front driveway of the school for example, drive 0.6 of a mile, establish the kilometer point, then finish the mile drive and establish that point. The pupils could then be told where the points are located and encouraged to walk the distances on their own time. It may be desirable to lay out a measured kilometer and a mile in two directions from school, or even in all four directions. Pupils could learn by walking that a mile is almost twice as long as a kilometer.

Perhaps the most common area measurement the pupil will read about is the *acre,* yet few pupils, particularly those living in a city, have any idea of how big an acre is. The dictionary is not much help. It tells that an acre in the United States and Great Britain is an area of 43,560 square feet or 1/640 of a square mile.

If the class measures the playground, some idea of the size of an acre may be obtained. Many playgrounds are rectangular. Measuring the length and width and multiplying them together gives the square footage. Suppose the playground is 300 feet long by 150 feet wide. Multiplying the length by the width gives 45,000 square feet or slightly more than an acre. (A football field is approximately one acre in area.)

An acre does not have to be a perfect square — in fact few farms are laid out in acre plots. The acreage of a farm is figured in much the same way as the playground has been measured.

To mark off an exact acre on the playground, the class can first use either side and divide that footage into 43,560 square feet to find the other dimension and then measure off that amount. If the 150-foot side of the playground is taken as a base and divided into 43,560, the other side of the acre would be 290.4 feet. This might also be measured on the 300-foot side of the playground and the acre approximated. If the 300-foot side is used as a base, the other side would be 111.9 feet. This would give a more elongated acre, but an acre nonetheless.

In the center of a large city, the playground may be less than an acre. The square footage could be found and that relationship to an acre determined. It may, for example, take two playgrounds to make an acre. An acre may have to be measured off on a nearby park if the pupils are to see an acre plot. The whole purpose of the exercise is not to give the pupils experience in the arithmetic involved, but to enable them to have the size of an acre in their background the next time they read about acreage in their geography assignment.

THE PHYSICAL SETTING

Some factors of the physical setting will vary so much from place to place that no general hints on how to study them can be given here. The underlying rocks, soil, landforms, vegetation, and climate should be investigated by the geography teacher and then explored by the pupils.

Other features of the physical setting such as day-to-day weather and change of season can be studied similarly everywhere. Some schools may have weather recording equipment for studying the daily changes in the temperature, wind direction, and various other factors. Others will need to develop their own weather stations.

Reading the weather report in the daily paper with its maximum and minimum temperatures, winds, humidity, and pressure, or listening to some television announcer read the same data cannot compare to reading the instruments for oneself and learning how hot one feels when the temperature registers 80°, how uncomfortable one is at 90 percent relative humidity, or how the combination of heat and humidity can be harder to bear when no wind is blowing. These things can be read about in the classroom, but they are remembered better if they are experienced and recorded in the outdoors.

Several instruments are necessary: thermometer (mounted out of the sun), a barometer (a simple aneroid is just as useful as the bulky and expensive mercury), a humidity gauge (which may be either a sling psychrometer or a registering gauge), some sort of a weather vane, and a rain gauge. Numerous useful gauges are on the market for the home gardener to use in measuring the watering of his lawn. These gauges register ordinary rainfall just as well. With these simple instruments the class can measure anything but wind speed. The emphasis should be on the students observing the instruments, recording the data — usually on large charts in the classroom — and drawing deductions from the changes in the data.

The pupils will first learn that their temperature readings will not agree with the official reports of the local weather bureau. Now is the time to explain about local variations in temperature. A trip might be made to the local weather bureau to see the setting. Is it at a higher or lower elevation than the school? Is it in a naturally warmer or colder place than the school? Students will learn, if they move their thermometers around, that it is hotter where their feet are than where their heads are.

Variations in pressure will seem less dramatic than variations in temperature, but the setting of the aneroid barometer each day will become a much watched ritual and the variation or lack of variation in pressure daily will bring out questions to be answered. Why does it not rain every time the pressure drops? Why is it sometimes cloudy in times of high pressure? Why is the fact that the pressure is rising or falling more important than the exact pressure reading at the moment?

The humidity gauge measuring relative humidity is also a source of data to be recorded. Why is low relative humidity accompanied by a dry feeling in the nose? Why is high relative humidity a source of discomfort?

The weather vane points in the direction from which the wind is coming. Remind the pupils that a wind is named for the direction from which it comes. A north wind blows from the north. Shifts in the weather vane can be recorded daily and correlated with other data at the end of the week, or whenever the teacher plans a summary lesson.

The rain gauge should record precipitation in tenths of an inch. A crude gauge, however, can be made out of a tin can, and the rain measured by dipping a ruler in it after a storm. Pupils can answer such questions as how many inches in the last storm. (It may be only a fraction of an inch.) The value of these recordings will come out in the summary lesson when pupils learn the relationship of temperature to pressure, humidity, and precipitation.

Perhaps the chief carry over into classroom learning will be when the pupil reads about a climate where the temperature never goes below freezing, or of a climate where less than 5 inches of rain falls in a year, or of another where only 6 weeks a year are without frost. The student carries with him in his memory the idea of how cold it is when the temperature is at freezing, how much is an inch of precipitation, how long is 6 weeks out of 52. The outdoor learning has given him a yard stick with which to measure things he can only read about.[1]

THE SEASONS

The change of seasons can be observed throughout the year, largely from the altitude of the sun above the horizon at noon and from the length of day. The sun is never directly overhead except within the tropics. Hence no one in the United States, except in Hawaii, can ever see the sun directly overhead; that is, the vertical rays of the sun never hit most of the United States. The sun's vertical rays migrate from 23½° N (at the Northern Hemisphere summer solstice, June 21) to 23½° S (at the Northern Hemisphere winter solstice, December 21) and crosses the equator twice in the process, giving us the spring equinox on March 21 and the fall equinox on September 21. All of this, of course, should be familiar to anyone teaching geography. Unfortunately, few geography teachers have ever taken a class outside to see the height of the sun at any time. Both of the solstices (June and December) come when most schools are not in session. It is possible to take a class outside on an equinox. The pupils should be shown the sun at noon local sun time and told to watch the change in the position of the sun until the next solstice. If the class begins at the spring equinox, the students can watch the sun climb higher and higher in the sky as the semester goes toward the summer vacation. Students may also be made aware of the length of the day. The two occurrences — the increasing altitude of the sun and increasing length of day — accompany the increasing warming of the season.

If the class begins with the fall equinox, the students can watch the sun sink lower and lower toward the horizon, as the days get increasingly shorter. By Christmas vacation time, the pupil will begin to see the connection between the heat of the sun and the length of day and increasing coolness of the season.

A good way to measure the difference in the position of the sun is with an erect stake outside. The shadow will shorten as the days go toward the summer and lengthen as they go toward winter. Marks in the ground at weekly intervals will keep tally. Some classrooms with south facing windows can keep tally of the changing days by marks on the wall where the sun penetrates. It is not necessary to make the mark at noon so long as all the marks are made at the same time of day.

---

[1] The Federal government issues a Weather Study Kit which costs $1.00 and may be obtained from the Superintendent of Documents, United States Government Printing Office, Washington, D. C. 20402.

If observations begin on an equinox, the sun at noon will be as many degrees off directly overhead as the location is north of the equator (Figure 6.7). For example, at the equinox the vertical rays of the sun are on the equator. At Towson, Maryland, the latitude is 39° 24′ N which means

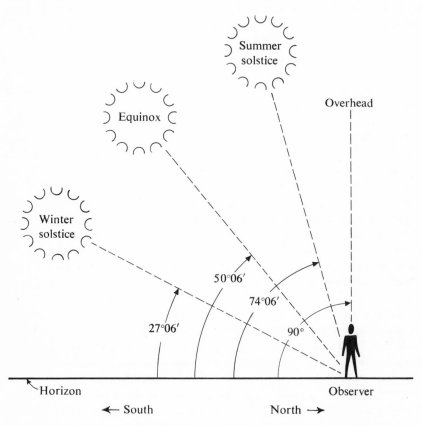

FIGURE 6.7.   *Angle of the sun at noon at Towson, Maryland.*

that the sun is 39° 24′ away from overhead at that time. Another way to express it is to say that the sun at noon is 50° 36′ above the horizon. (From overhead to the horizon is 90°.) As observations continue from the spring equinox until the summer solstice, the sun will climb 23½° higher, or to a height of 74° 06′ above the horizon. Meanwhile the length of day will increase daily by a few minutes.

If observations begin on the fall equinox, the sun will again be 50° 36′ above the horizon. Subsequently it will sink 23½° until on December 21 at the winter solstice, the sun will be only 27° 06′ above the horizon. Each day will be a few minutes shorter than the previous one.

Other factors are involved in change of season, for example, migrating air masses and cloud cover, but it will be easy for the pupils to see that the main reasons for the change are the altitude of the sun above the horizon (the higher the sun the hotter it is) and the length of time that the sun can warm the earth.

THE CULTURAL SETTING

The cultural setting, like the physical one, varies considerably from place to place and changes rapidly. The pupils can best learn about it in the outdoor laboratory by mapping various aspects of it themselves. The government topographic maps go out of date culturally as soon as they are printed, for man's works change much faster than the physical environment. A hill will remain while the roads running on it and the houses built on it will be much different this year than last.

Pupils can map cultural features fairly well if they have an adequate base map on which to plot. It is possible to make a base map when none exists by using the pacing method and graph paper. So many paces will equal one side of a square on the paper. A base map can also be made from cadastral maps usually available in the county court house or from insurance companies. Perhaps the easiest way to make one in a city is to copy a map of the city. Most schools have some type of reproducing machine so that copies may be made for each pupil.

Armed with a base map and colored pencils, the pupils can go out to locate and plot various aspects of population: single houses, multidwelling houses, stores, business establishments, supermarkets, vacant lots, parks, and recreation areas. Each class will have to establish its own legend of items to map, perhaps after a walking survey of the neighborhood.

The pupils will learn much about mapping while they are working outdoors; the legend may not include all the categories they need, or the scale of the map may be too small to show the location of all they find. Various pupils will probably classify things differently so that the composite map made on their return will vary from place to place. Some students may not be able to locate themselves on the map. All these are not failures, but opportunities for the teacher to bring out map characteristics about which the pupils should learn. Categories can be changed, small scale makes the mapper leave out certain items, individuals look at things differently, orienting a map is the first step in finding the reader's location on it. The class may make a series of maps showing culture. A transportation map may even include a traffic count of cars and trucks on a busy highway. Someone may wish to locate trees, sometimes even by variety.

One of the most interesting maps for the pupil to make is to plot the journey he makes from home to school. A large map of the journeys of all the pupils may even be of interest to the school principal. Teachers will think of other items to map that are important in the local environment, for example, the various fields of crops in a farm setting or the kinds of stores in a downtown area.

An excellent summary lesson is the plotted journey. The teacher gives each pupil a base map and written directions for a walking tour. The pupil plots the journey and then walks the route making observations as he walks. This is a test of the pupil's ability to use a map, adjusting to the scale as he goes. He knows by now how much in the world is how much on the map. On this understanding, subsequent map understandings can be built when he returns to the classroom.

FIELD TRIPS

After the pupils have explored the local area within walking distance, the teacher may wish to take them farther away on a field trip. First, see if the proposed trip is worth the bother of getting permission slips, disrupting the daily program, and hiring a bus. It is hardly worth while to go see a huge thermal power plant if the same principles can be taught through a conducted tour of the heating plant of the school. Suitable field trips might be made to outstanding physical and cultural features that are not a part of the local situation, for example, a park with a grotto, a hydroelectric plant, a dairy, a harbor, an airport, or a railroad terminal.

Successful field trips must be well planned. The teacher goes over the trip first. The pupils are then given an advance lesson on what they are to see, what they are to look for, and what kind of report they will make. On the day of the trip the pupils are given something to look for during the journey. If the journey is through a city, they might look for changes in housing on the way or changes in size of yards. The slower pupil might look for only one thing — chimneys, front doors — anything that varies from place to place and from which some interpretation can be made on return to the classroom. This active looking is part of a trip, and it is also useful in making the pupils easier to control in the bus. Transistor radios must be banned. Nothing should distract from the observations. Depending on the length of the trip, the teacher should plan for rest stops, meal stops, and chances to stretch legs.

The activities at the destination may be either under the direction of a guide or the teacher. The pupils should be shown what they have been prepared to see through the lessons in the classroom.

The return trip should be planned to follow a different route than that of the outgoing trip so that the pupils can continue their observations. If this is impossible, pupils might look for something else and compare observations with other pupils on their return.

In the lesson immediately following the field trip the experiences and learnings should be discussed. Here again, pupils should be encouraged to bring out their understandings no matter how faulty, so they may be compared with those of other pupils. Map work should be an integral part of the trip and its aftermath. No field trip is worth going on if the teacher does not prepare the pupils beforehand and check the findings afterward.

7

Pictures: moving and still

The prime requisite of all effective geographic thinking is the acquisition of clear-cut imagery of the items under consideration.

MARGUERITE LOGAN

THE TEACHING OF GEOGRAPHY can be enhanced through the judicious use of pictures in the classroom. To use pictures effectively, the teacher must develop the ability to recognize and explain the geography in a photograph, whether it is of general landscape or of detail such as the texture of soil particles. This ability, in turn, depends upon the thoroughness of his academic training as well as a self-taught system of analysis. Pictures can be scrutinized and the component parts discussed in a method analogous to the time-honored dissection and intensive study of the earthworm in courses in biology. Such analysis takes time and careful preparation. Before a teacher can use pictures to best advantage in his class, he must study them thoroughly. Readily available pictures, such as those illustrating a text, should be fully explored. Pictures that are ignored contribute nothing to the learning process.

Commonly, the selection may be limited to the illustrations in the text, and perhaps little attempt will be made to interpret aspects of the picture not emphasized by the accompanying caption. Certainly in twentieth-century America, with the proliferation of moving pictures and the great profusion of readily available still pictures, the teacher can draw upon this ever-increasing resource to enrich the classroom experience of his students. Properly used and interpreted, pictures can bring realism and relief to students bogged down in endless word descriptions buttressed by statistical tables.

MOVING PICTURES

Moving pictures, almost always popular with the students, provide a change of pace in regular classroom presentation. The student experiences the illusion of an actual visit to a far-off land, or he feels involved in the minute scrutiny of some activity. The motion picture is self-contained and self-explanatory. The sound track presents a ready-made interpretation of an "expert" who has had access to large amounts of data in preparing his commentary. Unfortunately, the teacher often tends to become a passive viewer, along with his students, and retreats from his role as interpreter.

The teacher must bring the moving picture into perspective. If it is to be used for a classroom showing, preview of the film is not only desirable, but mandatory. In viewing the film before it is shown to the class, the instructor can take notes on the organization as well as content. He is then in the position to explain to the students how the film helps to illustrate particular concepts. This briefing prepares the student to look for the parts of the film which may be of particular value to his study of geography.

Better learning results may be obtained if a synopsis sheet of factual data can be prepared and distributed to the student. The effectiveness of the moving picture is reduced, or even negated, if the student is preoccupied with taking notes on the commentary. His attention should be concentrated on the screen, not on the task of feverishly writing factual information in the dark.

If the motion picture is especially apropos, a repeat showing should improve its usefulness. A regular showing with the full sound track and prearranged commentary can be followed by a second viewing with the sound track silenced. This will enable the teacher to make his own points and interpretations about the geography which may have been ignored by the prepared script. This technique is especially desirable when the film is a travelogue.

A notable disadvantage of the moving picture is that frequently it moves too quickly, merely touching on the points to be explained visually. Commonly, too many topics are crowded into too few minutes. This failing is explainable by the high expense involved in production and resultant retail price of approximately twelve dollars per running minute for prints of the finished color film. Such costs dictate that motion pictures must be kept short if they are to be within the reach of most audio-visual instructional budgets. Brevity need not be a sin. Moving pictures can be more effective if they are more pointed. Short films arranged in logical sequence, each a part of a whole, are ever so much more useful than one long motion picture, a potpourri of successive fleeting impressions.

In some moving pictures the narration misses the geography almost completely. This is especially the case when the film is a travelogue and meant to be entertaining rather than instructive. Unfortunately many travel-adventure motion pictures concentrate on the scenic views and devote too much time to beauty and not enough to the people of a region and the work they do to make a living. Geography is present in this vast amount of moving picture footage, but commonly it is not recognized by the photographer who exposed the film or by the narrator who is explaining it.

Moving pictures about foreign lands have been advertised as contributing to the understanding of other nations and their problems. This, of course, is not necessarily true. A film concerned at great length with a ferocious fight between a mongoose and a cobra contributes little to a student's knowledge of India. To be sure, the student has been entertained, but has he learned anything of value from the movie? He may leave his class convinced that the principal pursuit of the Indian peasant is to spend much of the day watching such brutal entertainment.

Better quality moving pictures are being made for classroom use, in large part, a result of federal legislation. The National Defense Education Act in emphasizing the use of audio-visual approaches has stimulated film producers to correct many of the errors of the past. A great number of the films currently being issued are concept-oriented and are not the repetitive, pointless travel panoramas which preempt television channels.

Several large book companies have taken the initiative in upgrading the quality of instructional motion pictures in geography. This, of necessity, involves the expenditure of huge sums of money. The old practice of putting together a film from odds and ends is dying out and is being replaced by careful planning and shooting according to a script which dictates the photography to be done in the field. The results are amply evident. Although a story in itself, each film is a part of a whole, which consists of a series of films. The series is made up of several films concerned with one topic or region, to allow a more thorough examination of the subject matter. The rapid improvement in the quality of content in instructional moving pictures can lead only to their wider acceptance and use in the classroom.

Ideally, moving pictures that are to be used in teaching geography should be taken by a geographer who has mastered the techniques of exposing film correctly. In nearly all cases, commercial films are taken by professional photographers. A geographic editor is then consulted when the final film is assembled. The results of this practice are good, but moving pictures for the class in geography could be greatly improved if a well-trained geographer were to accompany the photographer in the field. The geography would be interpreted and photographed to bring the landscape indoors. Several such teams of professional geographers and photographers were used to great advantage in securing still pictures during World War II. Past experience can be drawn upon to improve the quality of the geographic material in the films we use in our classrooms.

TIME-LAPSE MOVING PICTURES

The motion picture can be used to capture movement involved in aspects of physical geography which can be brought into the school for classroom analysis, for example, the formation of clouds around the steep slopes of the Matterhorn, or perhaps the smoke and gases escaping from the crater of Stromboli. In either case it is difficult, if not impossible, to comprehend the subtle movements of the clouds involved. The continuous slow action takes place at a smooth and almost imperceptible rate of change. Such movement can be recorded on film, however, through a technique known as time-lapse photography. This involves taking single frames of the film at predetermined intervals of time. One frame exposed every five seconds results in a film which compresses a half hour of actual action into fifteen seconds of viewing time on the screen.

The time-lapse technique has been used for more than thirty years to study the growth and behavior of vegetation. Truly astonishing instructional films based on this technique have been made for classes in botany or biology. Little has been done to explore the use of this photographic method for the teaching of geography. It takes the trained eye of the geographer and the skill of an accomplished camera man to take such pictures.

In the field where the film is exposed, the action extends over a long period of time, hours, days, or even months. Consequently, great amounts of patience and sizable investments of money are involved. This, in part, explains why there is little time-lapse footage of motion picture film to illustrate the physical aspects of geography. The film that does exist matches the drama of the growing plants in biology. Truly, time-lapse films constitute one of the frontiers of visual education in geography.

ANIMATION

The name of Walt Disney is synonymous with animation. Over a period of almost four decades he perfected a technique which has not only contributed to entertainment, but to the education of a worldwide audience. Animation, an especially effective technique in the educational film, has been used to great advantage to explain the work of the forces of erosion and their resulting landforms. Beyond this, little has been done to put animation to work to explain geography. The technique could be applied to explore such timely problems as population explosion and urban sprawl. This would involve animated maps, maps which draw and explain themselves.

Until recently, the maps used in moving pictures were mostly unimaginative, almost illegible, and commonly static. What is the purpose of having a map in a film if the audience cannot read it? Why have a map in a motion picture unless it moves? Fortunately, the poor techniques of the past are being eliminated in many of the new films being produced for use in geography.

Animated maps are especially useful in the explanation of historical geography. Present-day patterns can be traced from their earliest beginnings through the long process of evolution. Years, even centuries, can be compressed into a few minutes of time on the screen. The advantages of such a technique are obvious. Why, then, are there not more animated maps in the film literature for teachers to use?

Animation is exceedingly costly. A rule-of-thumb estimate for production expenses is approximately $1,000 per running minute. If a sequence is to be eliminated from a proposed film, commonly it is the animated cartography, the part which could be so useful in keeping the student oriented. Producers for the market of films on geographic subject matter would be well advised to increase the amount of footage devoted to maps, despite the high costs involved. Their product would probably be in greater demand among teachers who use visual techniques in their classes.

SINGLE-CONCEPT LOOPS

The single-concept loop is probably the most revolutionary visual aid to be developed since the advent of television. It consists of a length of 8-mm motion picture film in a cartridge designed to run through a relatively inexpensive and sturdy projector. The student can operate the projector himself simply by inserting the cartridge and turning on the switch. The film runs for 4 minutes and then repeats. It continues the repetition until it is turned off.

The idea of the single-concept loop is sound pedagogy. A student is exposed to a visual explanation of one topic in a teach yourself or do-it-yourself atmosphere. He can repeat the film until the lesson is understood. The student selects his own pace in his attempt to assimilate the material. Based on the visual approach the lessons are concise and clear. Wherever the single-concept loop has been employed, teachers have reported a positive response among their students and remarkable results in retained learning.

The single-concept loop is in its infancy. New techniques of producing a larger and clearer image are being evolved. In recent months the size of the picture has been increased as much as 50 percent by use of film with perforation on only one side. The commercial companies that are pioneering in this area of audio-visual education deserve commendation for their efforts. As in the case with all of the visual approaches, quality must be emphasized if excellent results are to be achieved. The single-concept loop, with almost unlimited applications, can contribute much to the teaching of geography.

FILMSTRIPS

Filmstrips are particularly useful at the grade school and high school levels. They constitute a bridge between the moving picture and the still picture. The filmstrip consists of individual still photographs but is different from the collection of slides from which it is made in that a definite lesson or story is told. This can be done either in silent or sound filmstrips.

The silent filmstrip involves the use of captions printed on the pictures, and a set of teaching notes for the instructor. It can be argued that the caption helps the student to learn the material: one tends to remember what he reads. The caption, however, takes the attention away from the picture and often obliterates detail. Teachers welcome the opportunity to elaborate on features set forth in the teaching notes. The silent filmstrip has one notable advantage over the sound filmstrip; it can be projected for any length of time. This feature should enable the class to have a thorough exposure to the material covered.

The sound filmstrip has gained popularity as it has been perfected. Some teachers find that it has advantages over the silent filmstrip. The projected picture is not cluttered by a caption so that attention can be fully directed to the photograph. Furthermore, a self-contained, carefully prepared commentary is played on an accompanying record, which usually runs for twenty minutes. The number of pictures in the sound filmstrip is limited to fit into this amount of time. Although shorter in length than their silent counterparts, these filmstrips are ordinarily more to the point and better organized. The sound filmstrip is somewhat like the moving picture in having much to say in relatively little time. Listening to the recording along with the student, the teacher assumes a passive role. The record can be turned off, however, and the pictures viewed at a slower pace. After the filmstrip has been viewed, the teacher should summarize and show how the visual material illustrates geographic concepts he has been attempting to develop in class.

STILL PICTURES

Since World War II the color transparency, especially the 35-mm slide, has gained great importance as a means of visual presentation in the classroom. Before that time the cost of color film was beyond the reach of the amateur photographer. In the late 1940's color film became readily available, and a revolution in photography led to the increased use of pictures in teaching. Many teachers began to take their own pictures to use in their classes, and often students who were exposed to effective visual techniques were impressed with the method and started their own collections for future use.

The color slide, projected on the screen, can introduce a feeling of reality into the classroom. It is the instructor's responsibility to develop an understanding of the people, places, and things brought to the screen. The slides should be well chosen and arranged in some sequential organization. The principal advantage of color transparencies over motion pictures in teaching is that a picture can be kept on the screen for as long a time as the teacher needs to explain it. The color slide, especially if it was taken in the field by the teacher, can be the point of departure for fruitful classroom discussion. The teacher who knows how to use slides effectively will question the students about features in the picture and then will lead the aroused mind to the answers.

Pictures of people · Few photographs capture the student's interest so much as those which show people in the act of making their living. In the tropics where ocean water is let into the flat diked pans on white sand beaches, a man scrapes the silt into ridges and mounds in the evaporating brine (Figure 7.1). Leg muscles strain as the worker puts his weight and strength into the tedious labor. He wears a hat to protect his head from the near-vertical rays of the sun. His shadow is short; his shirt is drenched

FIGURE 7.1   *Worker in a Puerto Rican salt pan.*

with perspiration. Such a picture should awaken a sense of contrast in the student's mind. Not all of the world is like his home community.

The endless task of bringing water to the land in Southern India involves back-breaking labor (Figure 7.2). Two men work long hours literally lifting water from a well. One walks back and forth on a balanced log

FIGURE 7.2 *Indian farmers operate an irrigation well.*

putting his meager weight into the task of raising or lowering a basket attached to a long vertical pole. His co-worker strains to lift the basket of water and tip it into a leaky pipe made from a hollowed-out log (Figure 7.3). When the water reaches the field it must be worked into the mud. This is done by a third man who drives water buffalos back and forth through the paddy, dragging a board to break up the clods of clay (Figure 7.4). This process, known as puddling the paddy, prepares the soil for the planting of rice.

The teacher who uses pictures of people involved in agriculture may show the class maps of distribution of the crops which are under study. Legible and simplified maps in bright colors can be projected from 35-mm slides to create lasting impressions (Figure 7.5). Maps for classroom use should be made as legible and uncluttered as possible. This may best be done by using plastic tapes, colored paper, acetate, and pieces of felt to compile "swatch maps." These may be photographed to produce the legible map slide.

Pictures at different scales · Pictures, like maps, have the property of scale. The same subject matter may be photographed at varying distances

FIGURE 7.3   *An Indian farmer empties a basket of water into an irrigation trough.*

FIGURE 7.4   *An Indian farmer puddling the paddy.*

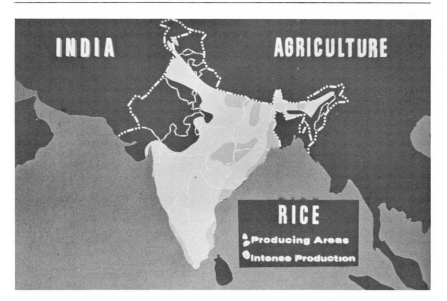

FIGURE 7.5   *A rice-producing area of India.*

FIGURE 7.6   *An Indian farmer spreads black peppers to dry in the sun.*

or through several lenses to achieve differences in detail. An excellent teaching technique is to present the overall view on one slide, and then present a close-up picture of detail on the next.

An Indian farmer squats in a hunkering position on a mat covered with black peppers (Figure 7.6). He is turning the peppers over so that they can be dried by the sun. With several mats to tend, he moves slowly and systematically over several hundred square feet of drying area. His hands in action roll the tiny peppers in the strong sunlight (Figure 7.7). The

FIGURE 7.7   *Detail of hands and black peppers.*

latter picture depicts the detail of the large-scale photograph. The use of two such pictures in conjunction produces better teaching results than if they are shown singly or separately.

Pictures of physical geography · Pictures of physical features contribute even more to the instruction of students than photographs of people in action. By means of a camera true representations of massive landforms, huge glaciers, and fleeting cloud formations can be brought indoors for study. Through the miracle of film they can be brought from all continents to illustrate with visual impact what the teacher is trying to explain.

On the Great Plains of South Dakota in the middle of an August afternoon, heat builds updrafts in the still atmosphere. An updraft of air is marked by the beginning of a thunder storm. A white cloud climbs several thousand feet into the clear sky (Figure 7.8). Twenty minutes later the cloud has taken on an anvil shape and spreads outward at an upper level (Figure 7.9). The birth of such a storm is a common happening in the

South Dakota summer, but may be uncommon elsewhere. Pictures tell the story better than words.

FIGURE 7.8 *Birth of a thunder storm on the Great Plains.*

FIGURE 7.9 *Anvil-shaped cloud, a later stage in the development of the thunder storm.*

High in the Alps, at the head of the Mer de Glace, stands a magnificent cirque (Figure 7.10). The vertical ice-plucked walls of rock merge with jagged arêtes to make a distinct landform. Ice slowly moves toward the

FIGURE 7.10   *A glacial cirque in the French Alps.*

foreground widening and deepening its valley as it moves. Farther down slope the glacier develops tension cracks (Figure 7.11), deep crevasses as the surface ice tends to move at a faster rate than the ice which is in contact with bedrock at the bottom and along the sides of the glacier.

Sometimes it is almost impossible to describe a physical feature so that the class can understand what it looks like and how it was formed. Devil's Tower in northeastern Wyoming will illustrate this point. An aerial view clearly shows how this magnificent volcanic plug stands hundreds of feet above the surrounding terrain (Figure 7.12). A close-up view of the top can be made only from an aircraft (Figure 7.13). The hexagonal columns are clearly discernible along the sides of the tower as well as at its base (Figure 7.14). If a student is shown pictures of the landform as its various features are being explained, his interest will be aroused and his comprehension improved.

Aerial photographs · Pictures taken from the air constitute an important visual resource which can contribute to the teaching of geography. Aerial photos taken either vertically or on an oblique angle can be selected to illustrate dramatic patterns etched by nature or built by man on the face of the earth. Differences between the seasons are especially notice-able in the vegetation or in the presence or absence of snow (Figure 7.15).

FIGURE 7.11 *Tension cracks in an Alpine glacier.*

FIGURE 7.12 *Aerial view of Devil's Tower, Wyoming.*

FIGURE 7.13   *The top of Devil's Tower.*

Each feature draws the student's attention and arouses interest in explanation.

If a classroom is equipped with simple stereoscopes, obtainable for a modest investment, three-dimensional study can be made of features on overlapping vertical aerial photos. Students should have the opportunity to see mountain topography seemingly rise from the flat photographs viewed through a stereoscope. It is a thrill never to be forgotten.

Aerial photos can be used to great advantage in teaching map reading. The photo-map correlation brings the oblique aerial photo and the detailed topographic map together into a useful tool (Figure 7.16). The limits of the photograph are plotted on the map, and the areas not covered by the air view receive less emphasis through a screening technique. This increases the ease of correlation. The photo is printed above the map so that the map symbol can be related to the real feature shown in the picture, and vice versa.

Aerial photos are some of the most exciting pictures available to the teacher. They arouse curiosity in the student, for they are different from other visual materials. Their general classroom use should be more common than it is.

USE OF PICTURES WITH OPAQUE AND OVERHEAD PROJECTORS

In addition to the aforementioned visual materials of moving pictures, filmstrips, and color slides, a teacher has the opportunity to use opaque

FIGURE 7.14   *Detail of columnar structure, Devil's Tower.*

(a)

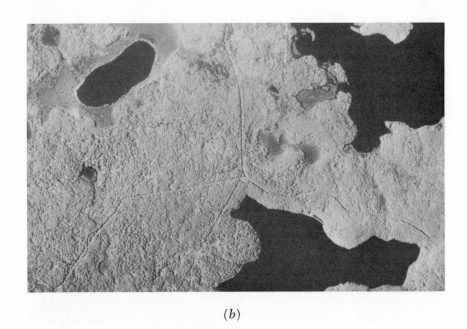

(b)

FIGURE 7.15   Aerial photographs taken in April (a) and July (b)
illustrate seasonal differences.

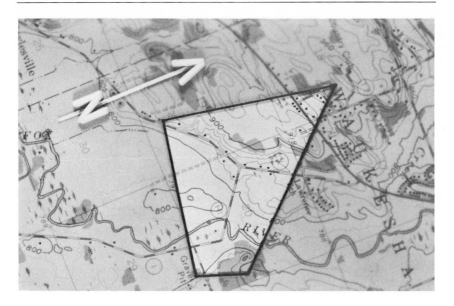

FIGURE 7.16 *A photo-map correlation. (Photograph courtesy of Benjamin F. Richason.)*

and overhead projectors in the classroom. The opaque projector, in greater popularity and use before the advent of color slides, enlarges and projects a photographic print by means of reflected light. Many opaque projectors are heavy and cumbersome, and the image projected on the screen tends to be less clear than one from a slide projector. The notable advantage of the opaque projector is that it can be used to transmit any map, graph, or picture, especially those in a textbook, to the screen for classroom viewing.

The overhead projector, much smaller in size than the opaque one, picks up the image from a transparency printed on clear acetate and projects the picture on the screen by means of transmitted light instead of reflected light. Teachers find the overhead projector an easy instrument to use. Overlays can be added to the printed transparencies to demonstrate spatial interrelationships or to develop a concept a step at a time. With the use of sheets of clear acetate and colored-felt pens, the teacher can literally draw lines to emphasize certain parts of the picture without harming the underlying printed transparency.

The overhead projector has a definite role in visual instruction, especially in the teaching of geography. The common problem of the illegibility of classroom maps is largely solved by use of clear, well-designed and easily read cartographic transparencies. As better-quality transparencies of all kinds are designed, printed, and marketed, the overhead projector will become increasingly popular and effective. Except for the introduction of the single-concept motion picture loop, perhaps no recent development has been so important to visual presentation as the increasing use of overhead projectors.

USE OF PICTURES WITHOUT CAPTIONS

An effective classroom technique in the use of black and white prints was developed by Professor Edith P. Parker during her distinguished teaching career at the University of Chicago. Miss Parker, who was full of ideas, would ask students to bring in pictures which they thought had geographic significance. From these she would select the best pictures, remove the captions, and mount the print on a piece of cardboard. The captions were pasted on the back of each board, out of sight of the viewer, but readily available for identification purposes. These cards with the captionless pictures were distributed to the class for study and discussion. She insisted that the student learn to recognize features in a photograph and to put his observations into an intelligent geographic synopsis. Without the crutch of the caption, the student was forced to draw upon all of his training in making his comments. Arguments which ensued between members of the class were settled only after Miss Parker would allow the contestants to peek at the caption.

Use of pictures without captions in Miss Parker's class was limited to relatively small classes where all of the students could see the print at a distance of a few feet. The same excellent technique can be used in large classes today through the use of projected pictures or even on television monitors. Miss Parker's effective methods of using pictures to teach the student how to read the landscape should certainly be adapted to all new tools of visual media.

CONCLUSION

Pictures are not of much use in the teaching of geography unless the teacher learns how to make photographs "come alive." This is an acquired skill involving careful analysis and interpretation. In classes where pictures are used effectively, students can be inspired to employ the same techniques in their own classes when they begin to teach. Good teaching begets good teaching. A more universal and intelligent use of pictures in the teaching of geography can result only in better comprehension and sustained learning.

8

Textbooks and supplementary reading

It goes without saying that the very nature of reading will always necessitate a greater measure of solitude than other forms of communication or artistic expression, but the solitude of the writer, like the solitude of the reader, is not antisocial. It is only the means where each may find the other. ROBERT ESCARPIT

WHAT IS A GEOGRAPHY textbook? Like many familiar things, textbooks are often taken for granted. Their meaning is assumed, and they may be infrequently analyzed or defined. Only as recently as November 1964 did a General Conference of UNESCO recommend a universal definition for a book. This conference resolved that a book is "a nonperiodical printed publication of at least forty-nine pages, exclusive of the cover pages." For those who would start to write a book by numbering the pages, this is a convenient definition.

In most instances, a book is a form of dialogue between an author and a reader. In the case of a compendium or other form of multiple authorship, the reader has a dialogue with several authors. What is seldom realized is that reading is an active rather than a passive process. Unless the reader mentally responds to what is on the page, the time and effort put into the reading are futile.

The two major categories of books are fiction and nonfiction. It might be assumed that textbooks are entirely nonfictional. However, instances of the use of fiction, particularly as a motivating device, may be found not only in reading books, but occasionally in geography textbooks as well. Hopefully, such use has a basis in reality.

Many books are written with the intent of changing the attitudes or behavior of the reader, and this is a particular attribute of the textbook. Content is selected and arranged in the expectation that ideas and concepts will be formulated by the reader. When this does not happen, the textbook author and the reader have failed to communicate. However, countless examples may be cited of successful textbooks which have not only influenced a generation of readers, but have also made a significant contribution to their field.

CHANGES REFLECTED BY TEXTBOOKS

Textbooks reflect the educational climate and the cultural milieu of the times in which they are written. Early American geographies, such as those of Jedediah Morse and William C. Woodbridge, reflected a knowledge of other places based largely on the accounts of sea captains returning to New England. The questions and answers in these books showed that the catechismal type of lesson prevailed at the time.

Expansion toward the west penetrated the life of the young nation during the 1800's and became embodied in the textbooks as well. For a time, some of them perpetuated the myth of the "Great American Desert." As a rule, the textbook descriptions of the western territories referred to the fertility of the soil and the nature of the plant and animal life. The process of adding new states undoubtedly caused problems in the revision of materials. The secession of the southern states also brought about school problems. From books published in Richmond, children learned about the Confederate States of America while northern textbooks reflected no such division. The transcontinental expansion of railroad lines was recorded on the maps of the textbooks, a practice which continues to the present day.

Historians and others have indicated that westward expansion and national development contributed to a spirit of isolationism in the United States. Toward the end of the 1800's, events in Cuba and the Philippines were impinging upon this isolation. Nevertheless, the geography textbooks revealed a missionary approach to Asia and Africa with considerable attention being given to race and religion.

The increasing number of students receiving secondary education around the turn of the century was concomitant with increasing popularity of high school courses in physical geography, as demonstrated by the wide use of *Physical Geographies* by Davis. The textbook has played an invaluable role by expressing the creative ideas of such individuals as William Morris Davis, Mark Jefferson, Carl O. Sauer, J. Russell Smith, Edith Parker, and Wallace W. Atwood. These and other great individuals demonstrated the happy facility of being able to combine professional and scholarly work with textbook writing on the elementary and secondary levels. This facility is still desired today.

In the first half of the twentieth century several significant movements in education occurred in the United States. The field of geography, in particular, saw the rise of human geography with its emphasis upon cultural factors of the environment. Closely related to this movement was the rise of the social studies movement which sought to integrate the study of history, geography, political science, economics, anthropology, and sociology. Both of these movements gained adherents and disclaimers who engaged in protracted debates over the relative merits of their positions. On the elementary level this dichotomy led to the publication of different series of textbooks for geography, history, and the social studies. The organization of the curriculum around a study of areas and eras seems to be one possibility for resolving these differences.

The position of the United States as a world power has meant that attention has been increasingly focused upon other parts of the world. Korea, Vietnam, emerging nations in Asia and Africa, and organizations like the Peace Corps all contributed to a rising demand that curriculums and textbooks give greater attention to non-Western lands and cultures than had previously been accorded. The successful launching of an earth satellite by the Soviet Union in October 1957 triggered a chain reaction in American education. The Sputnik scare caused the people of the United States to question their educational methods and procedures. The influx of federal money for research projects, teacher institutes, and the purchase of material first altered the teaching of science, mathematics, and foreign languages. Then similar benefits were extended to the fields of history and geography. This has stimulated the production of text materials by both public and private groups. In addition, ancillary geographic materials such as maps and overhead transparencies have proliferated.

One of the great problems of the United States at midcentury has revolved around the civil rights movement for the Negro. As a part of changing attitudes, more "integrated" photographs began to appear in textbooks. Various groups and individuals also studied texts to determine the treatment accorded Jews, Moslem nations, Communism, and other controversial topics. In preparing geographic materials for print, national publishers recognized such issues and attempted a balanced and rational presentation.

The content of geographic materials has recently been affected by increased attention to the psychological factors in learning. Such an interest is not entirely new, as can be seen by studying Guyot's *Geography Series* published in 1866 and Mary Hall's *Series of Lessons in Geography* published in 1880. Still much work remains to be done in understanding how concept formation takes place. The goal of having a student think for himself, rather than give a rote response, has always been the aim of good geography teaching. With increasing knowledge of the learning process, a sequence of experiences may be programmed into reading materials and other media to insure this desired result.

USING TEXTBOOKS

In the space age, the textbook may be thought of as the launching pad for the class. It is the takeoff point for discussions, further reading, and other activities. The reading of a basic textbook is one experience shared by all members of the class.

Beginning teachers especially may rely on what is called the textbook method; that is, classroom experiences seldom go beyond the reading and recitation of passages in sequence from the textbook. As more experience is gained with the subject matter and in working with children, a greater range of learning activities and a multiple-book approach may be used.

Ideally, the teacher should have a command of each subject taught. This includes a knowledge of the key concepts for the grade level, as well as an understanding of how these fit within the spectrum of the curriculum. The local or state course of study may enumerate the objectives and prescribe a sequence of topics or units. Frequently, however, the course of study and the basal textbook are not in agreement as to the areas to be studied or the order in which topics are to be taken up. In such situations should the teacher follow the course of study, the basic textbook, or make up his own organization?

Generally, more time, scholarship, money, effort, and attention to detail go into the organization of a basal geography textbook series than can be expended on a course of study by most school districts. Therefore, some school systems have taken to writing their courses of study after the textbook adoption has been made. In so doing, they select from available materials those which most meet their needs. Then they write courses of study which help their teachers to use the books within the context of local conditions and resources.

From the student's first lessons in geography, he must be helped with the special vocabulary of the subject. Terms such as *desert, equator, mountain,* and *contour plowing* may be far removed from the reader's experiences. Usually such terms are carefully explained when they first occur in the text. The teacher can assist in the pronouncing and spelling of the word and can determine from discussions if the correct concept was gained.

Teachers should recognize the importance of descriptive adjectives, not only in the textbooks, but also in their own speech. The descriptive adjectives help students to visualize as they read. Such words add color and life to a subject. Although geography involves much more than description, without it there can be no conceptualizing of regions or processes.

As an aid to visualization, photographs appear on almost every page of geography textbooks. Increasingly, these pictures are being reproduced in color in order to show the world as it is. A good geography photograph shows significant man-land relationships. For instance, a scene of lumbering activity may show forest vegetation on sloping land with moisture-laden clouds overhead. An aerial view of a city can help to explain its natural location, size, growth pattern, and functions. Accordingly, the photographs and captions should be studied and "read" along with the text.

Geography books are unique in having numerous maps which are frequently referred to in the text. Students, especially in the middle grades, should adopt the habit of stopping and turning to the map when directed to do so. They too often skip over these references in reading. By careful instruction of the class at the beginning of the term, followed by observing the students while reading, teachers can help them to acquire this desired behavior pattern.

Closely associated with map work are size, distance, and number concepts which occur throughout most geography books. Here the good teacher supplements the textbooks by helping students translate *acres, miles, populations,* and so forth into familiar comparisons. In the process the relationship between space distance and time distance is frequently brought out. Also, it is generally better to use a reasonably exact number, rather than such vague terms as *many, few, several,* when expressing quantities.

Place locations are another aspect of the vocabulary of geography. Knowing a place is somewhat like knowing a person. A person met frequently is more likely to be remembered. A well-known person will be remembered for a long time. The same applies to places. The student may soon forget places to which only a passing reference is made. Studies in depth permit meaningful associations with a place to be made, and thus contribute to retention.

Most geography textbooks come equipped with exercises either interspersed or at the end of each chapter or unit. A well-known geographer once said, "Geography is the questions we ask." Certainly the kind of question has considerable significance for geographic learning. At lower grade levels and for introductory purposes, questions based on simple recall may be used. In more advanced work, questions should stimulate geographic thinking. For this purpose, a "why" question is often used, and the answer may not always be in the book.

The problems of a wide range of abilities within the class have long beset teachers. Simultaneous use of a variety of instructional methods and materials within the classroom may be helpful, but such diffusion of effort is inefficient and difficult to perform and administer. To meet the individual's needs in today's consolidated and urbanized schools, it seems that each individual might progress through the schools on the basis of his accomplishments, rather than on the inexorable succession of his passing birthdays.

OTHER READING AND REFERENCE MATERIALS

Under Title III of the National Defense Education Act, funds have been provided for the purchase of reference books for school libraries. This removes one of the barriers to student research. Providing these funds, however, is but one step in the process. An intelligent selection of references should be made, and the necessary regulations must be met in ordering; once the materials are housed in an appropriate place, they should be effectively used.

Choosing the best encyclopedia for school reference purposes may be a difficult decision. A trained librarian can locate professional reviews and offer suggestions to assist in this choice. Atlases are even more difficult to evaluate. Here the advice of a local geographer may be sought. The accuracy of the data and toponymy, the extent of the index, the care with which shorelines and topographic features are drawn, the clarity of the type, and the control of color are some of the criteria by which an atlas may be judged. Since atlases may go out of date quickly, it may be advisable to choose one that is not too expensive and to replace it frequently. In addition, each student should have a paperback atlas at his desk if funds permit.

A copy of *Webster's Geographical Dictionary* belongs in the dictionary section of the school or classroom library. Large libraries may include a gazetteer, but these are expensive and soon out of date. A small library could provide some of the same information by having copies of the current editions of *The Statesman's Yearbook* and the *World Almanac and Book of Facts.*

Where statistical data are needed, particularly in the junior and senior high schools, the latest *United Nations' Statistical Yearbook* and the *United Nations' Demographic Yearbook* should be on hand. *Agricultural Statistics* and the yearbooks of the United States Department of Agriculture might also be available. The three volumes of the *Minerals' Yearbook* of the United States Department of the Interior Bureau of Mines are an excellent source of information on minerals. A practical and inexpensive form of information on other countries can be obtained by subscription to *Overseas Business Reports* of the United States Department of Commerce.

Even in the middle grades, boys and girls show an interest in mass-circulation newspapers and magazines. *National Geographic Magazine* and *National Geographic School Bulletin* are well known and widely available. The *Canadian Geographic Journal* and *The Geographical Mag-*

azine published in Britain are less well known in the United States, but deserving of attention. Among the popular magazines, *Fortune* is particularly useful in geography classes. Two rather specialized magazines which should be familiar to geography teachers are *Landscape* and *North*. Other magazines are generally available in the periodical section of medium-sized public libraries. By the time students reach junior high school, they should be familiar with the *Readers' Guide* and other indexes for locating information on specific topics.

Even though local newspapers often give good international news coverage, it is still desirable to have copies of the *New York Times, Christian Science Monitor,* or *Wall Street Journal* brought to the class daily. By rotating the responsibility among different students, pertinent articles may be cut out and placed in a clipping file. In time, this may become an extensive source of detailed information about many countries. In addition to the clippings, a pamphlet file may be built up from materials supplied by such organizations as the American Forest Association, American Iron and Steel Institute, American Petroleum Institute, American Dairy Association, as well as various large industrial corporations.

In addition to books for research, students should become familiar with books they can read for enjoyment. At the elementary level, students can develop the habit of recreational reading at the table in the classroom library corner. The selection of books for this purpose is especially important. Annotated bibliographies in teachers' guides accompanying basic textbooks can furnish some leads. Teachers' magazines, library journals, the *Saturday Review,* and daily newspapers also review children's books. One rather sure guide is to follow the selection of the Caldicott and Newbery Award winners. A well-written book can transport the reader out of his own environment and let him experience another time and place.

A word should be said about the teacher's personal library and reading habits. As a member of a profession, the teacher has an obligation to keep up with the events in his field by wide reading in books, journals, and periodicals. This is part of the continuing nature of his education. Since much of this reading must inevitably be done in the evenings, it seems that a quiet corner and a book are a necessary part of the teacher's image.

THE PAPERBACK REVOLUTION

The paperback revolution has affected teachers' libraries, classroom libraries, public libraries, and textbooks, as well as the habits of the entire population. Although paperbacks have existed in some form for a long time, the modern era of paperback books is considered to have originated with the famous Penguin series of books which started in Britain in 1935. Over one million paperbacks are now sold every day in the United States.

The savings in cost on a paperback book are the result of other factors than the method of binding. The inexpensive paperback uses low-quality paper and contains few illustrations. Often the text results from reprintings of original material. By making a wide range of books available in a low-cost, consumable form, the paperback has had a significant cultural influence on the nation. There is something about a paperback that lends itself to being picked up and read. Because of inherent motivation characteristics and because paperbacks make possible more frequent updating of materials, they will undoubtedly find additional uses as geography textbooks.

The quality of a person's reading experiences is often directly related to his ability to express himself orally and in writing. Thus, all the developing nations of the world are seeking more books for their people who are gaining literacy. Furthermore, they desire to produce their own books. This will involve having not only the machinery, but also the authors and editors to prepare them. With advancing technology and automation, it is possible that books will be altered from their present form. They certainly will be produced in less time and in greater quantities. In any event, the seen word will remain a primary means of communicating ideas and transmitting culture.

9

The audio-visual-tutorial
method in geography

Geography is the bridge between the humanities and the sciences and the tools of the geographer are nearly as manifold and varied as those required by the scientist. Therefore a special room or laboratory is as necessary to the geographer as the scientist. TOM W. BROWN

A WIDE VARIETY OF mechanical-electrical devices have been used in classrooms in recent years. Televised instruction, programmed learning, audio-tutorial, and audio-visual systems have been proposed separately and in combination for various types of learning centers. Their advent on the educational scene has aroused considerable discussion and speculation by academicians on their portent for the future. The technological possibilities are indeed impressive, but much exaggeration about their impact upon the classroom is fostered. Hopefully, the information presented will suggest to geography educators the possibility of using Audio-Visual-Tutorial instruction without necessarily revolutionizing a departmental organization or requiring a special budgetary grant.

The device developed for use in a two-semester introductory physical geography course at Carroll College is called the Audio-Visual-Tutorial system (A-V-T). The prior experience of Dr. S. N. Postlethwaite of Purdue University in the use of an Audio-Tutorial laboratory in botany has been of help in the design of the system.[1] The purpose of the A-V-T

---

[1] Conclusions drawn from two years of operation in geography of the Audio-Visual-Tutorial system at Carroll College paralleled many of those of Postlethwaite, Novak, and Murray as outlined in *An Integrated Experience Approach to Learning* (Minneapolis: Burgess, 1964). Their book provides additional ideas on some facets of the material presented here — most notably in detailing advantages of the system from the standpoints of learning and cost and suggesting techniques of preparation. Because an A-V-T system is not a standard program, those planning its use will want to take advantage of a wide range of ideas on the subject. Note that the A-V-T system at Carroll College differs from the Postlethwaite system in the use of slides as the primary visual device and in its adaptation to the study of geography.

laboratory is to improve course content, stimulate the students' interest in geography, and promote their independent work. Basic to the system is a series of ten independent study booths, each equipped with a tape-player deck and 35-mm slide projector (Figure 9.1). The lecture and laboratory

FIGURE 9.1 *In the Carroll College A-V-T system, ten independent study booths are arranged back to back. The laboratory is equipped with demonstration tables to which students may be directed in order to perform certain experiments that cannot be contained in the booths. A laboratory assistant is on duty during laboratory hours.*

portions of the course are presented by means of tape-recorded discussions, illustrated and expanded by means of colored slides. The laboratory work in the A-V-T system logically and immediately follows the so-called "lecture" topic, and thus becomes an integral part of the course, rather than an appendage to it, as is frequently the case in the traditional lecture-discussion-laboratory type of presentation.

Students perform the work independently in the A-V-T study booths on an unscheduled basis. An individual student may progress through a weekly unit of work at his own pace, repeating any portion of the presentation as many times as necessary to understand the concepts. Each student becomes an active participant in the course as he hears discussions on tape and sees them illustrated in an environment devoid of distractions (Figure 9.2). In addition to their work in the A-V-T booths, students meet once a week with the instructor in small discussion sessions.

The A-V-T laboratory at Carroll College is open from 8:00 A.M. to 10:00 P.M. Monday through Friday, and from 8:00 A.M. to 5:00 P.M. on Saturday. During these hours students may come to the laboratory and remain as long as they wish. Ten booths are open for a total of 770 hours each week, and were used during the 1966–67 academic year for an average of 65.2 percent of the maximum possible time. A laboratory assistant is on duty during these hours for the purposes of checking students in and out of booths, resetting tapes and slide trays, restocking expendable supplies, and aiding students with their work when necessary.

The enrollment in the A-V-T geography course at Carroll College during its first year of operation (1966–1967) averaged 145 students, as compared to an average enrollment of seventy-eight students during previous years when the elementary course was taught in the traditional lecture-laboratory manner. In a course such as the one at Carroll College where the lecture topic, laboratory observation, and experimentation are integrated, it is estimated that one booth will accommodate with ease twelve to fourteen students per week.

The A-V-T system is one that may be produced by any teacher or professor and implemented with modest equipment. Although the present A-V-T course at Carroll College is concerned only with the Elements of Geography course, there are probably few geography courses which in some way could not be taught in part or in whole by the A-V-T method. The system at Carroll College has been designed to incorporate both the lecture and laboratory portions of the course, but other uses of the system are also possible.

Upper-division regional and systematic courses lend themselves particularly well to this method of instruction. The fundamentals of an advanced course could be recorded on tape and slides. The basic content of the course would be required prior to meeting the class in a seminar session. For high schools the system could be used as a corollary part of a course.

VISUAL MATERIALS

The A-V-T system is predicated on certain well-established factors in education. Visual aids in learning are so extensively used and their value

FIGURE 9.2 *The independent study A-V-T booth provides an environment devoid of distractions in which the student may concentrate on tape-recorded lectures and laboratory experiments and/or observations which may be illustrated and expanded by means of various visual aids.*

so well established that the validity of this pedagogical procedure is not questioned. When combined with an individualized discussion by means of earphones in an isolated study environment, the visual presentation makes an impact on students in a way which classroom lectures, laboratory demonstrations, and group viewing fail to do.

The visual presentations in the A-V-T system take several forms. They are extensively used to place the student in a field situation where particular earth phenomena are being discussed. There is no substitute in geographic instruction for actual field observations, but the A-V-T method closely approximates the field situation when, for example, landforms are being discussed and the student is allowed to view a youthful valley, drift plain, drumlin, natural bridge, or sand dune, many of which may be completely inaccessible to him while studying the course.

As high school and college enrollments increase, the problem of taking geography classes on excursions into the field to observe features of unusual cultural or natural interest becomes difficult. One difficulty encountered on the field trip is the inability for all participants to observe prescribed features either in transport or on location. The visual presentation in the A-V-T method is so dramatic and stimulating that attention is attracted and interest held for longer periods of time than when exogenous factors are at play. As a result of such presentations the student has been led, not on one, but on many field excursions, and has thus viewed on location exhibitions of those facts and concepts presented in the course. Furthermore, the student may continue to view the slide on the screen as long as he wishes to study the phenomena.

In the A-V-T system slides are also used to aid in the discussion of problems. For example, if the altitude of the noon sun at a particular latitude is being presented, a slide of an actual situation can be prepared and discussed for the student. The pictorial mathematical problem is no farther from him than the projection screen on the wall of his booth, and he may replay the discussion of the illustrated problem as many times as necessary to understand the concept. Blackboard work is thus not eliminated by the A-V-T method; it is actually stressed and strengthened. The student always has good visibility, and he may study the problem for any period of time. Furthermore, he may return to the booth at a different time and review the concept on both the tape and slide.

Another use of slides in the A-V-T system is to direct the attention of students to specific features they are studying on maps or charts in their booths. Arrows or numbers placed on the photographed map will direct the student to that point on the actual map which is being discussed. In this way the student makes no mistake as to what is being discussed on the atlas plate, topographic map, aerial photograph, etc.

The slides which are used in the A-V-T system may also serve as the basis for laboratory work. For example, in discussing atmospheric pressure, it may be desired to teach the student how to read a mercurial barometer. Under the traditional laboratory method of instruction, it is impossible for an entire class to see the small main and vernier scales on the barometer during the discussion. The only alternative open to the instructor is to explain the problem to each student — obviously a time-consuming task. In the A-V-T method a colored slide would be made of the scale of the barometer. When projected on the screen in an A-V-T booth, the scale is magnified to about 15 inches. On tape the instructor explains how the scale is read, and the actual value of the reading is illustrated on the slide. Once this is done, the instructor on the tape directs the student to a mercurial barometer located in the laboratory room and instructs him to read the barometer and record that value along with the time of the reading. The accuracy of the student's work can be checked from a barograph. If the student does not remember how to read the scale when he arrives at the barometer, he can return immediately to his booth, replay, and review the tape discussion and slide presentation.

Slides are also used in the A-V-T system to illustrate concepts that under the traditional method of instruction have been presented as a laboratory demonstration by the instructor. For example, in demonstrating the Coriolis effect, water may be poured on a large stationary slate globe with the poles vertical. The student's attention is directed to the fact that the water flows downward parallel to the meridians. Next the globe is set into rapid motion from west to east and again water is poured on the globe at the north pole. In this case the student observes that the streams of water are deflected to the right in the Northern Hemisphere, but after crossing the equator the streams of water are bent to the left. In the A-V-T system this sequence of events is photographed and presented on colored slides along with a tape-recorded discussion.

Valuable laboratory work in the A-V-T system may result from requiring the student to observe certain phenomena on slides and to discuss what he sees on his laboratory report form. Also, the student may be required to solve problems which are presented on slides. Subsequent slides may give the student the answers to the problems he has solved in an effort to allow him to check his own work. In other cases the answers would be graded by the instructor.

Another type of visual aid to be considered in the A-V-T system is the 8-mm continuous-loop, single-concept movie films. Many useful and attractive single-concept films have been produced commercially, and the instructor may wish to incorporate this technique in an A-V-T system. In the A-V-T laboratory at Carroll College only two 8-mm continuous-loop projectors are utilized for the sake of economy. These are located on demonstration tables in the laboratory room, and the film is projected onto a screen, semidarkened by a hooded enclosure. The tape directs the student to proceed to a specific projector (which is numbered to avoid confusion) and view the film. He may be asked to write a brief summary of his understanding of the concept presented. In the event that several single-concept films are to accompany a particular A-V-T exercise, the cartridges can be numbered and the student himself may insert the designated cartridge into the projector.

The continuous-loop projector may also be installed directly in the A-V-T booth. At the appropriate time in the taped lecture the student can be directed to turn on the movie projector, and as he views the film he can also receive a discussion of the phenomena by the instructor on the tape.

Although the A-V-T system stresses learning through well-conceived and well-prepared slides and movies, it is recognized that the lecture-slide format itself may become monotonous and thus lose much of its effectiveness, even though the slides serve various purposes. Therefore, many other visual materials are placed in the booths for examination by the student. Depending upon the topic being discussed, the booth may be supplied with landform models, topographic maps, weather maps, climatic charts, cyclonic storm models, globes, projection models, rock and mineral specimens, soil micromonoliths, analemmas, tellurometers, stereoscopes, and aerial photographs, to list a few of the possible materials.

An integral part of the A-V-T laboratory is a demonstration table on which observational items or experimental equipment are placed (Figure 9.1). Students may be assigned the task of observing certain items here, or they may be required to carry out an experiment which is too large for the independent study booth. Materials used in this portion of the laboratory include old atlases and maps, weather instruments, maps of varying scales, the celestial sphere, Foucault pendulum, Geiger counter, and stream tables.

THE TAPE DISCUSSION

The principal value of the A-V-T system lies in the fact that each student hears the same taped discussion, coupled with the fact that each may listen to any portion of the tape for as many times as necessary to have a clear concept of the material presented. Teachers are aware of the fact that students learn at different rates and in response to varying sets of stimuli. The A-V-T method of instruction allows the use of the maximum number of senses at times and during intervals which the student finds best suited to himself.

The weekly A-V-T units of work in the beginning geography laboratory are written for an average independent study period of four hours. The lecture discussions and laboratory directions on the tape require approximately 90 minutes of playing time. With a seven-inch reel of one-mil tape at a playing speed of 3¾ inches per second (ips), it is not necessary to use the second track on the tape and the reel does not have to be reversed, thus saving time and eliminating potential damage to the tape and tape player. The remaining 2½ hours are consumed by note taking and laboratory experimentation and/or observation. During the first semester of the two-semester physical geography course at Carroll College, students spent an average of 3 hours 56 minutes in the A-V-T booths, and during the second semester of the course they spent an average of 3 hours 34 minutes in the independent study booths.

The time per booth visit per student varied according to the student's class schedule and attention span. The average time per visit per student in the booths for the first semester at Carroll College was 1 hour 34 minutes, and for the second semester it was 1 hour 44 minutes.

At first some students wanted to completely transcribe the taped discussions for study in their rooms, not realizing what a waste of time this was. One student came to the instructor following a series of weekly examinations and stated that he was discouraged because he was doing D work, notwithstanding the fact he was spending 7 to 8 hours each week in the study booths. An examination of his notes revealed an almost complete transcription of the taped discussions. He was prevailed upon to spend no more than four hours in the A-V-T booths the next week and to pace himself so he could complete the tape and laboratory work during this time. The following week he spent 3 hours 31 minutes in the booths and received a B on the weekly examination. Once he realized that the A-V-T system could teach him, he continued to work in this fashion throughout the remainder of the semester and earned a grade of B in the course. Other similar examples could be cited.

Each tape player is equipped with a fast forward, fast reverse, and a pause button, thus enabling the student to move with ease from place to place on the tape. The pause button allows the student to stop the tape instantly to take notes or to observe slides for any length of time. In addition, each tape player is equipped with an index counter. When a student wishes to leave the booth before completing the exercise, he merely records the number on the index counter, and upon returning to the booth uses the forward button to return the tape to that number and continues his work. Each booth is equipped with an outline of the unit presented on which the index number of the subject is printed. This permits the student to return to a booth for review purposes.

The laboratory work sheets, which are made available to students in the A-V-T booths, have blanks provided in which the student can write the index counter number from the tape player when he leaves the laboratory.

This enables the assistant in the laboratory to determine if the student has completed the laboratory work required up to that point on the tape. It is thought that for the student to obtain the maximum benefit from the A-V-T course, he must do the laboratory work prescribed at the time it is assigned on the tape.

An alphabetical list of new terms introduced on the tape is hung on the pegboard wall of each booth. Referral to this list enables the student to see the term and to learn its spelling. An alphabetical list of all new place locations mentioned on the tape is also placed in each booth.

PREPARATION OF TAPES

As the individual teacher begins to prepare material for an Audio-Visual-Tutorial course, he is immediately struck by the degree of inadequacy of the same course as it was previously taught. It is recommended that written scripts be prepared for all units of work. This demands a type of organization and thoroughness which was probably not present to the same degree in the traditionally presented course. The written script gives the instructor the opportunity to organize his material logically and concisely. A straightforward, friendly, personal type of script should be prepared. The script should be written after the illustrations have been prepared, and great care should be exercised to correlate slides and other visual materials used with the discussion. After the text is finished, the recording can be made. During the recording period it is an advantage to have the colored slides at hand on a slide viewer.

The instructor is cautioned concerning several pitfalls at the recording stage of the tape. In the first place, the recording should be made by the instructor in charge of the course. The students should identify this voice with the person they meet in discussion sessions and informally in office conversations. The recording should be made in a personable, conversational tone, but with the same enthusiasm that the instructor would otherwise display before his students in the classroom. This is not always easy to develop when speaking to a microphone only, but the instructor should practice this until the discussion sounds natural and exciting. Failure on this point can materially lessen the effectiveness of the course.

A recording error originally made at Carroll College was in speaking the tape recordings too slowly. When the students were told to observe something in the atlas, on the globe, or on maps or charts in the booths, periods of silence were introduced on the tape to give them the opportunity to perform that work. This was found to be not only unnecessary, but actually distracting and disadvantageous. If the student needs more time to locate or observe something he can always stop the recording. In view of the fact that the instructor does not repeat material on the tape, he sometimes thinks that he must speak very slowly in order to allow time for the students to take notes. This simply consumes large segments of tape which may make it necessary to reverse the reel. If the student misses a point, or wants to take more detailed notes, he can stop the recording or even reverse it to the point of the discussion missed.

Because the instructor is speaking from a well-organized script he does not digress in his lecture, and usually he does not repeat material. This makes possible the presentation of more material than in the traditional course where much time is consumed in reviewing previous lectures before proceeding to a new topic and in digressions that seem appropriate at the time. In the two-semester course at Carroll College, 40 percent more material is presented by the A-V-T system than by the traditional lecture-laboratory method of instruction formerly used.

Because of such a straightforward approach, the A-V-T discussion has a tendency to become very intense. Levity can be introduced by presenting anecdotes pertinent to the discussion. The student should be put at ease and given the feeling of great personal attention.

The tape-recorded presentation is the heart of the A-V-T method of instruction and great care should be exercised to produce a high quality master tape, as well as high quality tape duplicates. Many schools have language laboratories which can be used for the duplication of tapes. Even two tape recorders may be used for this purpose, but in such a system only one duplicate tape can be made at a time from the master. Although expensive, it has been found that a tape duplicator is a wise investment if many A-V-T booths are being used. The Geography Department at Carroll College purchased a tape duplicator with five slave units. Such duplicators can operate at a speed of 15 ips thus making it possible to duplicate tapes for ten booths in approximately 40 minutes. An additional advantage of such duplicating equipment lies in the ease by which tapes may be duplicated during the week in case of tape breakage; thus minimizing unusable time on a booth.

PREPARATION OF SLIDES

The 35-mm slides are an important part of the A-V-T system, and their preparation should not be looked upon as difficult by even the nonphotographic oriented teacher. Several commercial companies produce high quality slides of geographic topics, but their expense in lots necessary to supply many A-V-T booths may preclude their use on limited budgets. Some slide series are available at modest cost, but the most economical way of obtaining slides for A-V-T booths is for the instructor to produce them himself.

Elaborate equipment for slide production is not necessary. When the teacher does not possess slides in his personal files to illustrate the discussion, he may resort to sketches and diagrams which can be photographed. A single-lens reflex camera is recommended for this purpose because of the absence of parallax, but any inexpensive camera can be made to do a passable job. By use of an inexpensive copy stand the 35-mm slides may be photographed in a well-lighted room using natural light with outdoor color film, or with flood lights using indoor color film. After a few attempts, even the inexperienced photographer will become proficient in the production of very acceptable visual materials. Because color film is recommended for A-V-T slides, it is suggested that colors be used liberally on illustrative diagrams in order to increase the impact of the visual presentation. If rocks, minerals, or equipment are to be photographed, colored cloth or paper can be used as a background to increase interest in the photograph.

Problems, either for the illustration of a concept or for laboratory work, may be typed on a sheet of white or colored paper and photographed. In some cases, the instructor may wish to place a problem and its solution on the chalkboard and photograph them there.

Several visual specialists are at work in geography today. It may be well for them to offer some of their slides to instructors who are involved with A-V-T instruction in order that the students' reaction to their work might be tested. Such cooperation would be of benefit to both the A-V-T innovator and the visual aid specialist.

The 35-mm slide is preferable to a film strip in the A-V-T system because slides in a tray can be changed easily as the course is revised. Film strips are unsatisfactory because they are in permanent order and could result in a "canned" course that may be offered year after year without revision or updating.

The A-V-T instructor also may wish to incorporate 8-mm single-concept, continuous-loop films in his system. In order to implement this technique he may photograph many laboratory experiments or landscapes himself with an inexpensive 8-mm movie camera. Most commercial single-concept films are produced on *standard*[1] 8-mm film; to make use of these films, the instructor will want to purchase a projector which will accommodate that size. Therefore, he will need to purchase the type of 8-mm movie camera which uses *standard* 8-mm film. Once the film has been edited and spliced, additional copies may be made by a photographic processing company. There are several companies which will load this film in continuous-loop cartridges.

In the production of 35-mm slides and 8-mm motion pictures, the teacher may be as innovative and sophisticated as his ability and interest allow.

---

[1] Note the distinction between *standard* and other types of 8-mm film.

FIGURE 9.3 *The type of A-V-T independent study booth designed and built at Carroll College. 1. 35-mm slide projector with 3-inch lens. 2. Mat white screen, vinyl base (15 inches by 15 inches). 3. Recessed overhead fluorescent lighting. 4. Pegboard for displaying materials. 5. Ventilating fan. 6. Map rail. 7. Permanently mounted world relief map. 8. Glass shelf for displays and equipment. Other shelves may be added. 9. Alphabetical list of place locations described on tape. 10. Student identification card indicating number of times booth was used. 11. Alphabetical list of new terms discussed on tape. 12. Formica laboratory deck (48 inches by 32 inches). 13. Fast forward and reverse for tape player. 14. Tape-play control. 15. Electrical outlets. 16. Laboratory deck light. 17. Forward and reverse buttons for projector. 18. Projector switch (automatically shuts off overhead light and turns on deck light when projector is turned on). 19. Switch for occupancy light (occupied, red; unoccupied, green). Lights are located at end of series of ten booths. (See Figure 9.1.) 20. Ventilating-fan switch. 21. Guest pack for instructor. (See extra earphones in Figure 9.2.) 22. Earphone. 23. Earphones. 24. Laboratory programmed exercise, correlated with tape. 25. Laboratory work sheets. 26. Tape-player switch; volume and tone control. 27. Tape player with index counter. 28. Numbered drawers with dividers for reference to specimens. 29. Storage drawers for books, etc. 30. Booth dividing wall extends 12 inches from laboratory deck. (Figure 9.1)*

For example, the demonstration of Coriolis effect mentioned previously would be dramatized by the use of the 8-mm loop.

THE A-V-T INDEPENDENT STUDY BOOTH

The A-V-T booths which were designed and built at Carroll College cost approximately $600 per booth, including equipment, although a much less elaborate laboratory would serve equally well. Part of the expense of the system is defrayed by its use in shifts, whereby only ten students at a time are attempting to work in the laboratory. Equipment purchases for any given laboratory assignment are thus smaller than would be needed in a conventional laboratory session with perhaps thirty students needing the same material simultaneously.

For an illustration and explanation of the A-V-T booths see Figure 9.3. The system is not a commercially available unit, but rather the product of an evolution through the period of construction. While work was in progress, mock-ups were assembled and students were called in for their opinions. Small girls and husky boys were questioned concerning the comfort of the booth, the ease by which they could reach the control panel and the tape player, the placing of the projection screen, and the ease with which other items in the booth and on the walls of the booth could be attained and viewed. The present booths at Carroll College incorporate the opinions of many students.

THE A-V-T GEOGRAPHY COURSE

The Audio-Visual-Tutorial Geography course at Carroll College was introduced to conform to a general emphasis on independent study inaugurated by the college with a concomitant flexibility of class meeting times. The course is divided essentially into four parts: independent work in the A-V-T booths, a weekly discussion session, a weekly examination, and outside reading assignments.

The instructor meets once a week with several small discussion groups for the purpose of answering questions, clarifying ideas, and expanding concepts. Most students have reacted favorably to the discussion sessions because there they are brought into personal contact with the instructor.

Because the A-V-T class need not meet at a specifically scheduled time, the instructor's time is freed for individual consultations with students. In general, the operation of an A-V-T course is more informal for all concerned. The illness of either instructor or student does not stop progress with the material. The student unfortunate enough to miss work has an opportunity to make it up rather than hoping that the hiatus in the course will not be too damaging to the final result. The instructor is thus spared the pain of student alibi sessions, and student conferences can be confined to the content of the course.

Since the progress a student makes on a taped presentation can be measured, the exact segments of a course which cause difficulty can easily be determined. This also gives the instructor a considerable advantage in modifying the course content and testing procedures.

A weekly, in-depth examination is administered to the class each Monday morning. All examinations are cumulative in an effort to measure retention. Grades on examinations for two semesters have averaged more than 18 percent higher than on examinations given over a ten-year period under the traditional method of instruction in the course.

FIGURE 9.4   *Student use of booths is recorded on IBM cards. Such information as the day of the week, booth number, and time in and time out are punched by means of a portable IBM punch. The processing of this data gives information concerning the number of times each student came to the A-V-T booths during the week, the total time spent in booths, and the average time spent per visit.*

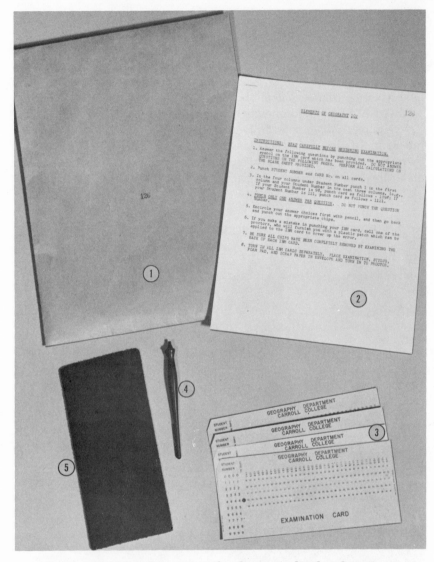

FIGURE 9.5 *The time spent in booths is correlated with performance on weekly examinations. Examinations are multiple choice and
are administered on prescored data cards designed and produced at
Carroll College. The student is provided with an examination packet,
which contains an examination booklet, one or more IBM cards, a
stylus for punching the card, and a foam rubber pad on which the
IBM card is placed to facilitate punching. Examinations are graded
and analyzed by an IBM 1620 computer. The punch-card system
was used because of the large number of students enrolled in the
course and the desire to assess the A-V-T method.*

In an effort to determine the effectiveness of the A-V-T system, the time spent in the A-V-T booths was correlated with performance on the weekly examinations (Figures 9.4 and 9.5). Students scoring A on examinations spent an average of 3 hours 52 minutes in booths; students scoring B spent an average of 3 hours 39 minutes in booths; students scoring C spent an average of 3 hours 21 minutes in booths; students scoring D on examinations spent an average of 2 hours 57 minutes in booths, and students who failed examinations spent an average of 2 hours 37 minutes in booths.

No textbook is used in the course, but a series of outside readings from a variety of sources is assigned. It was found that some students are more comfortable with a textbook, and several physical geography texts were ordered for the college bookstore where students could purchase them if they wished to do so. Physical geography texts were also placed on reserve in the library. In some cases a student arrives at the laboratory when all booths are filled. A seminar room has been provided in which these students may wait until a booth becomes vacant. A small library of books and articles relating to the course have been placed in this room and students have been observed to make modest use of these readings.

The geography instructors at Carroll College find that the A-V-T method is not only an exciting way to learn geography, but that it is one of the best methods by which a number of geography courses can be taught. Dormitory counseling has resulted in a 50 percent increase in enrollment for the second year of operation (1967–1968). Furthermore, the number of geography majors coming from the A-V-T course increased six times over those years when the course was being taught by the traditional methods. These figures, coupled with the fact that about 40 percent more material is being presented and grades are about 18 percent higher in the A-V-T system than in the former method, would indicate that this system should not be overlooked as an important change in geography instruction.

PART III
Geographic methodology

NUMEROUS AND VARIOUS methods are preferable in the teaching of all subjects, but in the field of geography this variation is an absolute necessity. The topics discussed in every geography class, whether at the primary or graduate level, are active and alive. The teacher should be presenting material "about places that exist and people that live." In many respects the interest shown by the students is a direct reflection on the preparation and enthusiasm of the teacher.

Since geography is a subject of *where, how,* and *why,* several different approaches may be made to the same topic and a variety of geographic tools used. By the skillful presentation of a topic the student can be guided into "discovering" some answers for himself. The discovery should lead to inquiries about other phases of the project and in so doing add to the knowledge of the individual. Several approaches may be used: comparative method, group reports, individual research, problem presentation, critical analysis, regionalization, etc. Regardless of the approach, however, the teacher must make constant use of the geographic tools available. Maps of the area being studied, both large and small scale, should hang on the classroom walls, a large globe is always an essential study tool, and a bulletin board for keeping up-to-date information before the student is a necessity. Thus, methods and tools must be completely coordinated.

The success of any class depends upon planning and preparation by the teacher. A well-prepared lesson plan takes considerable time, effort, and thought, but the results are readily apparent. A good lesson plan for a previous class, however, may be of little value for the current class. Lesson plans must not become like the yellowed notes of the college professor.

The plans must be kept current, for the active young minds of today are constantly gaining new insights into geographic problems via television, radio, news magazines, and newspapers. The old lesson plan can serve as a model, and some parts may be used again, but constant revision is a necessity.

10

The uses of the unit
in teaching geography

*A wise teacher will pace and adjust the unit to the ability and interest
of the children — lengthen and deepen it, or shorten and widen it as
the need arises.* WILLIAM B. RAGAN

TRADITIONALLY THE UNIT has been a problem- or activities-oriented
approach to the organization of learning experiences. For the purposes
of this chapter, the unit is a systematic procedure for introducing and
organizing learning experiences associated with basic generalizations
and/or concepts. These are derived from specific categories of geographic
elements which are fundamental to the core structure of geography.

The total of geography represents the relation of a set of subsystems, such
as climate, water, and land, to one another. As each unit is designed, the
planner must be aware of the overlay of the total geographic system to
the subsystem or subsystems dealt with in that unit.

The study of a continent or region, for example, would be incomplete
without a careful analysis of the subsystem of rivers as a process as well
as a function. In the past, too much attention has been given to the mere
descriptive nature of geography as opposed to the process associated with
geographic elements. Simply learning the name and descriptive characteristics of the Mississippi River is not enough; attention must be given
to the overall formation, conditions associated with the complete river
system, and how varying geographic conditions influence its operation.

Teaching a unit, or, for that matter, teaching any phase of geography,
requires the teacher to ask five fundamental questions:

1. How can I introduce this unit in such a way as to get an emotional
and intellectual commitment from each student?
2. What is it that I want to achieve?
3. How will I organize the basic working period?

131

4. What resources do I have available for my use and for the use of my students?

5. What is the best way to judge the extent to which I have realized my objectives and the extent of intellectual and effective growth which has taken place within each student?

INTRODUCTION OF THE UNIT

As noted in the model of a unit (Figure 10.1), Phase I has to do with the introduction. Any teacher would be unwise to undertake a new topic by simply assigning a given number of pages or a chapter to be read and

	PHASE I	
Introduction	Overview	
	Introductory activities	
	PHASE II	
Objectives	Teacher objectives	
	Student questions and concerns	
	PHASE III	
	Generalizations	
	Questions	
Working period	Problems	
	Activities	
	Terminology	
	PHASE IV	
Evaluation	Formal	
	Informal	

FIGURE 10.1   *Model of unit.*

discussed. The students would have little awareness of what is to take place for the next several days or weeks. The purpose of the introduction to the unit is to arouse interest and let the students know what they can expect to think about, read, and do.

The overview, which is a part of the introduction, should be designed and presented in such a way as to give the students a general summary of the specific content to be studied; resources to be used; description of activities, problems, and questions; and the general nature of evaluation.

The teacher should next present introductory activities which will create an emotional and intellectual readiness for the educational experiences which are to follow. For example, in a unit on South America, students may be asked to bring natural or manufactured objects from countries of South America. These materials may be put on display. Other students may write to various embassies or tourist agencies representing South American countries for colorful posters which would be placed around the room. Such activities may serve as clues to the students that something worthwhile is going to take place with the study of this new unit. The overview and introductory activities must serve the purpose of stimulating the students' imagination, curiosity, and involvement.

OBJECTIVES

Phase II of the instructional strategy should be devoted to developing immediate and ultimate objectives for both the teacher and the student. Traditionally these objectives have been too broad and nebulous in nature, or too completely centered in facts associated with specific events or conditions, and therefore of little use to either the teacher or the pupil.

As indicated by the Educational Policies Commission, the overriding objective should be that of developing the rational powers of each student, interpreted here to mean the development of the ability to think and to use thought in a productive and meaningful way. Therefore, the objectives should not be fact- or content-centered. They should facilitate a high level of cognition.

Specifically, the objectives should emphasize processes of analysis, synthesis, and judgment. They should give direction to an instructional strategy which will help the students to analyze the basic parts or elements of a problem, to put the parts together in such a way as to be able to make inferences which will lead to certain generalizations, conclusions, or hypotheses for further verification through the examination of new evidence.

Some specific examples of process-centered objectives are the following:

1. To understand the relationship of geographical land features to the overall transportation system of a continent.

2. To identify and understand the causal relationship between basic weather elements.

3. To be able to predict the consequences when given certain distinguishing conditions.

The implementation of fact-centered objectives requires little if any high quality thinking, but it does take a high level of thinking to examine a set of conditions and predict with a reasonable degree of validity what will happen or will be the consequences of these conditions acting upon each other.

> While statements of objectives for social studies should avoid the qualities of extreme remoteness and inclusiveness, they should also be significant. There is little point in working out statements of objectives that merely identify the topics or points of subject matter. An objective should identify a value to be achieved through the study of subject matter.[1]

The role of the students during the objective formulation stage must be considered. Through student-teacher transactions, student questions, concerns, and insights should be identified and categorized for directional purposes as the unit is developed. Information gained from the students should help the teacher to some extent in developing questions, problems, and activities which may be used during the working period.[2]

WORKING PERIOD

As noted in Phase III of the model of a unit, the working period has five parts: generalizations, questions, problems, activities, and basic specialized and technical terminology.

Generalizations · The heart of the unit is the basic generalizations. All information, data, and evidence should be focused on the development of the generalizations.

In Model 2 (Figure 10.2), it should be noted that the overall instructional strategy for the unit should have the following characteristics:

1. The content is evidence- or data-centered. Each hypothesis, question, or problem is dealt with through the collection of significant information by observation, experience, experimentation and discovery, research, and documentation.

2. The conceptualization processes use analysis and synthesis of data to determine cause and effect relationships and complex relationships.

3. The thinking may be inductive or deductive. The student may begin with a generalization and collect data to prove its validity, or he may

---

[1] J. C. McLendon, *Social Studies in Secondary Education* (New York: Macmillan, 1965), p. 60.

[2] For more information on the analysis of objectives, see: Benjamin S. Bloom (ed.), *The Taxonomy of Educational Objectives* (New York: Longmans, Green, 1956). This book serves as an excellent example of the trend toward identification of more specific objectives related to the broad statements often used. It deals with cognitive learning in several fields.

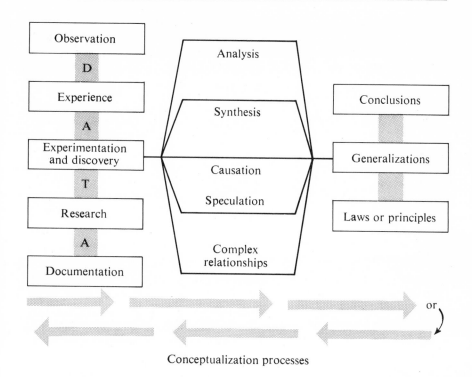

Conceptualization processes

FIGURE 10.2   *Factors associated with a system of instruction.*

collect data and develop a generalization by making inferences from the data.

The major criterion for the selection of a generalization may very well be this question: "Can the students be knowledgeable about the content and processes associated with this unit if this generalization is left out?" Because the total of knowledge cannot be taught, it is the responsibility of the teacher to emphasize the method and process of a geographer in relation to the basic substance and material with which the geographer works. A generalization is more than simply a random statement about a given geographical condition. A set of generalizations for a unit should serve as premises or hypotheses which, when verified, should help the student to predict geographical consequences in a variety of situations. The generalizations are of little value if they fail to give order to the randomness of geographic variables.

Questions and problems · The task of teaching might be described as one of posing thought-provoking questions. Unfortunately, teachers in general tend to direct fact-centered, recall, and recognition questions to individually designated students and elicit from them one-word or highly focused and limited responses. Such questions require little if any rational thinking. This is not to say that facts are unimportant. It simply means that a student must have an opportunity to make basic decisions based on facts or data.

More specifically, the instructional strategy will have the following sequence: identification of parts → patterning of parts into meaningful clusters → identifying and determining causal relationships → developing inferences or verifying generalizations → making evaluative judgments.[1]

The highest level of thinking occurs when determining of causal variables are manipulated. For example, a class might be studying the problem of the population explosion in relation to available resources. After basic information has been studied and analyzed, larger and more provocative questions must be posed which should lead to speculation in terms of consequences. Such questions might be, "If food production remains constant and the population continues to increase at the present rate, what will the conditions be like on the earth 200 years from now?" "In controlling the rate of population increase, is it possible that reality rather than basic values becomes the major factor in decision making?"

Another kind of questioning may present a set of conditions and determining consequences: "What would happen to the continent of North America if the major rainfall pattern were changed as a result of filling in the Gulf of Mexico and removing the Rocky Mountains?" The questions and problems should be related to the objectives in that they should require analytical, synthetic, and evaluative thinking.

Activities • No working period is complete without having a variety of activities geared to the special interests of individual students as well as to group participation. Traditionally many teachers have thought that if a student worked on a special project, he should report his findings to the total class. In some cases, this may be desirable. There may be times, however, when a student developing his own interests will engage in a study which may be too complex or technical for group presentation. In any classroom there will always be a wide range in ability, interest, and motivation. To deny the development of keen insights is to put a ceiling on the optimum development of certain individuals.

Conversely, some activity or project requiring the use of a variety of talent and levels of ability should be included. Each student should have some opportunity to participate as a significant member of a group in planning and developing activities.

---

[1] For more on conceptualization processes, see J. S. Bruner, *The Process of Education* (Cambridge: Harvard University Press, 1960).

Technical terminology • A knowledgeable student should be able to communicate geographic thoughts with coherence and precision. To do this he must have a keen understanding of the specialized meanings of the basic geographical terms. Particular attention should be given to the identification and pronunciation of terms and to discussion of their application.

RESOURCES

The major categories of resources in Phase IV of the unit are reading materials; audio-visual media; and community resources, including human, natural, and documentary resources.

The range of reading ability in a given classroom will be exceedingly wide. For example, in the ninth grade some students may be reading on the college level while others are reading as low as the fifth-grade level. This means that the use of one basic set of geography textbooks for the class is inadequate. Consequently, multiple-level materials should be used.

For each generalization or subtopic to be developed, readings should be available which are extremely easy to read, with many illustrations. At the other extreme sophisticated and technical materials should be provided for the gifted learners.

In terms of instructional strategy, through general discussions and teacher–student transactions, each student should have an opportunity to contribute evidence which may lead to the development of a generalization or the acceptance or rejection of a generalization.

Since any page in a geography book is of and within itself incomplete, the teacher must be prepared to expand, interpret, and extrapolate along with the students the meanings of various passages. Consequently, for each unit a teacher should have readily available highly specialized and technical references for his own use.

In the unit, emphasis will be placed on providing opportunities for the student to function and think as a geographer. He must work with materials and evidence that the geographer uses. Specifically, human, physical, and documentary resources from the area and community must be readily available.

EVALUATION

Evaluation must be compatible with the instructional strategy and the objectives to be achieved. Evaluation falls into two categories, formal and informal.

What is important in the curriculum must be measured and evaluated. One purpose that tests serve is to tell students what the teacher thinks is really of value. He should guarantee that his method of testing reflects the values he holds. The appraisal of a student's ability to remember the miscellaneous, unevaluated information that happens to be in a book that he happens to have read will provide little insight into the growth of social-study arts, skills, and understandings. If the teacher bases his grades on the student's abilities at miscellaneous remembering, then he affirms to the student that miscellaneous remembering is what is fundamentally impor-tant.[1]

Facts are important. Knowledge of facts should and must be measured. However, tests should be developed which use facts and data as they relate to questions of analysis and synthesis and to situational problems. Students should reveal their ability to discriminate between facts which are or are not valid and appropriate to a particular problem. Tests should measure evidence of critical judgment on the part of the learner.

The ability to analyze problems effectively involves an understanding of organizing concepts and the ability to use them — an understanding and an ability that need to be tested in problem situations. The teaching strategy for this testing is to identify clearly the organizing concepts that are to be observed and to invent a problem or setting that demands the use of these concepts.[2]

An effort must be made to design test items that will measure in the best way possible the students' ability to understand and apply principles involving complex relationships, to develop generalizations, and to recog-nize causal relationships.

Informal evaluation is much more subjective than formal evaluation. Student growth is assessed in terms of behavioral and attitudinal change as evidenced by what he says and does in work-study activities. Analytical descriptions of what each student is doing may report, for example, that he understands the nature, interrelationships, and interdependence of continents; he understands and is able to use map and globe skills; and he can collect, examine, and derive inferences from data. Credit in critical thinking should be given to the creative learner who is able to take existing data and rearrange them in such a way that he discovers new insights which may lead to new generalizations and/or principles.

As the terminal phase of the unit approaches, the whole-parts-whole theory of learning should become apparent. The wholeness of the unit

---

[1] H. M. Clements, W. R. Fielder, and B. R. Tabachnick, *Social Study: Inquiry in Elementary Classrooms* (Indianapolis: Bobbs-Merrill, 1966), pp. 149–150.

[2] B. R. Joyce, *Strategies for Elementary Social Science Education* (Chicago: Science Research Associates, 1965), p. 251.

is presented in the introduction and overview. The parts are examined during the working phase, and the wholeness of the unit emerges again during the closing phase of the unit as the parts are put together in clusters of meaningful relationships so as to give a completeness to the major concepts and processes which were developed.

11

The comparative method in the analysis of geographical regions

One of the prime objectives of geography is to clothe the map with meaning, to understand and evaluate differences in people and in the environment from place to place. GEORGE B. CRESSEY

THE STUDY OF REGIONS is fundamental to modern geography. No matter what the approach, it is generally agreed that geography is always concerned with the characteristics of places and with the obvious likenesses and differences existing among the places on the surface of the earth. The face of the earth is complex and continually changing as a result of various processes proceeding at different rates and with varying intensities. "The interaction of these diverse processes gives character to the face of the earth and produces contrasts and similarities of its differentiated parts."[1] Geography has been described as "the field that deals with the association of phenomena that give character to particular places, and with the likenesses and differences among places."[2] Areas on the earth's surface that are more or less homogeneous with respect to this or that phenomenon are identified as regions. Geographically, the term region implies an area of any size; an area homogeneous in terms of specific criteria; and one distinguished from bordering areas by a particular kind of association of areally related features and therefore possessing some kind of internal cohesion.[3] In a sense, then, geography itself might possibly be visualized as a comparative study of regions. This chapter is intended to illustrate how comparison may be employed to develop an interesting method of studying the characteristics of two or more regions.

The objective here is to compare two mining regions with the idea of revealing many of the geographical characteristics of each and to imply

---

[1] P. E. James *et al., American Geography-Inventory and Prospect* (Syracuse: Syracuse University Press, 1954), p. 5.

[2] *Ibid.,* p. 6.

[3] *Ibid.,* p. 9

how other comparisons could be developed. The two sample regions used to illustrate some of the principles of the comparative method are the Mesabi Iron Ore District of Minnesota and the Northern Anthracite Field of Pennsylvania. These two regions, although obviously different, seem to exhibit enough similarities to lend themselves readily to an application of the comparative method of analysis. It is always necessary to carefully select subjects which resemble each other but obviously differ in order to assure effective comparisons.

Maps may be utilized effectively in developing the comparative technique in geographical analysis. Various types of maps should be compared, such as those portraying topography, land use, or population density. It is always imperative that two maps of each kind used be made, one of each region illustrating the same thing. The two maps to be compared should be placed side by side if they are wall maps, or on the same page or on facing pages if in a book. Although the comparison will be most effective if the two maps are on the same scale, sometimes such an arrangement is not feasible. For purposes of convenience, it is better to make the two maps of the same general size so that they will fit on the same page or on facing pages. In some instances, the scales shown on the two maps will be different.

Figure 11.1 illustrates the use of comparative maps. In this case, population distribution in the two sample regions is analyzed. Although there is a striking similarity in the fact that the mining populations of both the Mesabi District and the Northern Anthracite Region reside largely in urban centers, the maps illustrate many sharp contrasts in the way the people are distributed.

In the first place, the Northern Anthracite Region is a narrow crowded valley. "There is not an agricultural landscape interrupted by sporadic evidences of mining, as is sometimes the case in mining regions."[1] Instead, the various types of mining land use mingle closely with a compact urban development. The region has over 500,000 people living in a series of agglomerated settlements. One mining town merges into the next. More than 100 square miles covered by the basin is decidedly urban. The density of population in parts of the basin is over 3,000 people per square mile. The map showing the distribution of population clearly illustrates the merging nature of the many towns and cities of the Northern Anthracite Region.

The Mesabi District, in direct contrast, consists of a series of detached and isolated urban centers. The great open pits and other features of mining, as well as agricultural land, are wedged in between the Range

---

[1] R. E. Murphy and M. Murphy, "Anthracite Region of Pennsylvania," *Economic Geography*, vol. 14 (1938), p. 338.

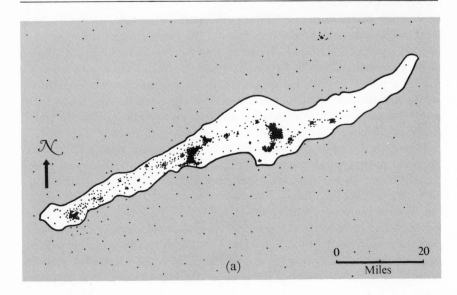

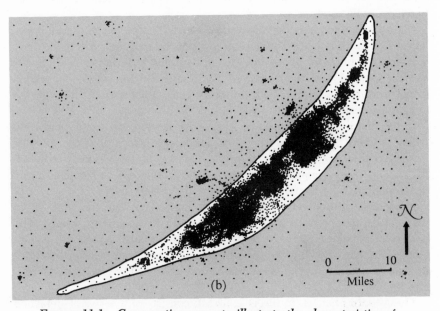

FIGURE 11.1   *Comparative maps to illustrate the characteristics of the distribution of population in the (a) Mesabi District and the (b) Northern Anthracite Region. Note particularly the detached nature of the urban centers in the Mesabi District in contrast to the agglomeration of almost contiguous urban centers in the Northern Anthracite Region. (One dot equals one hundred people.)*

towns. A visitor has little difficulty in detecting the gaps existing between the towns. Sometimes he will travel for miles among iron ore pits, waste piles, general farms, and forest before arriving at the next urban center. Despite this characteristic, most of the people of the Mesabi District, like the inhabitants of the Northern Anthracite Region, are urban dwellers. The Mesabi District covers a larger area than the Northern Anthracite Basin but has a smaller population (estimated at about 71,000). The two regions present a sharp contrast in the density of population.

Similarity is noticed in the fact that the density of population drops considerably as one approaches the edges of either region. One contrast can be noted in that the entire region surrounding the Mesabi Range is sparsely settled with no significant towns, while beyond the borders of the Northern Anthracite Region several isolated and detached urban centers appear in contrast to the agglomeration of urban centers on the valley floor proper.

Although maps comparing population distribution have been utilized here to illustrate a phase of the comparative method, it must be understood that many types of maps could be used in such an analysis. For example, topographical maps are often desirable. Such maps could be prepared and placed side by side for comparative purposes. Conspicuous would be the fact that the Mesabi District consists of a ridge or divide whereas the Northern Anthracite Region is a basin or valley. Further analysis would reveal that the walls of the Northern Anthracite Basin are much steeper than the sides of the range making up the Mesabi. Despite this difference in gradient, the Mesabi Range is just as conspicuous a ridge as the Northern Anthracite Basin is a decided depression. This similarity comes about largely because the Mesabi Range rises abruptly and rapidly above a country that is relatively flat for many miles on either side. Such significant impressions could possibly go unnoticed if the maps appeared singly.

When studying regions by means of the comparative technique, the utilization of many pictures is possible. Carefully compared pictures help to simplify understandings. Both similarities and contrasts can be effectively portrayed through the use of photographs. In either case, it is always urgent that the views to be compared are taken at approximately the same distance and that they appear on the same page or on facing pages. They should never be isolated from one another. Another advantage is the possibility of telescoping one picture into another in order to conserve space.

If the objective is to illustrate similarity, it is best to use two pictures, one taken in each region. They should so closely resemble each other that it is difficult to tell in which region the pictures were taken. In this case, the similarity is mentioned in the caption and then the two scenes are distinguished from one another by pointing out minor differences. Figure 11.2 illustrates this type of comparison. The photographs show

(*a*)

(*b*)

FIGURE 11.2 *Photographs to illustrate similarity. The pictures resemble each other so closely that it is difficult to detect the fact that they were taken in two widely separate regions. (a) Taken at Pittston, Pennsylvania. (b) Taken at Buhl, Minnesota.*

a familiar sight in both the Mesabi District and the Northern Anthracite Region and give indication of the intimate nature of the intermingling of mining activity and urban development. The scenes are so similar that one would have difficulty in explaining that they were taken in two different regions over a thousand miles apart. The obvious similarity would be pointed out in the caption, and the pictures would be distinguished from each other. Color photographs might be even more effective, since the scene at Pittston in the Anthracite Region would have a black cast, whereas that at Buhl in the Mesabi would have a rusty red cast.

Photographs can be just as effectively used in the illustration of contrast. Usually a view of some common feature of one region can be contrasted with a familiar scene in the other. There should be some relationship or similarity in the scenes, but this is not emphasized. Figure 11.3 illustrates this technique.

In Figure 11.3, a familiar school of wooden frame construction (a) in the Northern Anthracite Region is contrasted with the typical elaborate school found in the towns of the Mesabi District (b). In the view taken at Larksville, Pennsylvania (a), one can notice the obvious lack of landscaping around the building and the volcano-like stockpile of coal virtually in the backyard of the school. It illustrates that the residents of the Northern Anthracite Region "can seldom forget that coal is their mainstay."[1] In general, the schools of the Mesabi District give a much more favorable impression. There one finds large, expensive schools in small towns. In the view of the fine high school at Hibbing, Minnesota (b), one can readily see the sharp contrast. Hibbing High School cost over $4,000,000 when constructed, is well landscaped, and has an ornate interior. Even the very small towns of the Mesabi District usually have impressive schools. For example, Buhl, Minnesota (population 1,526), has a school that cost $1,700,000 when constructed. It is only natural that such a sharp contrast can easily lead to a discussion of differences in taxation policy, governmental administration, and the like.

A pleasant departure from the use of photographs is afforded by the use of diagrams and sketches. Numerous types of graphs lend themselves readily to use in the comparative technique of analysis. They should always be clearly and boldly drawn and are best utilized when they are placed together on the same page or at least on adjoining pages.

The double-flag graph utilized in Figure 11.4 is one of the most common devices of this type. It compares the population of the six largest urban centers in the Northern Anthracite Region with the corresponding six largest urban centers of the Mesabi District. The fact that the urban

---

[1] R. E. Murphy and M. Murphy, *Pennsylvania — A Regional Geography* (Harrisburg: Pennsylvania Book Service, 1937), p. 339.

(a)

(b)

FIGURE 11.3 *Photographs to illustrate contrasts. The pictures resemble each other since they are both schools, but this is not emphasized. The contrast in the type of school construction is obvious.*

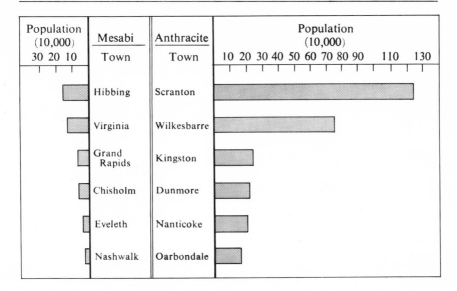

FIGURE 11.4   *The flag graph lends itself readily to use in the comparative technique analysis. In this case, the populations of the six largest urban centers in the Mesabi District are set off against the six largest urban centers of the Northern Anthracite Region.*

centers of the Northern Anthracite Region are much larger is emphasized, but an energetic teacher could easily explain other significant factors of the graph. Many other types of graphs could be used in a similar way. For example, the simple bar graph can be utilized or the circle or "pie" graph might be more appropriate under certain other conditions.

Among the most neglected of the graphs is the trend or line graph although it lends itself readily to use in comparative analysis. Figure 11.5 demonstrates the use of this type of graph. In this case, two lines are used, a solid line to indicate trends in coal production in the Northern Anthracite Region and a dashed line to illustrate the trend in iron ore production in the Mesabi District. In some situations, it may be necessary to use more than two lines, but one must be careful not to get too many lines. There is always the danger that the lines will intersect so often that the graph becomes confusing and loses its value as a tool. Although statistical information can be portrayed skillfully on various types of graphs, at times a simple table may be used to clarify significant contrasts and similarities.

The comparative method of analysis may be applied to many aspects of geography, and the techniques may be applied to other fields of study as well. The following illustrate the variety of possibilities in geographic analysis alone: comparisons of various ports, such as Duluth and Erie;

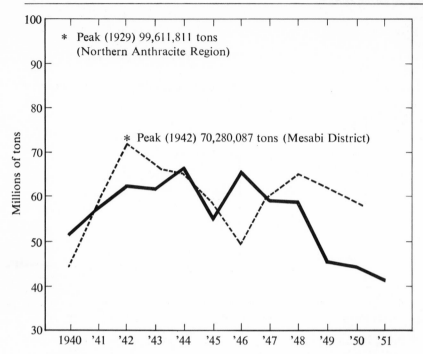

FIGURE 11.5   *The trend or line graph is a valuable tool in the comparative method of analysis, although it is often neglected. The graph uses two lines to compare trends in coal and iron ore production in the two sample regions. The solid black line represents the Northern Anthracite Region, whereas the dashed line represents the Mesabi District.*

comparisons of countries such as Switzerland and Bolivia or Alaska and Finland; comparisons of urban centers, such as Los Angeles and Philadelphia; comparisons of geographical regions, such as the Amazon and Congo Basins; comparisons of islands, like Java and Cuba or Fiji and Hawaii. In any case, if the comparative study is to be effective, subjects must be selected carefully for their resemblances and obvious differences.

Geographers, as well as teachers in various other fields, have often been taken to task because they failed to teach effectively and in an interesting manner. This chapter is merely intended to give ideas and to point out that the comparative method offers a variety of possibilities. There is little doubt that geographers need to develop interesting techniques of presenting information. "Not enough of their investigations have focused on the comparative."[1]

---

[1] E. VanCleef, "Must Geographers Apologize?" *Annals of the Association of American Geographers,* vol. 45 (1955), p. 105.

12

Group reports and current world affairs

*Whether to convert a class into small groups or committees involves
factors that the teacher should contemplate carefully. In general, small
group organization is desirable when the current objective of
instruction can be accomplished by students working with one to ten
others rather than individually or with about thirty others.*

JONATHON C. McLENDON

DURING THE LAST DECADE, increased emphasis has been placed
upon both the study of current affairs within elementary and secondary
geography classes and upon the introduction of more geography into world
affairs discussions with other social studies courses. The distinctive contribution that geography can make to an understanding of these and other
national and international developments has been continually reempha-
sized since the conclusion of World War II. Most teachers and admin-
istrators now realize that students cannot attain an adequate understanding of current world affairs until they are familiar with the natural, cultural, and economic environments which influence these events.

In the past, current affairs instruction has been limited mainly to class
discussions of ideological, political, and social issues and developments.
Many of the significant environmental factors which formed the bases of
these issues were completely ignored. For example, basic to the Sino-
Soviet dispute are elements of both physical and cultural geography. To
discuss only the ideological aspects of this conflict would be extremely
superficial. Likewise, any consideration of the Aswan High Dam or the
construction of a new interocean canal must be based not only upon a
knowledge of physical and cultural features but also upon the extent to
which these projects will alter or change the existing cultural and physical
characteristics of the area. Largely as a result of the increasing awareness of geography's importance, it is now generally recognized that pupils
cannot intelligently discuss and interpret political and social world hap-

149

penings without a thorough comprehension of the spatial relationships that are involved.

Similarly, nearly all educators accept the teaching of world affairs as a desirable method for achieving some of the ultimate objectives of pre-collegiate geography instruction. Just as it is the general consensus that a geography class without current events is inadequate and incomplete, it is also widely recognized that the study of current affairs constitutes only a part of the curriculum and that the study of world events alone would be highly insufficient. However, teachers must be aware that a broader definition of a "current event" or "world affair" is now being employed than was true in the past. Emphasis is placed upon the inclusion of a systematic consideration of the geographic and historical foundations of present-day happenings as an approach to the study of the events themselves.

The traditional practice of encouraging pupils to select current news stories indiscriminately, some of which possess little significance for geography classes, could result in a waste of class time from a lack of any coordination between the current event and the particular instructional unit being studied. Instead, the teacher must discriminate what events are of value for class discussion. He must select a few current affairs in which there are likely to be continuing developments throughout the course of the semester and which possess both student interest and applicability to the course of study. Most importantly, the geography teacher should attempt to identify some of the central issues which appear to form the bases of many contemporary world affairs and to prepare his students to analyze and interpret these issues and their geographic relationships. Through such an approach, students would be better equipped to apply their knowledge of geographic principles to many continuing world affairs. This broadened concept of current affairs instruction has developed from the realization that it is virtually impossible for students to obtain more than a superficial understanding of world events without some perspective of both the central or continuing issues involved and the geographic factors that influence these issues.

UTILIZING GROUP REPORTS

Values · Dividing a geography class of thirty into subgroups of five or six pupils and encouraging each group member to gather material and report cooperatively can achieve several constructive results. Small groups offer many more opportunities for individual participation than larger ones; if the pupil is one of five or six rather than thirty, he may participate more often and assume direct responsibility for more of the proceedings. Experimental evidence reveals that more effective learning may be secured by having small groups of pupils prepare, report, and discuss current problems and issues. Concepts may be clarified, hypotheses stated, generalizations formulated, and higher levels of critical inquiry attained. Group data collecting and reporting can provide numerous opportunities to meet the different needs of individual students as well as teach the complex skills required for working effectively with others. Finally, and perhaps most important, group reports in elementary and secondary classrooms may provide motivation and interest for both geography and the particular world affair being considered.

Limitations · It is equally important to be aware of some of the limitations of group reports. First, the use of group reports should be limited to events which are of common value and interest to the entire class. Second, if the topic could be adequately covered by one pupil or by several students working independently, there is no need to organize a group reporting effort. Third, unless the research and reporting assignments for each group member are carefully defined and coordinated, the activity will be a waste of time for both the individual group participants and the class.[1]

Using group reports as an approach for integrating geography and current world affairs may well yield disappointing results on the first attempt. Some teachers, especially beginning ones, may view the results of the first efforts as unsatisfactory and decide that such group techniques have little value in geography courses. They may decide that since pupils do not seem to be learning from research and reporting, class time would be better spent in formal lecture and discussion sessions. Even though the traditional instructional methods will characterize most class periods, it would be a gross mistake not to employ group reports at convenient intervals. Students need to be taught how to organize and present geographic material. Not only will they develop valuable skills of critical analysis and acquire more self-confidence for their later years of formal education, but also they will better prepare themselves to pursue nondirective inquiry. This should be the primary rationale for elementary and secondary education in a democratic society.

GROUP REPORTING TECHNIQUES FOR GEOGRAPHY CLASSES

The nature of national and international affairs necessitates that two basic procedures be utilized for group reports in geography classes. Short-

---

[1] For a detailed discussion of the strengths and weaknesses of various group procedures in elementary and secondary classrooms, see J. U. Michaelis, *Social Studies for Children in a Democracy* (3rd ed., Englewood Cliffs, N. J.: Prentice-Hall, 1963), Chap 8; and L. H. Clark and I. S. Starr, *Secondary School Teaching Methods* (New York: Macmillan, 1959), Chap. 7.

term or ad hoc groups can be used effectively for gathering information and reporting on selected day-to-day events occurring throughout the term which might or might not be directly related to the particular unit or curricular topic under consideration. Generally it is sound procedure to relate group reports of current affairs to the particular regions or topics being studied in the geography class. Obviously, when there is a tangible connection between the current development and the curriculum content, the problem of obtaining background material and giving perspective to the event becomes less difficult. However, certain world events will occur which are not related to the unit of study but which will attract such an unusual amount of student interest that class time must be taken to discuss them.

Many current affairs, however, will involve those central issues which have a greater degree of permanence and a more significant impact upon the contemporary world scene. Continuing groups could be assigned the task of identifying several of these major issues, gathering material, and preparing reports showing the geographic background and relationships involved. Such group reports could be used as a basis for discussing those world affairs which are likely to have continuing developments, for introducing the study of a particular world region or other geographic topic, or for organizing a separate instructional unit focusing on world affairs and their geographic relationships. Through the utilization of continuing group reports, the more significant current affairs can be discussed in greater depth and detail and can be better coordinated with existing curricular topics. Regardless of the individual variations applied to these two basic approaches for group reports, it is generally estimated that most geography and social studies teachers devote approximately 20 percent of their class time to the discussion of current world affairs.[1] In the majority of instances this means an average of one class day a week, usually Friday, is devoted to current affairs. Given the rationale of why geography instructors should teach about world events, a separation of curriculum content and contemporary affairs is both unnecessary and undesirable. If one of the primary purposes of geography instruction is to motivate pupils to develop the habit of keeping informed about world affairs, the activities necessary to achieve this objective should not habitually be restricted to any day or class period of the week.

AD HOC GROUP REPORTS

Ad hoc groups may be used to report on the geographic background of a wide range of current national and international news stories of con-

---

[1] M. R. Lewenstein, *Teaching Social Studies in Junior and Senior High Schools* (Chicago: Rand McNally, 1963), pp. 447–448.

siderable student interest and academic significance even though these happenings are not necessarily related to the instructional unit or a recurring world affair. The structure of such group reports is an important criterion for success. The geography teacher who, on the basis of an event in Brazil, only assigns group members to gather geographic information about the nation and report what they find may well listen to a series of presentations consisting of unrelated bits of information ranging from descriptions of the tropical rainforest to human conditions in the shantytowns of Rio. Unless students are assigned specific questions to answer, problems to solve, and definite relationships to establish, they have no systematic basis for selecting geographic information relevant to the problem. As a result, they have no way of knowing when they have done enough fact gathering. Length or number of pages, therefore, becomes the only criterion by which pupils evaluate their preparation. If group reports are to be useful to the individual and the class, each reporting student must be prepared to gather, organize, and present his material around common concepts or questions assigned to the group.

In addition to problems of structure, the teacher is confronted with a second major consideration before assigning group reports. What should be the nature of the geographic content contained in such presentations? Regardless of the event selected, group reports should include elements of both physical and cultural geography. Obviously, these two aspects of the subject are not mutually independent but together they form the subject's integral whole. When selecting report topics, particularly in elementary and junior high classes, the physical and cultural elements should be separated for descriptive purposes.[1] Students will be better prepared to comprehend and interpret the impact of both human and physical geography upon current affairs through a consideration of the two component parts. Above all, teachers should refrain from assigning report topics which imply that the primary function of geography is limited to that of providing only a physical basis for the study of historical and political events. Through these reporting activities, students must develop the ability to describe physical relationships, to view human and social relationships geographically and, thereby to observe the impact of both physical and cultural geography upon world events. The success of these reporting activities is largely dependent upon the materials available for gathering geographic information during the individual presentations.

An equally important consideration is the manner in which maps and globes are utilized during the individual reports. It is imperative that students be directed to make constant reference to maps throughout their presentations. Although the types of maps used will depend somewhat

---

[1] J. High, "Geography: Coordinating Element in Secondary Social Studies," *The Journal of Geography,* vol. 59 (1960), pp. 275–276.

upon the particular topic, most current world affairs cannot be adequately discussed without reference to both physical and cultural maps of the specific area being considered. Learning how to compare and correlate the phenomena presented on maps with the substantive content presented in the report is one of the primary objectives of geographic instruction.

Suggested report topics · One approach for presenting the geographic background of selected national or international events would be for the teacher to choose two groups of pupils and direct the members of group one to examine the physical aspects of the area in which the event took place while pupils in group two consider the cultural features. The following report topics and problems might be assigned to individual group participants. In some instances the teacher will need to restate these topics depending on the particular grade level of the students.

Group I   The Physical Setting

TOPIC 1   Location of the Event and Size of the Area Included.

A. Determine the direction and the distance of the area in which the event took place from your school.

B. Locate the latitudinal and longitudinal position of the area and its size in square miles.

C. Describe the area's relative location. What nations or regions border the area in question and what are the relationships of the area to neighboring regions?

TOPIC 2   Natural or Physical Characteristics

A. Describe the topography.

B. What are the predominant types of vegetation and soil?

C. Locate important rivers and water bodies.

TOPIC 3   Atmospheric Conditions

A. What is the predominant type of climate?

B. Describe daily weather conditions.

TOPIC 4   Primary Natural Resources

A. Determine the energy resources available for industry and manufacturing.

B. What ferrous and nonferrous metals are mined?

C. What are the environmental assets and limitations for agricultural production?

TOPIC 5 Relationships of the Physical Characteristics to the Current Event.

A. Describe the physical features which appear to influence the particular event being considered.

B. To what extent will the event alter or change the physical environment?

C. Do you think that the physical environment of the area will influence similar happenings in the future?

GROUP II HUMAN AND CULTURAL GEOGRAPHY

TOPIC 1 Population Characteristics of the Area

A. Determine both the size and population growth.

B. Describe the population distribution and density.

C. What proportion of the population is classified as rural and urban?

TOPIC 2 Cultural Characteristics

A. Determine the major ethnic groups inhabiting the area.

B. What are the predominant languages and religions?

C. Are there many smaller ethnic groups, dialects, and religions?

TOPIC 3 Predominant Types of Human Economic Activity

A. Describe the importance of agriculture to the area and determine the extent of subsistence and commercial agricultural activity.

B. Describe the manufacturing and industrial development and potential.

C. How dependent is the area on trade and commerce?

TOPIC 4 Human Resources

A. Describe the educational facilities found in the area.

B. What proportion of the population takes advantage of these facilities and to what extent?

C. Describe the development of scientific, technological, and communication facilities.

TOPIC 5 Relationships of Cultural Features to the Current Event

A. Describe the elements of cultural geography which might have an impact upon the current affair being discussed.

B. To what extent will the event alter or change the cultural geography of the area?

C. On the basis of your knowledge of the human geography of this area, do you think that similar political and social issues will develop again in the future?

Reporting procedures · In the investigation of many current world affairs, pupils might be directed to gather material and report on the above geographic topics. The nature of the event being considered, however, will determine which topics should receive most emphasis. For news stories concerning an independence movement within a colonial territory or a political revolution, the teacher might direct two or three students in Group I to examine and report on Topic 4, Primary Natural Resources, while the reports of Group II may emphasize Topic 3, Predominant Types of Human Economic Activity and Topic 4, Human Resources. Regardless of the nature of the event and the variations in emphasis, Topic 5, Relationships of Cultural Features to the Current Event, is most important for the reporting groups and for the class. Teachers may wish to assign all members of each group to consider this topic and present conclusions. In view of the significance of Topic 5 to any discussion of geography and world affairs, the teacher is confronted with an additional major responsibility: the necessity to reemphasize constantly to students that it is not the purpose of geography to prove any system of environmental or cultural relationships between man and his natural habitat. Geographic analysis of world affairs cannot disregard such relationships, but classroom emphasis should be placed upon describing and interpreting human-environmental associations individually rather than establishing any overall laws or principles of cause and effect.

The teacher may assign four or five students to each group, depending upon the amount of class time he wishes to devote to the particular world event. Group assignments should be made at least two to three days prior to the presentations. Participants may be assigned either to the library for parts of two or three class periods prior to reporting, or the members of the group might work together in the classroom if facilities can be arranged and if adequate reference materials are available. The latter procedure should be encouraged for elementary and most junior high students since the teacher would be present to direct the activities. In either case, it is imperative that the group participants be able to define the problems they are attempting to solve before they proceed to divide the labors of fact gathering.

Group reports should be presented orally and should be limited to fifteen or twenty minutes. To provide continuity, each group should appoint a chairman who is responsible for introducing the problem and organizing the order of individual presentations. At the completion of the individual reports, all group members should contribute to the discussion of the concluding topic — the relationships of physical and human geography to the specific event. Such a procedure affords group members the opportunity to summarize their findings, consider physical and human geography as an integral whole, and apply their inductive skills to an interpretation of the current issue.

CONTINUING GROUP REPORTS

One of the most effective procedures for studying world affairs in geography classes is to assign long-term or continuing groups. These groups, comprised of four or five pupils, could be directed to identify several of the central issues and problems which appear to be basic to many contemporary world affairs and to report on the geographic relationships involved in these issues. Through this approach, group participants may acquire the basic skills in using the geographic mode of inquiry as a method of investigating the environmental aspects of world political and social problems. As a result, they will be more prepared to apply both the method of intuitive inquiry and a knowledge of geographic principles to many recurring national and international affairs as they develop. Continuing group reports can be used to introduce class discussions of the more significant world happenings, or they may be organized into a separate instructional unit emphasizing contemporary world affairs and their geographic relationships. For a class of thirty pupils, the teacher might select four or five groups and assign report topics to be developed over a period of several weeks and presented at the appropriate occasion. The number of pupils assigned to report on each individual topic is dependent upon the nature of the topic and its relationship to the particular world affair being considered. Similarly, the structure and coordination of these more extensive continuing topics are requisite for their success.

The following report topics are exemplary of some of the central issues basic to many recurring world affairs for which a geographic perspective is vital to any intelligent appraisal or interpretation. Identified at the conclusion of each topic are some of the major geographic concepts that elementary and secondary pupils should come to understand. Similarly, both the topics and geographic understandings will need to be restated to correspond to the level of comprehension for students at individual grade levels.

GROUP I WORLD POPULATION GROWTH

World population growth is always a ready example through which geography can be introduced most effectively by group reporting techniques.[1] Through all varieties of news media, students are constantly confronted with the term "population explosion," the increasing fear of overpopulation, and the extensive measures that various nations are introducing to combat these trends.

TOPIC 1   World Population Increase

A. Determine what is meant by "natural" increase of population.

B. Describe the increase in world population since 1900.

C. Locate and name the nations which have the highest and the lowest rates of population increase.

Basic understandings

(1) The natural increase of population is the excess of number of births over deaths. (2) Because of the decline in infant mortality and the death rate, world population is increasing at an unprecedented rate of between 1.8 and 2.2 percent annually. (3) World population doubled in size between 1900 and 1962. (4) Population growth rates vary widely in different parts of the world. The fastest growing regions are Middle America and South America where the population is increasing at slightly more than 3 percent annually. (5) In contrast, the rates of natural population increase in Western and Northwestern Europe, and Anglo-America are less than the world average.

TOPIC 2   Population Distribution and Density

A. Determine the difference between the terms population density and population distribution.

B. Locate and identify both the population core areas and the vast empty spots on a map of world population distribution.

C. Compare world population density and distribution with physical features such as river valleys and deltas, mountainous areas, arid and semiarid regions, and densely forested areas. Where do the people live and why do they live there?

Basic understandings

(1) Distribution of population is a very general term which identifies the inhabited and uninhabited areas of the world or a particular nation while density is a more specific term, referring to the number of people per square mile. (2) The pattern of population distribution and density

---

[1] Three excellent sources for examining contemporary world population trends are W. Zelinsky, *A Prologue to Population Geography* (Englewood Cliffs, N. J.: Prentice-Hall, 1966); *The Future Growth of World Population,* Population Studies, No. 28 (New York: United Nations, Department of Social and Economic Affairs, 1958); *Population Bulletin* (Washington: Population Reference Bureau, 1963).

reveals the opportunities for gaining a livelihood. (3) The fact that much of the world remains relatively empty is not always because of the extreme physical characteristics in these parts of the world. (4) Discussing population density in terms of square miles is much more meaningful if the cultural level of the particular groups are considered. (5) A high population density may indicate overpopulation, but even a region with an extremely low population density may be over-populated.

TOPIC 3   Population and Resources

A. What are the differences between the natural resources and the cultural resources?

B. When is a nation overpopulated and when is it underpopulated?

C. What is meant by the term "carrying capacity" of the land?

Basic understandings

(1) A most important principle is that the term "resource" is less a physical fact than a cultural or technological achievement. (2) Although the natural environment sets limitations on human activities, man is able to impose his will upon the environment. (3) The degree to which human groups change or reconstruct their environment depends upon both the environmental limitations and man's technological ability to overcome these limitations. (4) Population density varies with geo-graphical factors, such as resources for agriculture and industry, and also the level of educational and technological achievement. (5) There are many densely populated areas where people exist in abject poverty in the midst of a natural resource base that could improve their con-dition. Also, there are dense population concentrations enjoying high standards of living in areas with a lesser environmental endowment. (6) Even though nature sets the extreme limits on man's activities, human attitudes and abilities determine the range of actual use within these limits.

Elementary and secondary students are extremely interested in all aspects of the human conditions. Thus, it is easy to integrate elements of geography into discussions of world affairs which involve problems of population growth.

GROUP II   GEOGRAPHY AND EMERGING NATIONS

Presenting a valid and meaningful appraisal of the emerging nation and promoting a student awareness of geography's role in shaping many of the social and political events in these nations are two of the foremost

tasks confronting elementary and secondary geography teachers.[1] The
following geographic topics could be assigned for nearly any of the nations
in Latin America, Africa, or Asia when a particular country within these
areas receives widespread coverage through the news media.

TOPIC 1   Population Characteristics of Emerging Nations

A.   Examine the rate of natural increase of population for several nations
     in South America, Central America, and Asia.

B.   Compare the population growth rates of these nations with the
     growth rates in several of the economically "advanced" nations of
     northwestern Europe and Anglo-America.

C.   Compare the pattern of population distribution in the particular
     nations under consideration with the physical features.

Basic understandings

(1) Overpopulation is a major problem confronting developing nations.
The population of many of these countries represents their greatest
liability or weakness. (2) The rate of population growth in many less-
developed nations is well above the world average and much higher
than growth rates in most of the economically advanced nations. (3)
One of the basic characteristics of many less-developed nations is the
extremely uneven distribution of population. (4) Underdeveloped
nations are confronted with the problem of producing a population
structure in which there are too many young people and too few adults
for economic development.

TOPIC 2   Regions and Regionalism

A.   Determine several regions within an underdeveloped nation or na-
     tions based upon patterns of population, religion, and language.

B.   Examine road and railway transportation systems within several of
     these nations.

C.   Determine what is meant by the terms "total national territory" and
     "effective national territory."

Basic understandings

(1) Peoples in the emerging nations tend to develop stronger attitudes
of devotion and loyalty to separate regions than to their nations. (2)
This lack of a widespread feeling of nationalism is partly the result of
the clustered pattern of human habitation throughout the country and
partly a consequence of the fact that the majority of the populace

---

[1] One of the most useful sources for examining the geographic characteristics of
developing nations is: D. W. Fryer, *World Economic Development* (New York:
McGraw-Hill, 1965), Chaps. 1–2.

occupies only a small fraction of the nation's territory. (3) The pattern of isolated concentrations of population results in the internal division of many underdeveloped nations into two distinct regions which have been designated as "total national territory" and "effective national territory." (4) Total national territory, or the political area over which a centralized government claims jurisdiction, must be distinguished from effective national territory — that part of the total area which makes the major contribution to the support of the populace and the nation's economic growth.

TOPIC 3   Types of Human Activity

A. Determine how the majority of the people in the emerging nations gain a livelihood.

B. What percentage of the people live and work in the rural areas as compared to the cities?

C. What types of manufacturing is found in these nations?

Basic understandings

(1) Among the numerous criteria used to define levels of national economic development are predominant types of productive activity in which a nation's population is engaged. (2) Countries which classify 50 percent or more of the population as rural are generally considered to be economically less developed. (3) Subsistence agriculture, which includes shifting cultivation, nomadic herding, and sedentary intensive production, is the most common in these nations. All human energy is consumed on supplying the basic human needs — food and shelter. (4) Manufacturing and industry in many emerging nations is not highly developed.

TOPIC 4   Economic Development and Resources

A. What resources are basic for industrial and technological development?

B. Determine several underdeveloped areas where the people exist in poverty in the midst of abundant natural resources.

C. Examine the educational system in several less-developed nations. What percentage of people in these nations are literate?

Basic understandings

(1) There are densely populated regions of developing nations where people live in abject poverty in the midst of resources for industry. (2) High population densities in underdeveloped countries may indicate overpopulation, but even a region with an extremely low population density may be seriously overpopulated. (3) Low technological and educational levels in many emerging areas is a larger hindrance

to economic development than the physical environment. (4) Many nations in Latin America, Africa, and Asia are "geoperipheral areas" or areas which export most of their raw material to technologically advanced nations rather than developing their own industry.

Since many current world affairs will continue to be centered around developments in the emerging nations, the well-informed teacher should be able to utilize group reports in such a way as to provide pupils with a background for understanding the human-environmental relationships that exist in these regions of the world.

GROUP III   BOUNDARY DISPUTES AND TERRITORIAL CLAIMS

Many of the most significant as well as frequent world affairs involve national boundary problems and territorial disputes.[1] Because of the roles they play, boundaries are of great importance to the functioning of a nation.

TOPIC 1   Definitions and Functions of Boundaries

  A. Describe the difference between a boundary and a frontier.

  B. What are some of the reasons why boundaries are so important to nations?

  C. What are some of the reasons why boundary disputes arise?

Basic understandings

(1) A boundary indicates certain well established limits of the political control of a nation and separates the control of one nation from another. (2) A frontier is not an exact line or limit but an area near the boundary which serves as a transition or buffer zone between two nations. A boundary is a separating factor while a frontier zone is a connecting factor. (3) Boundaries legally protect the resources and people of one nation from interference by another. (4) The existence of valuable resources as well as other interests in boundary areas will continue to result in territorial conflicts between nations.

TOPIC 2   Types of Boundaries

  A. Define a physical boundary and give several examples of national boundaries formed by different kinds of physical features.

  B. Define ethnic boundaries and geometric boundaries and give several examples of each.

---

[1] See: L. M. Alexander, *World Political Patterns* (Chicago: Rand McNally, 1963), Chap 4; and W. A. D. Jackson, *Politics and Geographic Relationships* (Englewood Cliffs, N. J.: Prentice-Hall, 1964), Chap. 8.

C. Determine what is meant by a complex or compound boundary.

D. Give examples of other types of boundaries that separate or divide nations and peoples.

Basic understandings

(1) Physical boundaries are those which follow some physical feature, such as a mountain range, river, seacoast, lake, or swamp. Many of the boundaries which cross sparsely inhabited territory, as in South America and Africa, are of this type. (2) Ethnic boundaries separate peoples of differing cultural characteristics, based upon such factors as language, religion, nationality, and race. (3) Geometric boundaries normally follow a straight line, a meridian of longitude, or a parallel of latitude. Such boundaries exist in areas of sparse population. (4) Complex boundaries are combination boundaries such as physical and ethnic, or geometric and physical.

TOPIC 3   Current Boundary Conflicts

A. What are some of the recent problems that have arisen in connection with physical, ethnic, or geometric boundaries between nations?

B. Describe in detail several contemporary boundary disputes. What types of boundaries are involved?

C. Determine the reasons and claims that each of these nations is making against the other. What resources or strategic territories are involved?

CONCLUSION

Geography occupies the central position in education for international understanding. Throughout the study of contemporary world affairs there is no more significant interrelationship than that between man and his natural environment. Too often pupils are encouraged to discuss and interpret current political and social events with little knowledge of the physical and cultural environmental factors involved and the extent to which these factors influence the particular event.

One of the most effective instructional techniques for introducing geography into the study of current affairs and promoting student awareness of the important role that geography plays in shaping these affairs is the use of group reports. The wise selection of report topics, however, is most important. Teachers should make every effort to choose current events in which there are likely to be continuing developments or in which there is some tangible relationship to a specific instructional unit. Also, geography teachers should identify and select some of these central issues or problems which appear to form the basis of many recurring world affairs and direct students to report on the geographic relationships involved in these issues. Such an approach would better prepare students to apply their knowledge of geographic principles and methods to many world affairs as they develop. Regardless of the variations of the two basic approaches, geography teachers must continue to experiment with techniques which will motivate pupils to examine world affairs within the context of their relative physical and cultural environments.

13

The problem or critical analysis approach

One of the greatest difficulties in any "problem approach" to the selection of content consists of the definition of "problem." If one is concerned with the teaching of conflict situations, how does he decide which of the multitude of conflicts among individuals and groups are most important to the survival of a multivalue society?

EDWIN FENTON

IN THE PROBLEM or critical analysis approach, the student may become an active participant in the teaching-learning processes. The problem approach is often considered to be synonymous with critical thinking. Problem solving is a form of reflective thought. It is a critical inquiry into the nature of our understanding which constitutes the highest form of thought process.

By its encompassing nature, geography is an ideal discipline for teaching by the problem or critical analysis approach. Geography uses facts and factors from both the physical sciences and the social studies. The ability to see relationships, order, and reasonableness in the complexity, totality, and reality of the landscape is the particular point of view of geography. Thus, geography classes provide an excellent place for integrating and unifying of data from the categorical disciplines with the broad viewpoint of the discipline of geography.

GEOGRAPHY AND PROBLEMS IN LIFE

As geography teachers, we can neither predict the knowledge of places that our students may find useful in the future nor the problems they will encounter in the future. However, we do know that more useful abilities and skills can be learned in problem solving than in the accumulation of facts and principles. Through classroom practice in problem solving, geography students learn to study, to analyze critically, and to think; and the more practice students have, the more likely they are to generalize what they have learned into a pattern of critical analysis that will enable them to solve the problems that they will face in the future. Out-of-school problems are interdisciplinary. Their solution requires not only data from several disciplines but also an approach, a method, or technique, for finding answers.

Too often, emphasis is placed upon the acquisition of knowledge rather than wisdom in the successful utilization of knowledge. The problem approach fulfills this need in our classes. The final test of efficient learning in our classrooms is the future performance of our students.

Teaching organized around problems rather than disciplines stimulates the use of a wide range of content materials and a variety of techniques. The problem approach stimulates thought about causes, relationships, patterns, and prediction. This approach works well in geography classes because geography itself is a way of thinking about facts — place facts.

If students are to think about the implications of some development or change, teachers must pose the problem of the effect of the development upon the place rather than give the class a resume of what occurred in other places at other times, or of what others have decided will be the effect. Teachers too often like to tell the answers or to give the "punch line" first, and then wonder why students have little interest in their presentations.

UNITY IN REGIONAL GEOGRAPHY

The teaching of regional geography comes closer to the spirit of geography and the problem or critical analysis method than the teaching of systematic geography. In regional geography, the class is presented with factual information about the cultural, the physical, and the societal phenomena of a particular region. Under the direction of a skillful teacher, problems can be posed in the classroom and the students guided in recognizing and understanding the significance of pertinent facts in the reality of their setting.

The unification of related factors into a larger concept necessitates the fusion of basic facts into basic patterns or principles, and finally into basic understandings. By the utilization of the basic facts and principles in solving problems, students learn the structure of the discipline of geography rather than solely the content of the discipline. The problem approach is particularly basic to the development of general ideas, skills, and concepts. The processes of conceptualization stimulate the student to analyze critically, to generalize, and to apply ideas to many situations and in varied combinations. The economic and political state of a country depends upon the ability and willingness of its citizens to analyze and to solve current problems. Among all the studies in school, the teaching of geography by the problem approach comes closest to being a laboratory for out-of-school problems and reality.

THE PROBLEM APPROACH

The problem or critical analysis approach received its great impetus from John Dewey over fifty years ago. Dewey stressed particularly that thinking involves first a state of perplexity or doubt in which the thinking originates, and secondly, an act of inquiring and seeking to find material that will resolve the doubt and dispose of the problem.

There are five broad steps in the sequence involved in the problem approach: identification of the problem by defining and clarifying it; collecting, organizing, and evaluating relevant information; formulating hypotheses; critically analyzing the problem by drawing comparisons, noting differences, and examining relationships to reach tentative solutions; and evaluation of the solution or conclusion resulting in its acceptance or rejection. It is not necessary that these steps be followed in strict sequence.

All thought processes exist on a continuum. The mind will move from thinking towards the solution of the problem to an analysis of some data, to new hypotheses, to possible solutions, or even to new sources of information. So students will move back and forth from one step to another in solving a problem. However, the teacher does need to keep the problem before the students during their work.

THE PROBLEM

In the classroom, the teacher may present major problems to the class with studies in regional geography, current events of geographical significance, and questions asked by curious students. The problem should be formulated, stated, or redefined in such a way that it is clear to each student. Care should be taken to see that all students understand the problem thoroughly before proceeding. The student can best demonstrate that the problem is clear to him by stating it in his own words in writing.

As the problem is identified, defined, and adapted to class instruction, the teacher can associate secondary problems with the interests and abilities of individual students. Students demonstrate good thinking when they can sense the presence of a perplexing problem, recognize clearly the nature of the problem, and hold the problem in mind as it is being studied.

Pertinent information · The study of units based upon problems necessitates the utilization of information and data from many sources and disciplines. It is here that geographical problems are similar to the problems encountered out of school. The teacher should provide a wide variety of material and activities both in the classroom and for the library and home. This will encourage students to contrast ideas from several references. The study of geography as analysis of problems becomes dependent upon history and the categorical disciplines of philosophy, the sciences, the social studies, and the humanities.

Once the class has begun solving a problem, certain assignments or subproblems can be given to individual students or groups. Gathering, classifying, reporting, and analyzing statistics require a variety of competencies adaptable to individual students. Such students can use a number of different techniques in their work and so develop a variety of skills useful in giving them greater insight and understanding.

To save time, teachers may supply references and materials for the class. Students like to do rather than plan, so the teacher needs to provide guidance for the class. Classroom study, library research, and field work provide the variety in materials and methods that promote favorable study habits and patterns of thinking. When facts, principles, patterns, and skills are learned in the process of solving problems, they become more meaningful and are more likely to be used in future situations than when they are learned as separate facts and principles or isolated patterns and skills.

Hypotheses · Good students will readily venture hypotheses and formulate possible solutions. The curiosity created by an unsolved problem stimulates the student to do his best in observing, describing, analyzing, evaluating, inferring, and predicting in order to find a solution to the problem. Problems are solved by using principles and old ideas in new ways and in new relationships. There are many diversions present to keep students from thinking for themselves, so the teacher must keep the thinking directed toward a tentative hypothesis. Nevertheless, teachers must be sure to give students sufficient time to hypothesize and to analyze.

Critical analysis · Critical analysis includes a variety of related processes: clarification, discrimination, classification, interpretation, and evaluation. Critical thinking proceeds by examining the available data in an organized manner, by verifying the hypothesis, and by rejecting or applying the conclusion reached. It is the logical examination of data and an evaluation in terms of accepted standards.

Critical analysis involves the organization and examination of a problem through comparison with relevant, objective, and logical evidence and the formulation and verification of hypotheses. For students to do well at critical thinking, they need the ability to study the problem objectively, a background of information, skills in relating standards and values to the problem under study, and an attitude of suspended judgment.

In critically analyzing the data collected, inconsistencies and untenable claims must be recognized and discarded. Students then need to sort items into their proper categories and to present the basis for their decision. They must also be able to describe the consequences that would result from the application of various hypotheses. Evaluation is the logical end of critical analysis; it is a judgment made on the basis of definite criteria. Creativity is shown by novel connections between concepts, by new applications of knowledge, and by different approaches to the solution of problems.

Both critical analyses and creative experiences are inherent parts of the problem approach. The discovery of cause-and-effect relationships requires critical analysis. Each student should be encouraged to pursue the solution of the problem in a depth appropriate to his ability or the goal of the teacher. The solving of problems demands decision making; once a student begins work toward the solution of a problem, a variety of ideas, materials, and data must be planned, collected, organized, and evaluated in relation to the problem. Unrelated and irrelevant data must be discarded. As the student works toward tentative solutions, problem solving requires an involvement of an attitude of openmindedness, willingness to withhold judgment, and the desire to reevaluate the established hypotheses.

In critically analyzing various hypotheses, the student may modify or discard a number of hypotheses and then select a new one. This preliminary work is not necessarily lost because it is related to the original hypothesis and may serve to clarify another problem. Thinking takes time, and students must be given an opportunity to think before judging the adequacy of their hypotheses. The problem approach may well provide the best means for learning.

As the students become actively engaged in solving a problem, they learn by doing and thinking. The students should have a wide range of problems to solve during their school career. The solving of problems in geography classes is multidisciplinary in nature like the problems encountered in life. As tentative solutions are reached, students tend to associate themselves with problems of concern. In this way, students learn the necessity of knowing the content of subject matter for facts and principles and the structure of the discipline for the method of thinking; these become the means for the creative pursuit of understanding.

The solution · All proposed solutions should be examined critically. Students should show a readiness to discard invalid hypotheses, should maintain an attitude of suspended judgment, and should exhibit a readiness to recheck conclusions to test their validity. Students often tend to generalize too quickly and too definitely. They need to be cautioned to maintain an attitude of suspended judgment and to study carefully all possible solutions. Some solutions may be reached rather quickly when a student perceives a clear means-end relationship. There is a constant shuttling back and forth from evidence to hypothesis to conclusions in the mind of the critical thinker.

Problems should be varied in nature and complexity so that different methods must be used in solving new problems. Persons taught by a single method or having been successful in solving a series of related problems will tend to cling to that one method despite repeated failures with it in trying to solve new problems.

Not all problems can be solved; students can appreciate the complexity of national and international problems and can discern the need for alternative solutions and the need to consider the consequences of different solutions. With the increasing complexity of modern society in an interdependent world, it is imperative that students be able to think as logically as possible. Students need to think critically about problems and conditions which are personal and social, political and economic, local and national, and regional and worldwide.

PROBLEMS FOR ELEMENTARY CLASSES

The work area in an elementary classroom might be used for the construction of the natural terrain of the community on a sand table or on a plain table with models. The main problem posed for the class would be — where do we place things in our community. Subproblems for individual students or groups could be — where do we place the houses, roads, city, factories, farms, airport, etc. Value judgments must be made in deciding how the space in the model community should be used. In this work, students can learn of the multidisciplinary nature of real problems in the community.

After the main problems are understood, the class should gather information on how the land of their home community is used and how other communities are arranged. Then the students need to consider how they should arrange their model community. In suggesting various locations for houses, roads, and other features, the students become aware of relationships between man-made things and between man-made things and the physical terrain. In trying to solve the problems, students must make decisions and compromises. Sites for factories compete with farmland. Does the city need an airport more than cropland? Just where should the major highways be placed? Here the intricate relationships between man's convenience and the present possibilities offered by the physical environment become apparent. What provisions can be made for water supplies? These are exactly the same problems which their parents help to decide in their role as citizens.

An intermediate class might be shown a battery of uncaptioned pictures. The problems posed might be — what region, what state, or what country is represented. What evidence is visible in the picture? Which items are relevant and indicative? What is the significance of the pertinent items?

In solving these problems, students must observe, weigh and consider, and support their tentative solutions with evidence and logical reasoning. Slides may be used for these problems also. The difficulty of the problems should be adapted to the level of the class and the ability of the students.

A sixth-grade class of students with a wide range of abilities might work effectively with a stream table. Again the terrain of a community could be made. Different students could work at various tasks on the stream table. The best student could compute the effects of rainfall run-off on varying surfaces while the poorest student might plant corn along a hillside. At the beginning of the class period, the teacher might read from a card the conditions to be shown on the stream table. For example, the card might state that there had been a 2-inch rainstorm last night. Then the student in charge of making it rain would produce a 2-inch rain over the area of the stream table. This would wash away the cornfield so laboriously planted kernel by kernel. While other students considered the effects on their areas of study, the poorest student, seeing the destruction of his work would be confronted with the problem of how to prevent a similar occurrence in the future. Problem, previous knowledge, hypotheses, critical analysis, and tentative solutions are all considered in random order, and before too long the possibility of making some type of ridge along the slope and planting the corn above it is proposed as a tentative solution. The words used may not be the current terms we use, but the ideas are the same. In the meantime, other students may study the effects of the storm on their projects and solving problems of special concern.

PROBLEMS FOR SECONDARY CLASSES

A small problem for junior high school classes uses unlabeled commodity maps. A set of dot maps showing the distribution of various commodities in the United States is presented to the class. Students have the problem of identifying each commodity by its distributional pattern. Background knowledge of the requirements for specific crops, livestock, and minerals can be tested and utilized. Each student is required to state his reasons for his tentative answers.

Dot maps of crops require the use of knowledge of different crop characteristics, of climate, landforms, customs, and other conditions. Dot maps of mineral production emphasize the relationships between certain minerals and landforms, bedrock structure, and size of deposit on the one hand and market demand, accessibility, and use on the other. Dot maps of livestock production can be used to clarify the relationships between certain kinds of livestock and economic demand, feed requirements, transportation facilities, and density of population.

Dot maps showing world patterns of distribution might also be used. Students must know and use facts and principles in identifying the patterns depicted on the maps.

In a world geography class, students might be given a battery of maps on a single country and asked to draw conclusions about life in that country. This approach might also be used in a regional course such as the geography of Europe or Latin America. It would be especially effective near the middle of the semester when the class has a fair background in subject matter but before it has completed the study of all of the countries. Although much intangible information is not mapped, the students can reach rather accurate conclusions with considerable understanding about a particular country using this approach.

A combination of "raw" data — tables of statistics, pictures, maps — of a state or country might be used with an advanced class, and the students asked to interpret them. Skills could be used in converting the statistics into graphs to make them more meaningful. Other maps may need to be made. A skills program works well with the problem approach. By requiring written conclusions from each student, everyone in the class becomes involved in solving the problem.

In the study of southeastern Asia, several groups of problems may be used. For the consideration of landforms and population, these three questions might be asked: How do landforms affect the life and the work of the people? What distribution pattern of population results from the distribution pattern of landforms? Why do the dense populations of the Orient occur in these specific regions? These three questions about shifting agriculture might be posed: What crops are grown and how are they grown? Where are the main areas having shifting subsistence agriculture? Why do these areas have shifting agriculture?

Other separate problems may also be asked. Why is India a land of villages? Why is rice a basic food in the Oriental diet? How do exports affect the economy on Malaysia? Why is Java so densely populated? What would present conditions be if there had never been a period of colonialism? Why does the land and climate, which support some of the largest forests known, fail to support crops?

THE PROBLEM APPROACH FOR A COURSE

An example of the problem approach for a course would be to study the geography of Illinois. This study may be coupled with the teaching of effects before causes. The entire course may be centered around four topics — location, population, agriculture, and manufacturing.

An outline of the course in the geography of Illinois based upon these four topics may include the usual physical and cultural elements. Numerous "where" and "why" questions are posed for all of these topics. Presenting the unity of the patterns observed is an important part of the study. Representative questions are listed in the outline which follows below.

It will be noted that complete answers will not be found within the study of each topic; instead each topic provides only possible answers for major problems. Why do the people live where they do? Why are there different agricultural areas in the state? Why is Illinois a leading manufacturing state? Others may be used as well. Students need to be reminded of the major problems as the class work proceeds from topic to topic. Some topics may contribute much insight into certain problems and none for others. These are occasions for bringing together the various factors. In this way, the unity of the total environment may be comprehended.

THE GEOGRAPHY OF ILLINOIS

A. Location: Where is Illinois in the United States?
    1. Size: What is the east-west distance across Illinois?
    2. Shape: What are the consequences of the shape of Illinois?

B. Population: How large is this population? (Compare with other states and with nations.)
    1. People and distribution: Describe the pattern of distribution of population in Illinois. (Wall map of density of population)
        Which region of Illinois was settled first? (Settlement maps)
        What was the population of the state a century ago? (Line graph)
        What are the major occupations of employed people in Illinois?

C. Agriculture: (Dot maps for major crops and livestock can be made from production statistics. Each student should make at least one map — determining a ratio for the dot, distributing dots over the county, and other cartographic techniques.)
    Describe the pattern of distribution shown on your map.
    Where are the areas of concentration? (A major "why" question is posed here)
    1. Livestock: What relationships exist between your map and the map of _____ (Some other livestock or crop)?
        Why is there a pattern like the one shown on your map? (A key question)
    2. Crops: Why are there areas of great density and sparsity on your map?

Why is your crop grown where it is in Illinois? (A key question which leads into the next topic)

3. Soils: What relationship exists between your crop or livestock map and the map of soils in Illinois? (Individual map of soil associations)

   Account for the pattern of distribution of soils. (This presents the opportunity for learning about soils and leads into the next topic.)

4. Vegetation: What relationship exists between the map of soils and the map of vegetation? (Individual map of native vegetation of Illinois)

   Account for the pattern of distribution of native vegetation in Illinois. (Consideration of the transitional area between the northern and southern forests and between the forests to the east and the grasslands to the west)

   Why did the settlers prefer the wooded areas?

   Where are most of the forests now?

5. Climate: Why do temperature and precipitation vary from south to north in Illinois? (From monthly temperature and precipitation data for a north-south series of stations, students can construct at least three climatic charts. Many questions are posed by these completed charts.)

   How does climate affect vegetation, soils, and crops? (An entire series of maps of various climatic phenomena can be used by each student.)

   Where do tornadoes occur most frequently and how do they affect your agricultural map?

   Why is there a general uniformity of climatic conditions over the state? (This leads into the next topic.)

6. Landforms: How has the physical landscape of Illinois been formed?

   How does the physical landscape of Illinois vary?

   What relationship exists between the map of glacial deposits and the map of soil associations?

   How do you know that Illinois is lower in elevation than surrounding states?

7. Water and drainage: Why is there a finger-like pattern of forests?

   Account for the pattern of alluvial and gray-brown soils.

8. Location of types of farming: Why is corn grown where it is in the state? (Consideration of custom, transportation aspects, feed crops, and hybrids in addition to economic and physical factors)

   Why is the dairying area in northern Illinois?

   How is the farmland of the state utilized? (Circle graph)

   Why are there different types of farming in different areas of the state?

9. Farms and settlement: Where are the individual farms? (To see the isolated farmstead pattern from various topographic maps.) Why are there larger settlements over the state? (From topographic maps; to lead into other economic activities.)

D. Manufacturing: (Present descriptions and statistics on various kinds of manufacturing in Illinois.)
Why are there different types of manufacturing in different areas of Illinois?

1. Kinds of manufacturing: What kinds of products are produced in Illinois? (Need, hence a market)
What are the main manufacturing industries? (Hypotheses on requirements)

2. Cities: What functions are served by towns and cities of different sizes?
Why has Chicago become so large?

3. Location of types of manufacturing: Why are cities the centers for manufacturing?
Why do certain types of manufacturing occur together or cluster together in specific areas?

4. Minerals: Does Illinois produce sufficient quantities of minerals for its manufacturing industries?
Why is so much limestone quarried in northern Illinois? (Maps and statistics. Besides a demand for the product, there is posed the question of why are the deposits there.)

5. Geology: What activities are influenced by the distribution and arrangement of rocks in Illinois?
Account for the location of the operating coal mines in the state.

6. Transportation: Of what significance is the location of Illinois on the western edge of the manufacturing belt of northeastern United States?
Why is the state a major center for all kinds of transportation? (This presents an opportunity to tie in ideas from location, crops and livestock, cities, etc.)

E. Summary: (Students must be permitted to answer the major questions, to summarize, and to offer new solutions for unsolved problems. Teachers can guide, encourage, and give sufficient time, and above all let the students do the answering.)

CONCLUSION

In the critical analysis approach, the teacher's tasks consist in posing questions, in creating perplexity, and in developing curiosity in the minds of the students in such a way as to get them to seek a solution. The teacher then supervises their efforts in redefining the problem, in gathering information, in hypothesizing, in critically analyzing, and in evaluating solutions.

In the solving of the major problems, many other questions pertaining to principles and facts may be considered also. The three major problems, and, to a lesser extent, the problems listed under each topic in the preceding outline may be analyzed critically by the students. Various hypotheses may be formulated, information studied and evaluated, and the hypothesis accepted or rejected.

Some problems should be solved in the geography class; some problems should be assigned for homework and the solutions presented briefly in class; other problems, by their very nature, cannot be solved definitely.

PART IV

Geographic methodology: the regional approach

IN THE ELEMENTARY SCHOOL most of the geography taught is of a regional nature. Frequently the subject is introduced to the third grade pupils by a study of their home community. From this, the study is expanded to the United States and the various continents. In some states the geography of the home state may be studied in the fourth grade. The continental studies in the fifth, sixth, and seventh grades are investigated from different points of view. In some cases the region may be formed by the political boundaries of a group of countries such as Norway, Sweden, and Denmark; in others the region may be a physical one like the Sahara of Africa or the Pampa of Argentina. If the country be a large one such as the Soviet Union, China, Canada, or the United States, it will probably be studied separately from its bordering nations. In some seventh grade classes an overview of the world, studied on a regional basis, constitutes a full year of geographic study.

For a long time geographers have been trying to give a technical meaning to the term region. The way the word region is commonly thought of, however, is well stated by Preston E. James.[1]

> There are many kinds of regions. Some are homogeneous in terms of the phenomena or associations of phenomena that occupy them; others are homogeneous in terms of the performance of a specific function — such as the trade area of a town. Some are simple because they are defined on the basis of a single phenomena or function; others are complex because they

---

[1] "Geography," in *The Social Studies and the Social Sciences* (New York: Harcourt, Brace and World, 1962), pp. 51–52.

embrace areas within which two or more phenomena, or two or more functions, are causally associated — such as a steel industry and its market area.

In the eight chapters of this section each author presents different ways and different points of view for the teaching of a region. The method suggested by any one author, however, can be adjusted to fit any of the other regions presented. In some cases outlines are presented, in others the principal concepts are stated; some authors present what they consider outstanding subject matter ideas; others present generalities about teaching.

14

The home community

*By drawing simple comparisons between life in the home community
and life in other lands, the child may learn something of the significance
of varying geographical conditions, and may gain some appreciation of
the interdependence of peoples round the world.*

NEVILLE V. SCARFE

THE HOME COMMUNITY is an important geographic region and is a
prime laboratory for learning. It is unsurpassed in the quantity and quality
of contributions it can make to the educational process for it provides
many opportunities to work with primary evidence. Association with this
method is basic in the learning process. If performance is the ultimate
evidence of learning, the opportunities for providing such evidence are
many and varied in the local environment.

The home community permits direct observation of natural, cultural,
and spatial phenomena. It also provides for the interpretation of relationships between the observed phenomena. The ability to interpret the
many intricate interrelationships that exist within a community is a difficult but important skill to acquire and may best be done in the setting
of the home community.

The home community provides real-life situations. Fundamental concepts can be developed on the basis of what is seen, heard, smelled, tasted,
or touched. Also, it permits intimate contact with what people have, what
they believe, and what they do. A good citizen should be able to interpret
these three in a related sense. Thus, the home community permits the
acquisition of a fund of knowledge which can be used in the development
of imagery of faraway places.

An understanding of the home community provides a basis for the
comparative evaluation of communities or regions. When making analyses
of likenesses and differences, it is natural to use that which is intimately
known as the key element of reference. A study of the home community
provides opportunities for learning about relationships between commu-

179

nities and regions. The evidences of exchange of goods and ideas can be readily observed. The understanding of a community requires, as a basic step, the identification of its elements. In a broad sense, these elements can be classified as spatial, physical, and cultural.

SPATIAL ELEMENTS

Spatial elements pertain to the location, size, and shape of a community.

Location · Where is it? This is a critical question that can be elaborated in a variety of ways. Where is it with respect to latitude and longitude, other communities, the state, the nation, water bodies, rivers, climatic regions, economic regions, specific landforms, transportation facilities, vegetation regions, soil regions, or population distributions?

Size · How big is it? Is the community a hamlet, village, town, city, metropolis, a town-country combination, or an open-country region? Size has an important bearing on the kind and quality of services a community can render. Some communities can support hospitals, clothing stores, museums, colleges, airports, and concert halls, whereas others cannot. Some may function within a limited area, whereas others may extend their operations over a large region.

Shape · What is its pattern or design? The shape of a community may be conditioned by water bodies, topography, transportation facilities, land availability, architectural design, basic function, legislation, or historical influences. Shape may significantly enhance or handicap the efficient functioning of a community.

PHYSICAL ELEMENTS

The physical elements are the natural features, including climate, landforms, water, soils, bedrock, minerals, and biotic resources.

Climate · Climate is a critical element in community analysis. The seasonal characteristics of temperature and precipitation have a significant effect on human activity. Food, clothing, shelter, agriculture, transportation, and recreation are a few of the human factors related to climate.

Landforms · Landforms can have a bearing on city design, kinds of agriculture, industrial location, transportation patterns, drainage, recreational opportunities, and other such matters.

Water · Availability of fresh water, either surface or underground, is a vital concern in the analysis of a community. Water serves many purposes — domestic, industrial, and urban uses, waste disposal, transportation, irrigation, power production, and recreation. Rivers, lakes, and oceans are frequently contributive to the locations of urban communities.

Soil, subsoil, and bedrock • The nature of the soil and subsoil are particularly significant when agriculture is an important consideration. Soil drainage is an item of concern in both rural and urban situations. The nature of the bedrock may affect its commercial use or it may be of significance in determining such things as subway or skyscraper construction.

Minerals • Minerals may be metallic or nonmetallic. The mineral fuels are man's prime sources of energy. Other minerals are critical in the construction of buildings, tools, machines, transportation media, and communications devices. The availability of minerals may appreciably influence the character of a community.

Plants and animals • Biotic resources may significantly affect the nature of some communities. Forestry, fishing, trapping, and hunting are primary economic activities that contribute a uniqueness to the character of a community.

CULTURAL ELEMENTS

The cultural elements are basically of three types — those that man has constructed on the earth's surface, those that relate to the nature of the people, and those that can be classified under human interests and activities.

Man's construction • These can be identified most easily by asking a series of questions. Are the residences single, dual, or multiple, and what is their quality and distribution? What is the nature of the schools, churches, and libraries, and do they provide adequate services? How are the parks and playgrounds distributed? What is the design of the street pattern? What kind of public transportation is available? What kinds of stores serve the community? Are there factories? If so, how do they affect the character of the community? What kinds of welfare establishments exist in the community? What kinds of buildings house governmental agencies?

The human factors • The following questions identify some of the things to be known about the people in a community. What is the population density? What is the age composition? What is the sex composition? How educated are the people? In what ways do the people make a living? What is the economic level of the people? What nationalities and races are represented? What is the class structure? What kind of associations are active in the community?

Interests and activities · Some of the items that relate to this category can be ascertained from the following questions. What are the people in the community thinking and what are they saying? To what extent is their way of life influenced by the past? What are their customs and traditions? How stable are the families? What is the nature of land use? What are employment opportunities? Are the communication devices adequate and of good quality? How much concern is demonstrated for the aesthetic aspects of the community? What provisions are made for the physical and mental health of the people and the prevention of accidents? To what extent do the people participate in civic affairs? What are the major problems of the community and what attempts are being made to solve them?

COMMUNITY RESOURCES FOR GEOGRAPHIC STUDY

The resources most usable for geographic study tend to fall into the following categories — the physical environment and the accumulated data related to it, data related to the people who live there and the relationships between them, the contributions made by man to the landscape in terms of direct use or alteration, the data which indicate how the past has contributed to current circumstances, the information that applies to economic, cultural, social, and political activities, and the data contributive to understanding the relationships of the home community to others.

The physical environment · This may be studied by direct observation, by recording information, or by gathering statistics and maps available primarily from government agencies. The data provided by the United States Weather Bureau, the topographic maps made by the United States Geological Survey, the information provided by aerial photographs, the studies prepared by the state geological survey, and the published results of private investigations are among the valuable sources available for the study of the physical elements of the community.

The people · Government census information ranks high as a source of data on people. Local societies, clubs, and churches have frequently made studies of the social structure of a community. These studies are ordinarily available to the public.

The man-made landscape · The present cannot be divorced from the past. The contributions of the past may be revealed by the character of buildings, the modifications of the physical landscape, the accounts of senior citizens, collections in museums, local historical writings, diaries, files in newspapers, church and government offices, business records, and the customs and beliefs of the people.

Economic resources • The sources of information related to economics are many and varied. Included are chambers of commerce, civic groups, labor organizations, farm organizations, business enterprises, and government agencies. It is in the area of economics particularly that the relationships of a community to others may be identified and often measured.

Cultural and social resources • Some basic sources of data are the following: records of schools, churches, public and private welfare agencies, social service organizations, zoning and planning boards, various departments of government, newspapers, and labor and management organizations.

Political resources • Activities and facilities related to government responsibilities may be observed frequently. However, information is also available from people involved in government or politics, from various kinds of records that agencies of government must keep, and from newspaper accounts.

Community relationships • The relationships of a community to others depend primarily on its major functions. If it is agricultural or manufacturing in character its outreach may be to the opposite side of the earth. If it is primarily a residential community for senior citizens its outreach is quite limited. However, in the latter case there may still be the factor of dependency on products from distant communities.

The sources of data for the study of interrelationships are as varied as the kinds of communities being studied. When analyzing community functions it is necessary to distinguish between those that are of direct service to the people living there and those that render a service to people in other communities. For example, a bakery may serve people within a limited environment, whereas a manufacturer of ball bearings may serve the world.

WAYS OF STUDYING THE HOME COMMUNITY

The home community may be studied in a number of ways: making field trips or surveys, studying documents, using local materials, using resource persons, recording on maps, preparing pictorial and graphic materials, exchanging information with students in other communities, and conducting service projects. Before using any of these devices, a decision must first be reached on whether the community as a whole is to be studied or whether the investigation is to be confined to one or several facets. The method to be employed is determined to a large extent by the substance of the inquiry.

Field trips • Field trips rank among the best of instructional devices in the field of geography, if they are managed with care. They provide access to primary information, encourage learning through the use of a variety of sense perceptions, give new meaning to the landscape, arouse curiosity about the environment, and enrich instruction. Ordinarily, a field trip is designed to examine one or a few elements of the community, not its total structure. Field trips may range from a visit to a fire station by preschool children to an examination of wholesale marketing by college students. Visits might include such diverse places as dairy farms, factories, department stores, museums, government facilities and functions, newspapers, transportation terminals, power plants, zoos, scientific laboratories, radio and television studios, and notable physical landscapes.

A different kind of field trip may be the recording of things observed along the two sides of a selected street. This may range from a few blocks to a complete cross-section of a community.

At the college level, a look at the landscape from the air has been a successful instructional adventure. Similarly, bus trips with professional instructors have merit.

Effective field trips require careful planning, meaningful motivation, approvals of responsible parties, safe and insured transportation, and follow-up learning procedures.

Surveys · Surveys are ordinarily designed to be comprehensive in character. They acquaint the students with the totality of the community structure. Surveys focus attention on the significant elements of a community and their interdependence. They expose the problems with which citizens must cope. Surveys can be conducted effectively by dividing a class into committees. Each committee assumes responsibility for one aspect or element of the community. The results of the investigations are ultimately synthesized.

Some rules that must be observed when doing a community survey are the following: Define clearly the purpose of the survey and select carefully the elements to be investigated. Concentrate mainly on the people — who they are, what they do, and how they think. Do not exceed community tolerance. Select judiciously the techniques to be used. Gather data objectively, with care and caution. Make the data as understandable as possible through pictures, maps, graphs, diagrams, models, and stories. Synthesize the work of the various groups or committees and then present the accumulated information to the class and to the community.

The results of a survey, especially graphs and maps and their interpretations, are often welcomed by a community newspaper. The results may also be presented through an open house at the school or at the meetings of community organizations.

Community materials · These materials are of many different types and may be as diverse as historical documents, pictures (either historical or current), industrial products, aerial photographs, maps (old and new), mineral samples, agricultural products, soil samples, and records of different organizations and agencies.

Resource persons · Resource persons must be selected with care. Some may be knowledgeable with regard to a topic but do not have the capacity to communicate at a specific grade level. Others may evade their intended purpose by propagandizing for a specific noneducational cause. A well-selected resource person can make significant contribution to the understanding of a community. The following types of people should be considered: long-term residents, librarians, public officials, newspaper editors, farmers, industrial managers, scientific workers, labor leaders, social workers, ministers, health officials, scientists, and college teachers.

Recording on maps · Much of the data gathered during the course of community study can and should be recorded on maps. The map is probably the most compact device for recording and the most lucid device for revealing information about a community. Recording may begin in the primary grades by putting things observed in the landscape on a large, simple base map of the area immediately adjacent to the school. With the advance of grades the area depicted by the base map will increase and the data recorded will grow more complex. If the community is not too large, a map of its entirety can serve as a base. Different symbols are used for transportation routes, schools, churches, factories, parks, residences, parking lots, government buildings, and other items. The symbolism will change from the pictorial to the abstract with advance in grade level.

Preparing pictorial and graphic information · Pictures and graphs have the advantages of making information clear and concise. Pictures may be used either in the historical study of the community or in portraying the existing scene. They must be used with care and caution so that the representation is honest. Graphs are useful in presenting quantitative data. Such data are usually available on the nature of the people and on their economic activities.

Exchanging information · One of the more interesting ways of motivating children to study a community is to arrange a school correspondence or pen-pal program. Ordinarily letters or homemade booklets with maps, pictures, graphs, and descriptions are exchanged between students in two distinct and remote communities. The subtle competitive aspect of such a project tends to yield high-quality production. Furthermore, the children not only are encouraged to learn more about their community through this instructional device, but also about another one.

Technological advances permit a refinement of this device. Telephone companies can connect two different grades in two different communities in a way so that all the children can hear what each one is saying. There are microphones and loud speakers in each room. Furthermore, to add to the educational value, the children of Grade Y in Town A send pictures (transparencies) of their community to children of Grade X in Town B and vice versa. When a picture is discussed, it is projected on the screens in the two schools simultaneously. Two different groups of students at the same grade level living miles apart can in this way share their inquiries and interpretations.

Service projects · Service projects are activities designed to promote civic welfare. Although they require considerable tact, they are democratic in action. As such they deserve to be promoted.

Possible projects include the following: A study might be made of safety measures as related to traffic control, especially in the neighborhood of the school. The recreational facilities of the community could be reviewed in terms of possibly suggesting places where new ones could be added. Civic beauty might be a project worthy of consideration. Service projects are most successful when teachers ally themselves with the constructive forces of a community.

SOME PROBLEMS; SOME BENEFITS

With an increase in urbanization, communities are becoming more difficult to define. With advancing time, functions are growing more and more complex and boundaries are becoming harder to find. Furthermore, increasing population mobility tends to diminish interest in community affairs. However, these obstacles should not deter community study.

The benefits of home community study are many. The student increases his faculty of observation. He learns the art of selection, works with measurement and classification, and becomes acquainted with pictorial, graphic, descriptive, or cartographic methods of recording. Also, the student gains experience in the art of synthesis as he develops skill in interpretation. He acquires the art of dealing intelligently with community problems and opportunities. Coupling these skills to a desire for improvement is a big first step toward good citizenship.

15

Anglo-America

The North America of today is one of the most fully developed
continents on earth. No comparable area is anything like as productive.
None has a higher standard of living.   J. WREFORD WATSON

ANGLO-AMERICA CONSISTS OF two large countries, Canada and
the United States, plus the world's largest island, Greenland, which is a
county of Denmark. The region extends from the Atlantic seaboard to
mid-Pacific and from the frozen Arctic to tropical lands along the Gulf of
Mexico. Within this vast region are examples of all of the world's major
types of landforms and most of its climates. In population density, settlement patterns, and livelihood activities, the region is also varied. The two
nations provide an excellent example of neighborly cooperation, and
together comprise the world's greatest center of economic and military
strength.

There is no single "best" approach to the study of Anglo-America. In
any case, the most useful approach is determined by the interests and
competencies of the teacher; the interests, capabilities, and maturity of the
students; the instructional materials available; and the amount of time
allotted for the study. Indeed, the teacher may wish to approach the study
of the region in several ways rather than in a single way. Therefore three
possible approaches are suggested.

A study of the entire continent can provide the student with an overview of the region. Anglo-America occupies most of North America but
not all of it. The student should at some point examine the entire continent and the seas and lands beyond it in order to see well the areal
framework within which the region lies. The continental overview may
come early in the study of the region, but it need not; its usefulness may
be as great in the middle or toward the end of the study.

An examination of national patterns may be a useful approach to the
study of the geography of Anglo-America. The two political units, Canada and the United States, are familiar realities, and each is so large

territorially that interesting internal patterns are easy to discover. The study of national patterns in Anglo-America is made easy by the availability of reliable data on both the United States and Canada. The study will reveal similarities and striking differences between the United States and Canada, as well as important variations within each country. Students should be encouraged to develop the "comparison habit;" it will contribute to regional understanding.

Regional analysis of Anglo-America may be approached through examination of "natural" or "human-use" regions. Such regional divisions are based on selected biophysical or cultural criteria, or a combination of the two. These regions may ignore political boundaries. Being smaller in area than either the United States or Canada, they offer the possibility of a closer, more detailed view of particular parts of Anglo-America.

DESIRABLE OUTCOMES OF GEOGRAPHIC INQUIRY

Desirable outcomes of geographic inquiry, regardless of the region or topic under study, include the following:

1. The student is made aware of the importance of sources of information: In a time of explosion of knowledge, the "walking encyclopedia" is an anachronism. The educated person in any field of study knows where to find the information he needs. Training in geographic research should begin early in the child's school experience.

2. The student learns to examine critically both textual and cartographic materials: Important though it may be, the ability to gather data is not enough. The data must be interpreted and evaluated, the useful retained, and the useless discarded. Lacking critical skill, the student may skim the surface of a problem, gathering ill-founded impressions or opinions without identifying basic issues.

3. The student learns to think geographically: The study of geography can provide a way of thinking, a distinctive approach to reality. Teachers of geography at all levels should realize that geography is the only field of study that invites students to try to characterize areas and trace interactions between one area and another. Only geography challenges the student to sort out and arrange the threads in the skein of complex relationships between man and his earth home. Leading the student to think in these ways helps toward an understanding of Anglo-America and equips him to initiate the study of any area.

SUGGESTED THEMES FOR STUDY

Some themes or topics that students may fruitfully examine in the study of the geography of Anglo-America are listed below.

1. Anglo-America: Major World Power Center
   (a) Agricultural and industrial leadership.
   (b) Military cooperation.
   (c) World relations and commitments.

2. United States–Canada Boundary
   (a) Evolution of the boundary. Ease of crossing. International trade.
   (b) International cooperation.

3. Filling the Land: Progress of Settlement
   (a) Indian America. Origins of post-Indian settlers. European rivalries.
   (b) Routes. Territorial expansion of the United States. Canadian territorial expansion.

4. Crowded Lands and Empty Lands: Present Distribution of Population
   (a) Areas of heavy density. Areas of light density. United States–Canadian contrasts.
   (b) Contrasts within the United States. Contrasts within Canada. Correlations.

5. Light and Dark: Variation in Sunlight
   (a) Earth–sun relationship. Latitudinal variation. Seasonal variation.
   (b) Correlations.

6. Air Masses of Anglo-America
   (a) Nature and role of air masses. Polar versus tropical. Continental versus maritime.
   (b) Fronts. Associated weather types.

7. Warm Lands and Cold Lands: Distribution of Temperature
   (a) North–south gradients. Influence of water bodies. Seasonal changes.
   (b) Correlations.

8. Wet Lands and Dry Lands: Distribution of Rainfall
   (a) Definitions of dry land and wet land. Average annual rainfall.
   (b) Seasonal patterns. Snow cover. Water resources.

9. The Physical Frame: Landforms of Anglo-America
   (a) Major highlands. Major lowlands. Similarities of the United States and Canada.
   (b) Glaciated lands. The work of wind and water.

10. Power Resources
    (a) Coal. Petroleum. Water.
    (b) Cooperation and trade between the United States and Canada.

11. Iron Ore and Other Metallic Minerals
    (a) United States–Canadian cooperation and trade relations.
    (b) Physical aspects of area in which mined.

12. Travel in Anglo-America
    (a) Waterways. Railways and roads. Airways. United States–
        Canadian contrasts.
    (b) United States–Canadian cooperation.

13. Agriculture in Anglo-America
    (a) United States–Canadian contrasts.
    (b) Crops and livestock.
    (c) Types of farming.

14. Manufacturing
    (a) Types and distribution.
    (b) Investments by United States companies.

15. Recreation
    (a) Growth. United States–Canadian comparison.
    (b) Types and distribution.

16. Urban Studies
    (a) Almost three-fourths of the people of the United States and two-
        thirds of the people of Canada live in urban places; moreover,
        urban population is increasing year by year at the expense of the
        population of rural areas. In addition, urban population tends to
        concentrate more and more in "urban strips," or linear areas
        where several cities are in the process of coalescing. A study of
        selected urban strips will help toward an understanding of Anglo-
        America's most rapidly expanding areas of population and eco-
        nomic productivity. The following list of the larger urban strips
        may be supplemented.

        1. Megalopolis (Boston to Washington, D, C.).
        2. Southwest Lake Michigan Shore (Milwaukee to Chicago to
           Gary).
        3. The Niagara Frontier (Toronto to Buffalo).
        4. Cities of the Piedmont (Richmond to Atlanta).
        5. The Gold Coast (West Palm Beach to Key West).
        6. Upper Ohio Valley (Pittsburgh, Youngstown, Johnstown).
        7. Rocky Mountain Front (Boulder, Denver, Colorado Springs,
           Pueblo).
        8. Salt Lake Oasis (Ogden, Salt Lake City, Provo).

9. Puget Trough (Seattle to Portland).
10. San Francisco Bay Area (San Francisco, Richmond, Oakland, Berkeley, Alameda, San Mateo).
11. Southern California (Los Angeles to San Diego).
12. St. Lawrence Valley (Montreal to Quebec).

(b) Urban studies need not be limited to large urban strips or centers. Investigation of the student's home community, the county seat, or the nearest city can induct the student into one useful approach to the study of human geography.

17. Studies of Roads

(a) Roadways (including railroads, waterways, and trails) have helped to build the nations of Anglo-America and maintain their unity. The study of roads can show how the nations grew, how regions differ, and how people and goods move from one region to another. Such a discussion can be used to display the dynamics of interregional and international relations. Studies of the great roadways of both nations could include:

1. The Canadian National Railway.
2. Early transcontinental railways of the United States (The Union Pacific, The Southern Pacific, The Santa Fe).
3. Trails to the West (The Wilderness Road, The Mohawk–Erie Route, The Oregon Trail, The California Trail, The Santa Fe Trail, The Mormon Trail).
4. Modern Highways: The modern highway systems of Anglo-America are so extensive that it would be necessary to select a limited number of routes for study. Canada's transcontinental highway project would provide excellent opportunity to examine Canada's east-west contrast. U. S. 40, cutting across the grain of the United States, can be used to illustrate regional contrasts and relations. A study of the Interstate System of highways can point to future patterns of travel and transportation.
5. Waterways: The historic role of numerous waterways and the contemporary importance of a few may highlight the study of water routes in Anglo-America. The Great Lakes–St. Lawrence system is important historically and today. Most of the rivers of the Atlantic Seaboard have declined as avenues of travel. Many of the rivers of the interior and the far west are maintained as navigable waterways through construction of dams and locks, dredging, levees, and watershed protection. The study of a single river or river system can be a challenging study and may lead to examination of

other stream functions such as drainage, land sculpture, water supply, and power.

Although the preceding outline suggests themes that may be pursued in the study of Anglo-America, it is not complete, nor are the themes listed in any intended order. The list is intended to suggested pertinent topics which teacher and students may adopt for study.

MAP PORTRAITS OF ANGLO-AMERICA

The study of Anglo-America may involve the student in a variety of activities: use of textbook and atlas; in-depth investigations of topics, areas, or problems; supplemental readings for enrichment; discussions or reports. An activity that has proved useful with undergraduate classes and may be adapted for use at other levels is the preparation of map portraits. Working individually or in groups, students gather data and prepare their own maps. Charts and graphs are also prepared, but maps are the central focus. Assembled in a binder, the individual student's maps may become his own atlas. The process helps him to learn more about the area. Moreover, the preparation of his own regional maps almost invariably heightens his interest and enthusiasm. Students are likely to remember well those things they discover and present, either in maps or in text. The world of maps is the world of discovery, and geography teachers should capitalize on this obvious way to exciting new discoveries through maps.

A second and perhaps more important reason for requiring student map work is that it may be the key to increased geographic literacy. A major cause of the much discussed condition of geographic illiteracy in America lies in our failure to teach well the language of maps. Furthermore, this failure may result from students experiencing maps largely as observers rather than as makers of maps. We may learn from instruction in other fields: Children learn English language usage by employing its symbols in building words, sentences, and paragraphs. Reading, important as it is, will not alone develop excellent language usage. Likewise in mathematics and music, proficiency is attained through use of the symbols; and the chemist learns chemical reactions by inducing them. Proficiency in the language of maps requires nothing less than the use of cartographic symbols in preparing one's own maps.

The themes listed earlier may suggest maps for students to prepare. Maps may range from simple sketch maps to meticulously prepared ones. The student should be allowed a measure of freedom to experiment in map design and choice of technique or symbol, but always under supervision. The purpose of maps is to convey a message, not merely to provide a means of self-expression for the map maker.

The student should be required to interpret each map he prepares, and each should be relevant to the general orientation of the course. The student should have the opportunity to look for correlations between maps as well as for patterns within an individual map. Used in this way, map portraits may become a highly useful component of the study of the geography of Anglo-America.

16

Latin America

Latin American nations are caught up in the storms of economic and social transition. Country by country, the continent is experiencing the dislocations of peoples, social and political groups, and economies.

HERBERT L. RAU

To LOVE THE Latin American as thy neighbor, or as one in need, calls for a correct image of the Latin American as he goes about his daily activities in the city and countryside. To acquire such fundamental information, it is necessary for the teacher to research correct geographic facts and concepts from primary or documentary source materials and first-hand experiences as distinct from propaganda or mere hearsay. Having gained such a correct and fair image of the Latin American lands and peoples, the teacher has the responsibility of translating that body of geographic knowledge to the level of instruction desired in such a way that the student will be challenged to want to go beyond the basic requirements of the course of study.

True, this is a theoretical goal, for there are those who have spent much of their lives living, working, and studying in Latin America who would be among the first to admit that to cast the Latin American in one single mold is an impossibility. One region or country cannot typify the whole of Latin America, for each has its own particular combination of geographic features which give it uniqueness. However, it is best to introduce Latin America to the newcomer first in terms of the grosser generalities, then work toward the refinement of those geographic concepts that differentiate countries and regions and impart character to Latin America as an outstanding world cultural region.

OBJECTIVES OR UNDERSTANDINGS

The following logical and sequential objectives or understandings center attention at the onset on the contemporary geographic importance and implications of Latin America among nations and in the western hemisphere. This experience is then followed by a geographic analysis of the macroregions of Latin America. The culminating experience is to identify the major problems of Latin America and to catch a glimpse of the dynamism that will typify the next two or three decades in Latin America as efforts are accelerated to achieve a higher standard of living with respect and dignity for all.

To indicate the unique geographic features of Latin America when compared with other developing nations and the advanced or developed nations in the world today, the following points need to be stressed.

1. Geographic location and implications (cultural, social, and economic).

2. Population characteristics: geographic distribution, the large primate city, and open space from low population density; demographic characteristics: highest growth rate in the world and young population.

3. Agriculture and industry: nearly half the population engaged in agriculture and the early stages of industrialization.

4. Vast resources, largely unexplored and unexploited, of forests, grasslands, minerals, soils, fisheries, and water power.

5. Economic integration: Central American Common Market and Latin American Free Trade Association.

6. International trade: Latin America's exports mostly primary products from farm, pastoral land, or mines; world economy depends on Latin America for much of its foods and raw materials.

To compare and contrast Latin America with Anglo-America for the purpose of showing the nature of and need for the increasing interdependence between the major macroregions of the western hemisphere, the following points need to be emphasized.

1. Physical comparisons and contrasts: terrain, climate, natural vegetation, soils, minerals, hydrology, nature of harbors, position in relation to world trade lanes.

2. Cultural comparisons and contrasts: population totals, trends, and gross reproduction rates; predominant economies, major agricultural regions, leading products for domestic and foreign consumption, surface transport facilities and ocean and air transport, composition of trade, and international boundaries and their implications.

3. Cultural exchanges: getting to know students and professors, Peace Corps members, tourists, people-to-people programs, diplomats, Voice of America.

To be able to identify and explain geographically those cultural and socioeconomic features of the lands and peoples of Latin America that help to make a distinct cultural world region the following points need consideration.

1. Ethnic characteristics.
2. Religion, language, and education.
3. Customs, food, clothing, shelter, etc.
4. Types of land tenure, patterns of land use.
5. Nature of governments.

To separate the component geographic regions, or macroregions, for convenience of geographic analysis, and to suggest procedures for the study of a geographic region in Latin America, the following macroregions should be studied.

1. Mexico
2. Central America
3. The West Indies
4. South America

Through a detailed study and geographic analysis of the regions of Latin America, appreciation and respect may be developed for those particular cultural, social, and economic characteristics and anomalies that help to make the Latin American different from the Anglo American. Such understanding may be based on the following points:

1. Wealth and conspicuous consumption of elite class and abject poverty of masses.
2. Ultramodern architecture of Brasília and make-shift shelters in the *favelas* or slums.
3. Large cities with thriving, modern business economies, but small, remote subsistence communities not tied into national economy.
4. Use of human and animal power in a machine age.
5. A high but varied rate of illiteracy from country to country, but only a recent inauguration of popular education and a textbook program: the case of Mexico and Central America.
6. Well educated medical men, yet many communicable diseases and helminthiases to be controlled and eliminated.
7. Great need for pure drinking water, public sanitation, and personal hygiene.
8. Low wage scales and child labor: coffee *fincas*, tending herds.
9. Much unemployment and underemployment.
10. Contrasts in pattern of living: Upper Amazon, Altiplano, Patagonia, Rio de Janeiro, or other large city.

One must recognize that Latin America, like other world cultural regions, has particular problems; the solutions must be worked out by the .

peoples themselves, aided by the technology of advanced nations. The following problems need to be identified:

1. Nutritional levels in Latin America are below the standards set by the United Nations for that area.

2. The gap between the rate of population growth and per capita food production is widening in Latin America.

3. Postwar import-substitution industries developed at the expense of the agricultural sector of the economy.

4. Economies must now be planned and restructured with more attention given to the agricultural-pastoral-fisheries sectors.

5. Very great are the needs for better communications and transportation, especially access roads.

6. For longevity and socioeconomic advancement, disease control and elimination must be stepped up.

7. Urgently needed are improvements in pure water supplies and sanitation.

8. For more effective manpower in all sectors of the economy, power development should be greatly increased.

9. To raise literacy levels more homes, schools, and textbooks are needed.

10. Democratic tendencies should be strengthened in the ideological struggle between capitalism and communism in Latin America.

11. A more correct image of the United States and its world obligations is desired as well as an understanding of our ambitions for free peoples everywhere.

12. Population pressure on worn-out land resources should be minimized by continued colonization and settlement of the *tierra caliente* zone.

It should be stressed that the dynamic aspects of the geography of the Latin American lands and peoples — changes in the landscape, in ways of work, patterns of living, and leadership are coming about largely as a result of the initiative and drive of the Latin American peoples for a higher standard of living. The following points are basic to such understanding.

1. Agrarian reform is bringing about better methods of agriculture and more foods and fibers for home consumption.

2. Relative stability in government is aiding socioeconomic progress.

3. Land reform is favoring the landless peasant.

4. New leaders are coming from the growing *mestizo* and middle class.

5. Modern construction and industries are helping revamp the large cities.

6. Popular education and production of their own textbooks are occurring.

MATERIALS FOR DEVELOPING GEOGRAPHIC UNDERSTANDING

An excellent start in the acquisition of correct overall geographic facts and concepts pertaining to Latin America is for the teacher to use a good atlas, to itemize, then summarize, and analyze geographically the information on Latin America from three points of view: Latin America's world role; Latin America's position in the western hemisphere; and Latin America's regions. To build upon this basic information it will be helpful to research the documents of the United Nations, Organization of American States, United States Bureau of Mines, and the United States Department of Agriculture, as well as census reports and publications by each Latin American country. Professional and scientific journals, together with the *New York Times, Wall Street Journal,* and various news magazines will supply recent data.

While the teacher is adding to and updating his own fund of knowledge on Latin America, he should be building up his file of geographic materials that will enhance the various stages in unit planning and presentation. The following is a minimal outline of suggested materials useful for such activity.

I. Pictures of high geographic quality which show both cultural and natural features (Kodachrome, black and white, and aerial photographs; film strips and motion pictures).

   A. Panoramic views of typical landscapes from plane, high mountain, or tall building.
      1. Temperature zones in tropical highlands: *tierra caliente, tierra templada, tierra, fría, paramos,* and *tierra helada.*
      2. Major land forms.
      3. Major vegetation associations.
      4. Stages of economic development.
      5. Colonization and settlement of new lands.
      6. City and town layouts.
      7. Transportation.
      8. Farm layouts.
      9. Poor use of resources.

   B. Typical close-ups: cultural and physical features.
      1. Market facilities.
      2. Types of homes.
      3. Methods of work.
      4. Different ethnic classes of people.
      5. Types of transportation on vehicles.
      6. Foods and beverages.
      7. Clothing.
      8. Educational facilities.

II. Maps of high geographic quality: large and small scale.

    A. General purpose maps: Physical-political maps (wall and atlas maps) of Latin America, Middle America, and South America.

    B. Special purpose maps.
       1. Population.
       2. Predominant economies and stages of economic development.
       3. City and port layouts.
       4. Elements of physical environment as they relate to socioeconomic and resource development.

III. Charts, diagrams, statistics, and models.

    A. Compiling data, constructing graph, interpreting graphs: line, bar, climatic chart, etc.

    B. Statistical analysis of a problem or a region involving gathering statistics, organizing statistics into meaningful tables using such sources as *Statistical Abstract of Latin America,* United Nations *Demographic Yearbook* and *Statistical Yearbooks;* United States Department of Agriculture, *Agricultural Yearbook.*

    C. Models (clay or sand): a typical Latin village, the Atacama Desert and *garua,* the hut and artifacts of the Amazon rubber gatherer, the Baia de Guanabara, the harbor at Callao, the estuary at Buenos Aires and Montevideo, the site of Brasília, the Cubatão Power Station at Santos, a coffee *fazenda* in Brazil, *a sítio* on the Brazilian frontier, the terrain of Ecuador showing generalized land use, and others.

SUGGESTED TEACHING PROCEDURES

Having formulated an up-to-date geographic image of Latin America, the teacher should next consider how to refine and synthesize the complex association of geographic facts and concepts that characterize the Latin American cultural region and differentiate it from all other world cultural realms. This calls for dividing the entire area into broad macroregions, each of which is made up of a group of political units that are generally uniform in structure. The boundary lines between the macroregions are of little import; of more concern are those basic and dynamic geographic concepts that identify the core regions of Mexico, Central America (isthmian countries), the West Indies (insular nations), and South America.

Structurally, Mexico to about 20° N is a continuation of the North American land forms. While the structure of southern Mexico, Central America, and the West Indies trends generally east and west, that of South America has a north-south alignment.

Mexico should be the first macroregion studied, for it offers certain similarities of terrain, climate, natural vegetation, and land use to those of the adjacent areas of the United States. In addition, the student will be confronted at the onset with many surprises and challenges having to do with the various cultural, social, and economic features of Mexico. Mexico has a large and significant core region, the Central Plateau, the study of which will help the student become acquainted with the study procedure.

A Suggested Procedure for the Geographic Study of Mexico on the Secondary School Level

I. Major Objectives: Have the students discover for themselves the physical and cultural similarities and differences between Mexico and the United States, the many contrasts within Mexico itself, importance of the Central Plateau, the major problems confronting the Mexican, and then, delineate the problems for study.

II. Materials: Assemble maps, pictures, graphs, models, globe, diagrams, reading materials, statistics, work sheets, and a reading list of library materials.

III. Procedure
    A. Introduction or motivation.
       1. Picture study: landscapes of different parts of Mexico and close-up pictures of the people.
       2. Map study: latitudinal extent, nature of the United States–Mexican boundary, landforms, climate, population distribution, surface transport, predominant economies, and major agricultural regions.
       3. Statistics and graph study: population of Mexico in 1960, age distribution and longevity, size of family, rate of population growth and of agricultural production, and international trade.
       4. Special reports: the uniqueness of Mexico's social revolution and the contemporary relations of Mexico with the United States and the Caribbean nations.
       5. Summary and statement of problems: Why is the Central Plateau Region the population and economic heart of the country? Why are other parts of Mexico considered outliers? How are the hydrological problems being solved? What is the present status of the social revolution in Mexico? What is Mexico doing to relieve population pressure on land resources?
    B. Assimilation or individual study: Reading and research in the school library and presentation of findings to class through such media as panel discussion, oral reports, or other procedures.

   C. Summary of understanding: Research papers, class summary of findings, and testing.
   D. Application of understandings to new situations.
      1. What advice about Mexico would you give to those wanting to participate in the games in Mexico City?
      2. Indicate what you would like to know about Mexico from a pen pal.
      3. State what a prospective Peace Corps volunteer should know about Mexico.
      4. If you were asked to accompany a group of youths from the United States on a reconnaissance tour of Mexico, state what you would tell them in the orientation session prior to departure and describe the itinerary you would follow so as to give the group a fair assessment of the Mexican and the land that he occupies.

CENTRAL AMERICA AND THE WEST INDIES

The suggestions for geographic study of Central America and the West Indies, might be similar to those suggested above for Mexico. A survey should first be made of the overall characteristics that have to do with the strategic nature of the countries surrounding the Caribbean Sea and the similarities and differences between the isthmian countries of Central America and the insular nations and dependencies of the West Indies. By now, the student should be able to make his own investigative outline for a detailed study of the Central American countries and of the West Indies. He might be encouraged also to suggest how the research on such a divergent and fragmented area may go forward, where to look for information, and how the knowledge gained may be presented to the class and also rationalized in relation to the lives of the students. As a culminating activity each student should then be asked to summarize in essay form the comparative geography of Central America and of the West Indies. Guidelines for preparing the essay should be forthcoming from the class. It would indeed prove beneficial if representative essays were read to the class, followed by one that the teacher prepares.

The teacher's summary might be constructed along these lines:

Caribbean America is made up of the seven countries of Central America, and the insular West Indies that surround the Caribbean Sea. The many narrow land crossings and water passages, together with commodious landlocked bays and an intermediate position in the Western Hemisphere, place this area of Latin America well to the forefront strategically.

Those small countries have an east-west trending structure in latitudes with a northeasterly trade wind flow in winter, and an easterly trade wind flow in summer. This results in marked contrasts in rainfall on windward and leeward exposures. These countries lie in the paths of tropical storms and devastating hurricanes. Also, seismic and volcanic activity occur from time to time.

In Central America the *tierra templada* zone contains the larger population nuclei, except for Belize, San Pedro Sula, Managua, Panama City, and Colón. However, largely because of historical precedent and balmy sea breezes, island littorals of the West Indies are the most populous.

Ethnically, the Central American is a *mestizo*, though the largest segment of the population in Guatemala is Indian, in British Honduras, Negro, and in Costa Rica, Caucasian. The West Indian, moreover, is a mulatto, with Negroes in a majority in Haiti, Barbados, and several other islands, but with predominant *mestizo* elements in the Dominican Republic and Puerto Rico. Except in a few small isolated areas the native Carib and Arawak Indians have disappeared.

Economic advancement is making headway in those Central American countries that are members of the Central American Common Market (Guatemala, El Salvador, Honduras, Nicaragua, and Costa Rica), and in Puerto Rico under "Operation Bootstrap." Advancement is less in Jamaica and Trinidad, and even retrogressive in Cuba.

Largely because of the dearth of economic mineral deposits, except in Jamaica, Trinidad, and Cuba, the peoples of Central America and the West Indies have long depended more on the soil for a livelihood than have the Mexicans. They do not have Mexico's variety of products for export. Their national income has been derived singly from the sale of a few commodities from the farm (sugar, bananas, coffee, cotton, tobacco, cocoa, fibers, and spices), from the mine (oil, asphalt, and bauxite), and from the forest (pine, mahogany, and cedar).

Industrialization, the new way of life, is firmly established in Puerto Rico. It is making rapid strides in Jamaica, Trinidad, and the Central American countries, and for some time will produce largely consumer goods for the home market.

Problems particular to these small countries have to do with population pressure on land resources, especially in El Salvador, Puerto Rico, Jamaica, Haiti, and Barbados; construction of a new interoceanic canal capable of handling future world shipping; and political problems growing out of independence for Jamaica and Trinidad, communism in Cuba, dictatorship in Haiti, and colonialism in the nonself-governing territories of Britain, France, Netherlands, and the United States.

SUGGESTED IDEAS FOR STUDYING SOUTH AMERICA

The student by now should demonstrate his capability for gathering geographic data from different media and should be encouraged to do so in the case of the last macroregion of Latin America to be studied. He should also be able to state in scientific language the outstanding geographic facts and concepts concerning South America, with respect to geographic location, terrain, climate, natural vegetation, power and mineral resources, and other natural phenomena; areal distribution and density of population, total population, gross reproduction rate, projected population for 1980, and ethnic characteristics; predominant economies, major systems of agriculture, leading products for domestic and foreign consumption, nature and direction of international trade, and other cultural and socioeconomic features.

The student would be expected also to show facility in stating broader comparisons and contrasts between South America and other macroregions of Latin America and to point out the unique features of South America. To state the problems for further research becomes his next task, together with a suggested organization of the countries, and a study outline for each country. At this juncture he may expect some help from the teacher. As an aid to the teacher the outline below is offered.

I. Tropical lands with less advanced economies.

    A. North Coast Countries: Colombia, Venezuela, Guayana, Surinam, and French Guiana.

    B. Indo-Andean Countries: Ecuador, Peru, and Bolivia.

    C. Brazil and Paraguay.

II. Midlatitude lands with more advanced economies.

    A. Chile, Argentina, and Uruguay.

Very briefly stated, the study outline for each country should incorporate these major understandings and in this order: generalizations that have to do with both physical and cultural features; unique geographic concepts; geographic regions (South America lends itself best to regions based on terrain) described and analyzed from the point of view of contemporary land use, developed and potential resources, and problems; and last, how this information may be of value to the student.

CONCLUSION

After the detailed study of each country group, attention should return to the initially delineated views about Latin America for purposes of clarification, explanation, and refinement, and perhaps, for a look into the future.

The teacher should make sure that no student leaves the course with only half-truths. What does he know about Latin America's world role; her place in the democratic world; her current relations with the United States and western Europe; the efforts of the Latin Americans to strengthen intracountry ties; the new leadership that is developing in Latin America; their efforts and contributions toward the solution of the food and population problem; the reasons for the frustrations, anxieties, and impatience expressed by the Latin Americans with respect to their standard of living; the reasons they will need foreign aid in increasing amounts for the next two or three decades; the meaning and reasons for frontier colonization and settlement; the effects of changing world commodity price on countries that produce and export such primary raw materials and foodstuffs as coffee, bananas, cotton, sugar, oil, iron ore, bauxite, copper, tin, and others?

What has the student learned about the real meaning of remoteness, of lack of power, communications or access roads; the modernity and problems particular to the large primate cities of Latin America; the true meaning of poverty, hunger, and disease; the reasons for such high percentage of workers in agriculture, of unemployment and underemployment; the reasons for population pressure on land resources and the many landless people? What does he know of the function and significance of the Organization of the American States and how the member nations are now trying to strengthen that organization; of the objectives of the Alliance for Progress; of the great latent wealth of natural resources — soils, forests, grasslands, minerals, and water power — upon which advancing economies depend; and, of the proper attitude and respect for the Latin American, who he is, and what he desires to become?

17

Europe

Europe does not stand for quantity but for quality, not for size but for variety.   PAUL COHEN-PORTHEIM

THE PLACE WHICH Europe holds in the modern world and its relations to the United States make the study of that continent most interesting and important. Economic, political, and cultural ties bind the people of the United States more closely to Europe than to any other continent. As a consequence, Europe has exerted and continues to exert a profound influence over many aspects of American life.

Economically Europe is more important to the United States than is any other continent. With it Americans carry on a large portion of their foreign trade. American investments abroad and many other economic relationships are of considerable importance. Consequently, the prosperity of the United States rests in no small part upon a sound knowledge of European conditions.

The cultural relationships between Europe and the United States are as close and as important as the economic relationships. Most American culture either originated in Europe or has been built upon European foundations. We have long looked to Europe for inspiration in such fields as art, music, literature, drama, education, and philosophy. Modern scientific agriculture, scientific forestry, modern medicine, and many improvements in manufacturing and communication are of European origin. America has drawn upon these discoveries in the building of its present-day society and within recent years it has made important contributions of its own which have been adopted throughout Europe.

Close political ties bind the United States to Europe. The American form of government is largely European in background. The makers of our constitution were well acquainted with European political ideas. Our Bill of Rights includes rights previously won by Englishmen. Our system of law was inherited from English law. Our ideas of democracy are much the same as those of Northwest Europe. As Europe's political influence is world wide, such vital matters as peace or war, and America's position within the family of major nations, must depend upon its relations with the European powers.

A study of the nations of Europe will enable the student to see his own country and culture in better perspective. It will help him to realize that his own nation is but one of a family of nations with common elements yet distinctive characteristics, evolving through time from common antecedents with differentiation, but with much cultural borrowing.

The majority of young people are eager to study Europe. Their school work and their reading have included stories, the scenes of which are laid in Europe. They know and use products that have been imported or have been brought back by friends who have visited there. They have seen pictures, articles in newspapers and magazines, telestar television, and world-wide news reports concerning people and events in Europe. Their personal association with the continent has usually been through relatives who have traveled or have lived there. As a result, the student will bring much background to the study of Europe.

ORGANIZING THE SUBJECT MATTER

With the great amount of material to be covered in teaching the geography of Europe, good organization and presentation are essential. The subject matter in the study of Europe may be presented regionally or systematically. Each approach divides the subject matter into pedagogically convenient categories.

As geographers utilize the term, a region is "a device for selecting and studying areal groupings of the complex phenomena found on earth. They are areas of any size that are homogeneous with respect to specific criteria,"[1] and as such there are many kinds of regions that can be recognized. Europe may be divided into regions based upon climate, surface features, population, industrial concentrations, countries or groups of countries in order to provide a framework for geographic study. The size of the region will depend upon the physical or cultural features that are considered pertinent to the purpose for which the region is being established. The systematic approach would deal with such topics as climate, soils, transportation, and population. Within a course organized on a regional framework, it is desirable to use the systematic approach to analyze phenomena within a region.

Methods of dividing the continent of Europe into regions and of ana-

---

[1] D. Whittlesey, "The Regional Concept and the Regional Method," in P. E. James and C. F. Jones (eds.), *American Geography: Inventory and Prospect* (Syracuse: Syracuse University Press, 1954), pp. 20–21.

lyzing them will differ from one course to another depending upon the level of instruction. The regions studied at the elementary level are for the most part countries or groups of countries. It must be remembered that young students are primarily interested in people in other countries — how they live, what they do, how they are like us, and why they do some things differently from ourselves. To be sure the emphasis varies in different grades, and in the upper levels more consideration is given to the social, economic, and political problems which face the nations of Europe and our relationships to them.

The following sequences of regional units on Europe are presented as resources from which selection may be made and direction obtained:

A. SEQUENCE OF UNITS*	B. SEQUENCE OF UNITS†
1. The British Isles	1. Physical features on the continent of Europe
2. France and Benelux countries	2. British Isles
3. Northern Europe: Norway, Sweden, Denmark, Iceland, Greenland, Finland, and Faeroes	3. Northern Europe: Norway, Sweden, Finland, Denmark
4. Central Europe: Germany, Austria, Switzerland	4. Western Europe: France, Belgium, The Netherlands, West Germany, Switzerland, Austria, Luxemburg
5. The Mediterranean lands	5. Southern Europe: Spain, Italy, Greece, European Turkey, Albania
6. Eastern Europe, including Balkan Countries	6. Eastern Europe: Poland, Czechoslovakia, Romania, Bulgaria, Yugoslavia
7. The Soviet Union	7. Soviet Union in Europe

* *A Program of Geography Education from Kindergarten Through Grade 12 for Improving Curriculum in the Pennsylvania Schools* (Chicago: Pennsylvania Council for Geography Education, 1962), p. 8.

† M. V. Phillips, "Suggested Sequences for Geographic Learning," in Wilhelmina Hill (ed.), *Curriculum Guide for Geographic Education* (Normal, Illinois: National Council for Geographic Education, 1964), p. 40.

The sequences of units described by the preceding table were selected on the principal of adjacency of one region to the following region (the study of one region is followed by a region adjacent to it). This will enable the learner to attain a knowledge of the design of these regions, and thus he will acquire an association concept of their relative positions and an awareness of the patterns of their given physical, biotic, and cultural aspects.

ATTITUDES, CONCEPTS, FACTS, AND SKILLS

In teaching the units, the content and materials should be selected so as to develop important attitudes, concepts, facts, and skills about each region.

ATTITUDES

An *appreciation* of the diversity of the countries of Europe in physical elements and resources, in economic activities, in political organization, and in cultural change.

An *understanding* of the diverse cultures of Europe, each with its particular viewpoints, achievements, and problems.

A *recognition* that Europe and the United States are linked together by economic ties of trade, by political ties in international organizations, by scientific ties of education and research, by cultural ties in art, music, and literature, and by common dangers of disease, war, and catastrophes.

CONCEPTS

Man–land relationships · Man's activities are intimately interconnected with human and physical phenomena. They depend not only on the physical quality of the land but also on man's culture, that is, the attitude of the people toward the land and their technical skill in using it. The nature of agriculture in an area, the economic structure of a nation, or the pattern of transportation routes in an area cannot be studied meaningfully apart from the land. Conversely, the activities of man are continually modifying the soil, the vegetation cover, the surface of an area, and other aspects of the natural environment in varying manner and degree.

Regionalism · The region is another concept of strong geographical interest. It is a device to comprehend likenesses and differences on the earth's surface. Cultural and natural conditions vary greatly from place to place. These variations are often associated in meaningful ways which make possible the recognition of a practical and reasonable unit or region. For example, physical regions, such as those of climate have associated agricultural possibilities. Cultural regions often are characterized by the coincidence of types of economic activity, stages of economic development, types of resource utilization and political organization. The political geographic region is another kind of region which possesses agencies which gather meaningful data.

Changing pattern of geographical complexes · The world is in a process of continual change. Almost nothing either human or natural is static. The changes in the region and the rates of change are not everywhere the same. Some regions are undergoing rapid economic development and cultural changes while others are relatively stable. These changes have repercussions which affect the present and the future.

Areal structure · The continent of Europe and each of its regions have areal structure with a specific layout of land and bodies of water, plains and mountains, forests and farms, roads and railroads, cities and towns, and distribution of language, religion, and occupational groups. The map is the most important tool for depicting this structure.

Interrelationships · There are many interrelationships in the study of regional geography. For example, we can, in a given region, interrelate the weather and climate, landforms, soils, vegetation, and man with land use and tenure. The development of manufacturing regions reflects resources, labor, skills, and markets not only of the present day but also of the past. The agricultural regions reflect diversity of climate and soils on the one hand and the method of cultivation on the other.

FACTS AND SKILLS

Facts · The most significant elements of the cultural and natural environment in the various regions of Europe and their functional relationships should be understood. The pattern of distribution of the major physical and cultural elements of the environment should be learned. The important place locations studied need not be large in number but should include key places, both cultural and physical, within the continent of Europe.

Skills · Students should learn to secure and interpret geographic information from landscapes, pictures, maps, globes, graphs, statistics, and reading materials; prepare and present data by means of maps, charts, statistics, graphs, and written materials; and raise significant geographic problems from facts gained and effectively organize facts from various sources in order to solve geographic problems.

SUGGESTIONS FOR TEACHING EUROPEAN GEOGRAPHY

From the many ways of studying the countries of Europe, a competent teacher can select the ones most appropriate to his own teaching style and to his particular group. The combined use of many of these approaches in the study of a country can enrich the understanding of it and provide a variety of methods for building and maintaining the students' interest.

While it is beyond the scope of this chapter to indicate even in a brief way all the approaches to the study of a region, a few have been selected for discussion.

Using a problem-solving approach · The problem approach to geographic studies provides teachers with a flexible teaching procedure which can be used effectively as a point of departure and for action based on fact finding and generalizations. The problem approach is the application of the thinking process or the scientific method to class procedure. When problems are utilized, they not only furnish intrinsic motivation for vital study, but they bring into lively and personal focus principles in geography which might otherwise remain to the students mere abstractions concerning the region.

The teacher might begin with a problem he believes to be of greatest concern to the pupils. Another point of departure would be to draw students into the project by ascertaining what they think important in the area. A planned survey would yield many problems of concern to them. Pupils can be helped to recognize certain problems as of immediate concern to them through visual aids, guidance, discussion, dramatic incident, and capitalizing on the significance of current events.

Teaching European geography through audio-visual experiences · Pictures of landscapes are vital materials, for they are the nearest reflection of actual scenes. We cannot take students to each country we explore, but we can bring scenes they would see there to them. Pictures should not be thought of as supplementary, but as material from which young people are to be led to discover many facts for themselves which they can check and add to from reading.

In selecting wisely any audio-visual material for use in the study of Europe, one should take into account the specific understandings, abilities, and attitudes which one is seeking in the unit of instruction; the background of understanding possessed by the individuals involved; the specific contributions which materials can make to the development of the understandings, abilities, and attitudes sought; the technical qualities (clarity, legibility, composition, etc.) of material appropriate in nature and content.

In using material selected in accordance with the foregoing general principles, one should introduce the material when the contribution it makes is most needed in the development of the major objectives of the unit; prepare the student by supplying specific terms and background as may be needed to grasp the significance of the material; make clear to those using the material what they are to find from its use; give opportunity for expression of findings.

Map study as an approach · The use of several maps at the beginning of a unit may give an effective reconnaissance. By the use of a physical-political map or of a group of maps giving the rainfall, temperature, vegetation and population of a region, the class may be challenged to see how much they can learn about the region from maps. Have the students study their maps and state their inferences. Then have them read materials to verify and modify their inferences.

Personal contact with Europeans · Direct contact with persons of various nations of Europe, made under favorable circumstances, is among the most valuable experiences in forming desirable attitudes. If it is possible, make use of pupils in your school, or parents, or other adults in the community who have come from abroad or have visited there.

The use of creative activities · The resourceful teacher will find many ways in which to involve pupils in creative activities in conjunction with their studies of the countries of Europe. For example, writing a travel account describing an imaginary journey or experience in a region is an excellent creative activity for geography. It involves reorganizing the pupil's knowledge and the ability to visualize people and lands. The following are similar types of activities: to write a geographic play or pageant; prepare a newspaper account featuring a geographic incident such as a storm; compose a story using geographic materials; and write a critical review of a book on a geographic subject.

The expression of ideas by painting murals or drawing pictures is a legitimate form of study and application. Students might paint or draw a picture of a scene or activity described in a paragraph. Also, geographic relationships can be represented by means of drawings. For example, on the left-hand side of a sheet of paper, a picture of lumbering, or any other economic activity can be drawn; on the right-hand side, a scene of the natural environment characteristics of where the activity took place can be drawn. A series of these drawings representing the work activities and the natural environment could be made for the continent of Europe.

Other activities involving drawing are making charts, graphs, sketch maps, and recording information by means of map symbols on an outline map. All of the above should be for a definite purpose, such as to illustrate a geographic concept, or to express geographic content in a clear and functional manner.

Manual activities, such as the construction of models and miniatures, are of value if their construction is an application of facts learned. They not only involve research but they give a better image of the region or the work activity.

Other creative activities include making notebooks, performing an experiment to illustrate some process such as soil erosion, making posters, and collecting and mounting pictures related to the unit. These types of activities must be evaluated carefully if they are to have real learning value.

Teaching through reading · Reading about the countries of Europe has value and most of the approaches and activities just discussed cannot be carried on adequately without reading. The following suggestions should be helpful when making reading assignments: Material to be read should never be introduced unless it can contribute something directly to the unit. Read and discuss the material in the text to establish fundamental ideas before wide reading is started. The student then has a basis for selection and a chance to apply understandings. Keep in mind the gradation in reading material: Give young students the specific pages to find specific facts; later give him chapters, and at higher levels, only the name of the book is necessary. Read snatches from various sources to students to show that additional ideas may be gained from a great variety of books. Fortunately, many books with geographic content are authentic and interesting for young people and include stories, biographies, plays, poetry, and novels.

The supplementary readings assigned do not have to make all relationships obvious, but they can bring out things which can be related to content and cores of thought that the students already have.

SUGGESTIONS FOR REVIEWING EUROPEAN GEOGRAPHY

After a consideration of the various regions of Europe, the continent should be studied as a unit so that the chief geographic factors and human activities may be correlated. Such a study is needed so that children may have an awareness of the essential unity of the continent. This may be done by grouping the countries for review or by using a problem which will compel the reorganization of the student's information regarding each unit studied and its application to Europe as a whole. The countries may be grouped as follows: the central plains, the mountain countries, the interior plains, the Mediterranean region, the uplands of central Europe, and the great river plains of Europe.

The following are problems which may be used: Why is Europe a dominant continent in spite of its small size? In what respects may the continents of Europe and North America be compared? Why are so many people able to make a living in Europe?

Another good review may be secured through the building up of a series of maps on Europe. This may be done by making a class or individual atlas of Europe. Outline maps of Europe should be used, the students filling in the outlines. The following maps would make an excellent series: annual rainfall, physical, forest, mineral resources, chief agricultural regions, manufacturing regions, product maps, chief transportation routes (land, water, air), and major urban centers. Each map should be accompanied by a brief explanation of the information given on the map.

EVALUATION

The outcome of a series of units on Europe will depend upon the grade in which the continent is taught, the mental ability of the students, and their background. To measure accurately the results of the work, preliminary tests could be made of the knowledge students already have of the various units. Thus the teacher will be able to judge in his final tests what he really has accomplished.

It is important that the evaluation of the desired outcomes should be as comprehensive as possible. The evaluation of each objective must be a continuous and integral part of the instructional activities. Otherwise statements of objectives are but sterile phrases.

The teacher should use a variety of testing techniques such as essay examinations, standardized tests, and teacher-made objective tests. The tests that the teacher makes may be of the multiple choice, matching, completion, one-word, underlining of significant words, and other types. The teacher should also evaluate pupil-made charts, maps, and pictures, pupil reports of their own laboratory investigations, and pupil projects which are conducted in or out of school. In some instances the teacher should permit pupil participation in the evaluation of their own learning activities.

These methods of evaluation will reveal how much knowledge the student has acquired in the way of facts and general information, concepts, understandings, work habits, and study skills. They will also show evidence that interests and attitudes are being developed. The items in the evaluation will measure elements closely related to the objectives of the unit. These include the ability to interpret data, think both deductively and inductively, attack problems, and use geographic facts, generalizations, and principles in new situations.

18

Soviet Union

In the Soviet Union, physical elements such as relief, climate, soils, and vegetation, have combined to produce a series of broad geographical regions. These natural zones have become effective keys to regional differences in life in the Soviet Union and also in differing regional potentials for future development. HUEY L. KOSTANICK

O NE OF THE MANY problems in teaching the geography of the Soviet Union concerns the pronunciation and spelling of place names. It is advisable for the teacher to acquaint the students with the map of the Soviet Union by pointing out the more important cultural and natural features. During this process the proper pronunciation and most appropriate English spelling of these features can be given. To make the names remembered by association, one can relate to the student something of significance concerning each. A good rule to remember is that the Russian language is phonetic and all spelling and pronunciation should be handled accordingly.

SPATIAL CONCEPTS OF THE U.S.S.R.

The objectives in teaching spatial factors is to present to the student in a practical and simple way the significance of location, size, and shape of the largest country in the world.

Location can be shown in terms of position on the Eurasian continent, and pointing up the fact that the country is in Europe, Central Asia, and the Far East. The U.S.S.R.'s location can also be displayed on a world map with reference to other continents and particularly to the location of Canada. Location can be impressed on the student's mind in terms of latitude and longitude. The most southerly and northly points of the Soviet Union should be compared to the latitudes of well-known places in the United States and Canada. The position of the Arctic Circle may be emphasized, and its significance brought out in terms of seasonal length of daylight and darkness north of this parallel. The latitudinal position may be stressed in a practical way in terms of the growing season and its effect on man's use of the land. The longitude may be described by the fact that mathematically the U.S.S.R. is in the western and eastern hemispheres.

Size can be brought out in terms of the area it occupies in square miles of the Eurasian continent, and in terms of the greatest distances across the country in the north-south and east-west directions. The size of the U.S.S.R. can best be depicted on physical-political maps of Eurasia and the world. Traveling time east to west across the U.S.S.R. by rail from Vladivostok to Kaliningrad may be compared with that between New York City and Los Angeles. Another method of showing size is to use equal area maps of the same scale and projection of the U.S.S.R. and the United States, and see how many times the United States will fit into the area of the Soviet Union.

The shape (form) of the U.S.S.R. should be taught as compact. This concept can best be portrayed on a historical map showing how the territory was expanded after the Czardom of Moscovy was established. The expansions from the Czardom of Moscovy through 1946 may be shown on historical maps depicting territorial accretion and acquisition. Thus, from 1147, when Moscow first appeared on the map under the Descendants of Rurik to the present day, the shape of the U.S.S.R. has changed but little. The significance of compact form should be stressed in terms of stabilizing and unifying factors for the U.S.S.R.

GROSS RELIEF FEATURES

The objectives in presenting the gross relief features of the U.S.S.R. should be the following:

1. To describe the nature (geologic and glacial) of forces that have shaped the three broad plains (the West Russian, the West Siberian, and the Caspian–Turan Plains) of the U.S.S.R., and to describe the surface configuration.

2. To describe the nature of the river plains, outside of the three broad plains areas mentioned in objective one — namely, the Lena, the Indigirka, the Kolyma, and the Amur.

3. To describe the natural forces that have shaped the upland.

4. To describe the mountains along the southern and eastern peripheries of the U.S.S.R.

5. To describe the four broad river patterns of the U.S.S.R. These river patterns should be brought out with the accompanying physiographic area wherever possible.

To teach these broad objectives it is necessary to have a large and detailed map of the relief of the U.S.S.R., of the Wenchow or Haack type, plus large-scale geologic and topographic maps, if possible, to show finer details of the topography.

Before studying the three broad plains of the U.S.S.R. in detail, the student should be introduced to the physical map of the country by outlining the large plains areas of the Soviet Union, generally less than 600 feet above mean sea level. The large plains area, which includes the West Russian, the West Siberian, and the Caspian–Turan Plains, should not be treated as one unit because the natural forces that developed each and the surface configurations are different.

Plains · The West Russian Plain is the eastern extension of the North European Plain, which widens in the form of a wedge in Poland and western U.S.S.R., reaching its maximum width at the foot of the Ural Mountains. It must be stressed that the Ural Mountains are not a formidable barrier between the West Russian and West Siberian Plains. Roads and railroads cross the Urals at a little more than 1,000 feet above mean sea level.

To understand the causes of the rolling nature, the radial drainage, and the distribution of mineral resources of the West Russian Plain, it is necessary to explain the geologic forces that have created these features. Structurally the West Russian Plain should be subdivided into the Moscow, the North Ukrainian, the Donetz, the Black Sea, and the East Russian Basin. Each structural basin is known for its mineral resources, such as the Moscow and the Donetz for coal, and the East Russian Basin for its oil in the "Second Baku" area.

It is important to show the extent and effects of glaciation of the West Russian Plain. The glacial map should show the morainic systems, the lake, till, and fluvioglacial plains which are dotted with hundreds of lakes, and the deranged drainage system. Bogs and marshes that were left behind as a result of glaciation should be pointed out. The combined effects of the Great Baltic Terminal Moraine and the Valdai Hills should be stressed to show how they form a drainage divide between the northward-flowing rivers that empty into the Baltic, the White, and Barentz seas, the south-flowing tributaries of the Volga River which empty into the Caspian Sea, and the Don and Dneiper rivers, which empty into the Black Sea.

The West Russian Plain can be described as a rolling plain, varying from less than 300 to about 1,450 feet above mean sea level. It may be noted that the West Russian Plain has two longitudinally trending hilly belts — the Central Russian and the pre-Volga uplands. The former should be subdivided from north to south into the Valdai Hills, the Smolensk–Moscow, the Central Russian, and the Donetz ridges. The Black Sea Plain, with its gently sloping surface and underlying sedimentary strata which dip toward the sea, is unglaciated. The Baltic–North Russian–Pechora Plain which slopes toward the Arctic is drained by north and northwest flowing rivers. The radial drainage pattern of European U.S.S.R. should be pointed out as having its source in the Valdai Hills and the Smolensk–Moscow Ridge.

The West Siberian Plain is to be associated with the lowlands of the Yenisei and Ob rivers, the large tributaries of the Ob, and the Khatanga River. The vastness of this plain can be emphasized by pointing out that it measures 1,200 miles from east to west and 1,500 miles from north to south, and is one of the largest and most monotonously level areas of the earth's surface. The flatness of the plain can be explained, in part, by the fact that when the area was raised above sea level, its uplift was very slight. Even though the West Siberian Plain was covered by ice sheets, the depositional materials that might have added relief to the flatness are lacking bacause the deposits were reworked by a glacial marine transgression. This transgression was created while the ice sheet covered the northern part of the West Siberian Plain, and blocked the mouths of the north-flowing Ob and Yenisei rivers, forming a glacial lake between the Kazakh Upland and the ice front. The flatness is evident in that it is waterlogged, that the central part of the plain is occupied by the Vasyuganye Marsh, and that the Ob River meanders back and forth and has a braided channel for many hundreds of miles. The flatness of the surface can also be stressed by stating that the slope of the land is so gradual that at the confluence of the Ob and Irtysh rivers, 500 miles upstream, the elevation is only 200 feet above mean sea level. The river drainage of the West Siberian Plain is classed as a northward flowing pattern. Stress should be placed on the fact that the rivers flow in the wrong direction as far as economic advantage is concerned, and that they pose flooding problems in the spring when the headwaters and upper reaches of these rivers thaw first, causing inundation downstream.

The objectives in treating the Caspian–Turan Plain should be to explain the flatness of the saucer-shaped surface, and the internal drainage pattern. Emphasis can be placed on the fact that throughout most of geologic time this plain was part of a sea which embraced the present Aral, Caspian, Black, and Mediterranean seas. During the Pleistocene the Aral and Caspian seas formed one large body of water which drained into the Black Sea by way of the Manych Lowland. With further uplift and the cessation of the drainage of glacial waters from the West Siberian Plain via the Turgai Gap, the Caspian and Aral seas separated to form two flat, saucer-shaped plains.

The Lena, the Indigirka, and the Kolyma rivers are a part of the northward flowing river pattern of the U.S.S.R. These river plains should be discussed immediately after the West Siberian Plain, as they are also comprised of deposits laid down by a marine transgression and are a part of the same glacial lake which occupied the Ob-Khatanga lowlands. Indicative of the sediment load of the Lena River, which rises in the Baikal Range, is the Lena Delta which is three times larger than the Volga Delta in the Caspian Sea. The New Siberian islands should be pointed out as a continuation of the Lena River Plain.

The larger rivers which comprise the eastward flowing river pattern are the Amur-Ussuri, Anadyr, Penzhina, and Kamchatka rivers. The largest, the longest, and the most important from the standpoint of use is the Amur River and its valley. The Amur River is navigable for ocean going vessels from its mouth to Khabarovsk, a distance of about 550 miles.

Upland areas · The upland areas can be treated in two groups — those forming pre-Cambrian shields and those that do not. The Kola-Karelia, the Azov–Podolian, and the Central Siberian Upland, comprise the shield areas of the U.S.S.R. The Byrranga Plateau and the islands of Severnaya Zemlya are northern extensions of the same type of rock areas and topography. Uplands that do not form shield areas are the Ural and Kazakh uplands.

The Kola–Karelia Upland should be stressed as being part of the Baltic Shield. The geology, the nature, and the kind of rocks in this upland are related to the mineral resources of the area. The Azov–Podolian Upland is similiar in the nature of rocks, but was not glaciated. Instead, after the latest ice sheet retreated from the northern flanks of the area, a veneer of loessal material was blown into parts of this upland and subsequently was highly dissected.

The Central Siberian Upland includes the pre-Cambrian rock areas of the Anabar Shield and the Byrranga Plateau in the north and the Baikal–Aldan Shield in the south. The rivers that have greatly dissected this upland are the Angara, Stony Tunguska, Lower Tunguska, and Upper Lena. Relationships of rocks to mineral resources should be brought out.

The Ural Upland may be subdivided into three parts: the Ural Mountains proper, the Ufa Plateau, and the Timan Ridge. The Ural Mountains can be compared to the Appalachian Mountains in the United States. The structure of this range is described as consisting of a narrow belt of tightly folded Paleozoic rocks with an exposed granite core. The age of the rocks and the structure of the area are related to the great variety of mineral resources found in the Ural Range. Novaya Zemlya should be considered a structural extension of the Ural Mountains. The Urals have a topographic "saddle" in the central part, with both the northern and southern extremities attaining elevations above 5,000 feet. The Ural Range is old and worn down, having been subjected to a long period of erosion. The Ufa Plateau may be related to the Ural Range and compared to the

Appalachian Plateau in the United States in terms of structure, topography, and resources.

The Kazakh Upland can be described as a broad anticlinal arch of Paleozoic rocks with extruding granitic cores of the same age. Here the slightly disturbed coal beds are related to the carboniferous strata of the Paleozoic age. This upland forms a watershed between the rivers that drain northward into the Ob and those which flow into Lake Balkhash.

Mountains · The mountains should be stressed as ramparts surrounding the vast Russian Plain and the lesser plains. The mountains appear in irregular concentric bands, with the oldest nearer the plains and interior uplands, while the youngest and most rugged mountains form the outermost band of ranges.

This band of young, rugged mountains includes the Yaila (on Crimean Peninsula), the Caucasus and its associated Stavropol Plateau, Kopet Dag, Pamirs ("roof of the world"), Sakhalin, Kamchatka, and Koryak Mountains. The mountain range on Kamchatka Peninsula, the Koryak Range, and the Kuril Islands are studded with volcanic peaks, some of which are still active. Geysers and hot springs are found in this volcanic belt, which is frequently referred to as the "Ring of Fire."

CLIMATE

The climatic regions of the U.S.S.R. should be treated in association with the natural vegetation regions and the major soil groups, because of the close-existing relationships, and the accordancy in the regional patterns of each. Delimitation of the regional patterns of climatic, vegetation, and soil regions should be emphasized with maps depicting these physical phenomena.

In treating the climate of the U.S.S.R. the obpectives to be achieved are:

1. To stress the controls of climate in the U.S.S.R.
2. To characterize the climate of the U.S.S.R. as continental in nature. and to prove this continentality by description in terms of temperature and rainfall.
3. To present a classification and description of the climatic regions of the U.S.S.R. and to point up the salient features of each.
4. To relate and describe the vegetative regions and the major soil groups to each climatic region.

Climatic controls · The principal climatic controls are latitude, size of the area and position within the U.S.S.R. with reference to the oceans, topography including mountains as barriers, oceans and ocean currents, pressure systems, and associated air masses and winds.

The influence of latitude can best be analyzed in terms of the mean monthly temperatures for the warmest and coldest months for weather stations at the various latitudes in European U.S.S.R. and Siberia. Another approach is to point up the variations in the growing season from north to south in European U.S.S.R., in western Siberia southward to the Turkmen S.S.R., and in the Soviet Far East. Effects of latitude can also be stressed in terms of the average length of the days from sunrise to sunset for June 21 and December 21.

The influence of size can be shown best in terms of the diminishing temperatures and rainfall from the west toward the east, the only appreciable source of moisture and the tempering effect being from the Atlantic Ocean to the west.

The effects of topography can be stressed with the fact that the vast Russian plains areas are open toward the Arctic Ocean permitting the flow of cold air masses to reach as far south as the Turkmen S.S.R. The barrier effect of the Yaila and the Caucasus Mountains should be mentioned as producing subtropical climates on the south coast of Crimea and in parts of Transcaucasia. The barrier of high mountains along the southern frontiers does not permit tropical air masses to enter the central Asiatic republics; nor do the mountains of eastern Siberia permit Pacific Ocean moisture and tempering effects into the country from the east. The far eastern ranges limit the deposition of moisture to the mountain slopes facing the Pacific Ocean. Stress should also be placed on the fact that when weather fronts move from the north toward the mountains along the southern frontier, precipitation takes place on the mountain slopes facing north and northwest.

Emphasis should be placed on the minimal effect of the Atlantic and the Arctic oceans in providing moisture for precipitation, even though the Atlantic provides about 85 percent of the moisture for rainfall along the western frontier. Mean annual rainfall figures for such places as Kaliningrad, Moscow, Kiev, and Leningrad could be used as proof of this phenomenon. The lack of moisture for rainfall from the Atlantic is caused by the great distance to that ocean. The lack of moisture for rainfall from the Arctic Ocean is the result of that ocean being frozen in the winter. In summer the near coastal ice-free areas provide only very small quantities of moisture for rain. The influence of ocean currents can only be emphasized in the Barentz Sea area where Murmansk and Petsamo (Pechenga) are ice-free ports.

A high pressure system prevails over the U.S.S.R. in the cold months and a low pressure system during the warm months. Here emphasis should be on the wind directions, associated with these pressure systems, in all parts of the U.S.S.R. as they either bring moisture or affect the temperatures. Associated with daily pressure changes are the cold and warm air masses. It should be stressed that the cold fronts during January and July move into the Soviet Union predominantly from the Arctic region and only occasionally in July from western and southern Europe. Warm fronts in January and July move into the Soviet Union predominantly from the western sectors — anywhere from the Mediterranean–Black Sea areas to the North Atlantic, and secondarily from the Middle East via the Caspian Sea region into Siberia toward the East Siberian Sea.

Climatic regions • Regions can be made on the basis of an empiric or genetic approach. In the empiric method the climatic elements (temperatures, precipitation, winds, etc.) are used in formulating classifications and regions. In the genetic approach, climatic controls (latitude, elevation, etc.) are used as a basis for classifying and formulating climatic regions. Regardless of the system that is used, both the elements and the climatic controls should be brought out in the description of the climates.

For each station within a region, the mean annual temperature can be compared to emphasize the coldest and warmest stations. The mean monthly temperature regimes can be shown with statistical tables. The July and January mean temperatures can be presented by using an isothermal map, for these months which will show the north-south shifts of the isotherms, the bending of the isotherms, the coldest area in January, and the effects of ocean currents and the gigantic size of the U.S.S.R. on the largest continent in the world. Extremes in temperature can best be shown on a map of the average annual range in temperature. Temperatures should also be correlated to pressure and winds, and movement of air masses and fronts.

The mean annual precipitation within a climatic region should be shown with more than one climatic station to illustrate variations or similarities in the total rainfall, and to give valid reasons for these variations or similarities. The mean monthly regimes of precipitation can be presented statistically or by season with one precipitation map for the period from November to May and the other for the months from May to November.

NATURAL VEGETATION REGIONS

Because of its value as a resource, as a habitat for wildlife, and as a recreational and tourist attraction, natural vegetation should be given the same emphasis as climate and soil. In discussing the natural vegetation of the U.S.S.R. it is important to stress the regional variations which are determined by the physical environment. Since plants respond to all elements of climate, soil, topography, and organisms, one element in the environment always seems more important than all others, and emphasis should be placed on these more important elements from region to region. In the broad sense, climate, particularly rainfall and temperature, have the greatest effect on regional distribution of plant life. Where variations occur within a natural vegetation region, one must look for causes for these variations in local changes in soil, local climatic conditions, the effect of man's long-time occupation of an area which can affect vegetation regions through burning and exploitation, and in the effect of biotic factors such as overgrazing, pollinating insects, and parasites.

It must be remembered that the natural vegetation regions of the U.S.S.R. cover broad areas, which have similarity and general uniformity throughout in their physical environment. As such, certain plants, though unrelated to each other, but requiring a certain physical habitat will be found growing together in plant associations covering broad areas. Thus, it is necessary to point out the predominant species within each association, and where possible, the ways in which certain elements of the environment control certain species.

NATIONALITY, ETHNOLOGY, AND POPULATION

The objectives are as follows:

1. To differentiate between nationality and ethnology.
2. To show the great diversity in national and ethnic groups.
3. To describe and account for the population distribution.
4. To show and account for the more recent changes in population distribution.

In presenting the nationality and ethnic groups of the U.S.S.R., it is best to relate these groups to the political map of the country. It should be brought out that the fifteen major republics of the Soviet Union represent the major nationality groups. The numerous autonomous republics, autonomous oblasts, and national okrugs which have been set up for the minority groups are all, except five, in the Russian Socialist Federated Soviet Republic. Although the major republics have been created for the major nationality groups, other groups have found their way into them, or have been in them since early historical times. Emphasis should be placed on the spread of the Great Russians to all parts of the country, to "russify" the other nationalities in terms of language, education and training, ideology, and economic development. The Soviet Union cannot be stressed as a melting pot, even though it is a conglomeration of some 189 nationalities of varying ethnic groups, who speak 151 different languages and several hundred dialects. Reasons should be advanced why the U.S.S.R. is not a melting pot, and that nation could be compared and contrasted with the United States. In connection with the nationality groups, comments might be made as to origin of their languages or relationships to other tongues. From a cultural point of view, their religions, mode of attire, and possible relationship to other nationalities should be discussed. To teach the ethnic composition of the peoples of the U.S.S.R. it is best to classify them into racial families and groups.

Population distribution within the U.S.S.R. can be analyzed by geographic regions, namely, the Caucasus Republics, the European U.S.S.R., the Urals, the Central Asiatic Republics and Kazakhstan, the West Siberian, the East Siberian, and the Far Eastern regions. Population distribution and densities can be described in terms of the land. By this method the average population density can be computed for the total area of the U.S.S.R., the average density per republic, and the geographic regions. Population distribution and densities should also be computed for rural areas in terms of arable land. In this method one can relate the high rural density areas to the soils, to the climatic conditions more favorable for agriculture, and to irrigation possibilities. Urban population can be treated separately, as urbanization points to industrialization. Major shifts in population from rural to urban areas from 1926 to 1939 should be pointed out; and shifts from European U.S.S.R. into the Urals, eastward into Siberia, and southward into Central Asia should be explained. The appearance of new cities and towns on the map and the growth of older ones was particularly spectacular during this period. Increased urbanization since 1939 should also be noted. Future population trends for the U.S.S.R. may be analyzed in terms of yearly numerical and percentage increases in population, in terms of a lowering death rate, and in terms of an increasing life span.

SOVIET ECONOMY

The objectives in teaching the Soviet economy are:

1. To explain the nature of the Russian economy.

2. To explain why it was possible to impose a planned economy on the Soviet people.

3. To describe the Five-Year and Seven-Year plans — their proposed goals and achievements.

4. To describe the nature of Soviet agriculture, its productivity, its relationships to climate and edaphic conditions, and explain its lack in expected productivity.

5. To describe the distribution and production of mineral resources of the U.S.S.R. and the relationship of these resources to the Soviet manufacturing regions and their potential.

In attempting to describe the philosophy of the Soviet economy, it is best to define the economic objectives of communism and socialism and then note the differences in each. It should be stressed that the nature of an economy cannot be divorced from its political ideology, both of which make a political economy. After examining the differences between a communist and socialist state and their objectives one can say that the economy of the Soviet Union is not truly a socialistic one. The U.S.S.R. may aspire to be a true socialistic state, but in its practices it is at best a form of centralized state capitalism.

In explaining why it was possible to impose a planned economy on the people of Russia, it is necessary to describe the chaotic economic, political, and social conditions under the Czars. Economic troubles began about 1880 when the position of agriculture and the conditions of the farming classes worsened, while industry rapidly developed and the working population increased, causing labor organization and strife. Likewise, the setbacks for Russia in the Crimean War (1854–1856) and the Russo-Japanese War (1904–1905) did not help matters socially, politically, or economically. The latter war led to the Revolution of 1905, which dissolved the medieval social structure of Russia, and in 1905 forced Czar Nicholas to promise an elected assembly to help in forming and discussing legislative proposals. At first this promise failed to materialize. In reviewing this period of history (1880–1917), one can establish the factors that led ultimately to the formation of a popularly elected Duma in May 1906. The Duma experienced upheavals and many prime ministers came and went, the fourth and last Duma (1912–1917) having six prime ministers. With all this upheaval and unrest, another revolution was inevitable and began on March 12, 1917.

The proposed goals of the Five-Year Plans and the one Seven-Year Plan (1959–1965) in agriculture, mining, industry, and transportation should be stated and compared to actual achievements. The Third Five-Year Plan (1938–1942) was interrupted by World War II and the German invasion in 1941. The Fourth Five-Year Plan (1946–1950) called for the reconstruction of the Soviet Union after the destruction of the war and a continued interest in heavy industry. Here the area occupied by the German armies and the nature of destruction may be described.

Study of Soviet agriculture should center around the fact that the U.S.S.R. is to a large degree an agricultural country, with almost half of its people engaged in this pursuit. Here an analysis could be made of the acreage of agricultural land in percent to the total land area, in total number of acres plowed, and in the number of people engaged in agriculture as compared with that of the United States. Increases in land in agriculture from 1913 to the present could also be brought out, with some stress on the use of marginally productive land and reclaimed marsh areas.

Irrigation areas with acreages and type of crops grown in each area should be included.

Emphasis in Soviet agriculture should be placed on the grain crops, since they take up the large part of the acreage and since the cropland is mostly suited to grains. Other areas of importance are vegetables, industrial crops, and forage and feed crops. In presenting statistical data for each of the crops, it is important to show past production figures as to increases or decreases in productivity, analyzed in terms of imports and exports, which reflect shortages and surpluses.

The U.S.S.R. has a great variety in mineral resources which should be classified as fuel and power resources, ferrous metals and alloys, or nonferrous metals. The industries may be classified into those of engineering, chemical, textile, food processing, forestry, and fishing.

For each natural resource the following topics might be covered:

1. The location of primary and secondary sources of each natural resource.
2. The past and present production, and the reserves of each resource.
3. The adequacy of each resource in terms of national requirements.
4. The quality or purity of each resource.
5. The location of the resource with respect to centers (places) of their use in industry.
6. The location of each with respect to transportational facilities.
7. The number of people employed.

In presenting the statistical data, comparisons can be made to world total production and the leading countries of the world. These data can be presented statistically and on charts.

The topic of industries should include the following:

1. The location of each type of industry.
2. The decentralization or dispersion of each.
3. The sources of raw or processed materials.
4. The commodities (finished products) that are produced.
5. The quantity of each item produced.
6. The position or rank of the industry in the U.S.S.R. with respect to number of persons employed, and in terms of value in rubles or dollars.
7. The market (domestic and foreign).

Statistically, comparisons in production can be made to world totals and the leading countries of the world. Statistical data can, for better teaching techniques, be presented on charts. On the basis of the production of the various commodities, location of industry, the manufacturing and mining regions of the U.S.S.R. can be established for the student.

TRANSPORTATION

The transportation systems of the U.S.S.R. consist of railroads, water transport (coastal, canal, and river), roads, and airlines. It is imperative to account for the mileage and the density of the rail net in different parts of the country. The importance of railroads in the Soviet Union should be explained in terms of the inclement weather most of the year, and the percent and tonnage of freight that is hauled annually. The strategic character of many of the railroads should be discussed. Isolation of the U.S.S.R. in terms of rail line crossings into the middle and far eastern countries of Asia can be examined. The importance of Moscow as the hub and rail center of the U.S.S.R. should be stressed.

The lack of a good and extensive road net, and the predominance of dirt roads might be explained by the fact that there is no great need for roads when, comparatively speaking, the number of vehicles is small, and most uses for roads are to haul local farm produce to the city or to a railroad.

Important items relative to the water transport system of the U.S.S.R. are that it has the longest navigable waterway system in the world, but only a little more than one-fourth is used, and that the inclement weather freezes the rivers for three to nine months. Particular attention should be given to the Volga River because it passes through varied economic regions, has adequate depth, drains a large and populous region, and is the key river in the canal system of the U.S.S.R. Here stress should be placed on the Moscow–Volga, the Volga–Don, the Baltic–White Sea, and the Mariinsk canals. It should be noted that these canals make Moscow a port on five seas and link the capital with the ports on these seas, that these canals link the Volga with most industrialized regions of European U.S.S.R. The river to be noted especially in Siberia is the Amur which is navigable to Khabarovsk. The important coastal transport to be brought out is that between Vladivostok and Murmansk via the Arctic Ocean during the short summer season. This route is shorter by 7,000 miles than that by way of the Suez Canal.

The best technique in presenting the airline routes of the U.S.S.R. is by the use of a map. On it one can see the pattern of air lines radiating out from Moscow to distant points within the country and to distant places on the Eurasian continent.

To summarize the transportation study one can compare freight tonnages and present percentage figures for each mode of transport. To compare the rivers of the U.S.S.R. as to the use of each, tonnage figures and percentage figures based on total river transport can be utilized.

19

Asia

*Asia is not one but many. On this, the largest continent, live 60 per cent
of the people of the world, not evenly distributed throughout the vast
extent of Asian territory, but localized in certain major concentrations,
which form the core lands of the various Asian states.*

NORTON GINSBURG

WHAT IS ASIA? In recent decades just what the term Asia implies
has become more and more ambiguous. Physically, Asia is not a continent
because it is not a large land mass surrounded by water. It is undoubtedly
the largest part of the continent, Eurasia, but there is no universal agreement on the boundary between Asia and Europe. The largest country in
the world, the Soviet Union, occupies a continuous area stretching from
the Atlantic Ocean on the west to the Pacific Ocean on the east. This
chapter will give a brief geographic overview of all of Asia and its associated archipelagoes of Japan, the Philippines, and Indonesia except the
territory in the Soviet Union.

POPULATION

Number · In 1968 approximately 1 billion 900 million people, or over
one-third of the world's population, lived in Asia. The ratio is ten persons
for each one living in the United States. If an American family of four
entertained a group of Asians at this ratio, the American family would
need to play host to forty Asians.

People per square mile · If these 1.9 billion Asians were evenly distributed over the 10.5 million acres, the average population density would
only be approximately 180 per square mile. In 1968, the ratio of people
to land in the United States was approximately fifty-seven persons to one
square mile. Consequently, if only area is used as a criterion, there are
approximately three times as many people in Asia attempting to gain a
living from one square mile as there are in the United States. This average

population density is very misleading both in Asia and the United States. In Asia over one-half of the land is so arid, semiarid, cold, hot, swampy, and mountainous that, in areas with these limitations, the population density is less than twenty-five persons per square mile. The bleakness of parts of this region is further emphasized by 2 million acres which are either uninhabited or have an average of less than two persons per square mile.

In contrast with the vast, vacant, or almost vacant expanses of central and western Asia are the overcrowded parts of China, India, Pakistan, and other smaller areas where the population density is greater than 250 per square mile. In these same areas even the rural population is over 200 persons for each 640 acres. Sections of many countries in east and south Asia support over 2,000 people per square mile of crop (arable) land. In Japan, the population density soars to over 4,000 for each 640 acres of cultivated land.

Statistically density of population in this region and the world reaches its peaks in the crowded residential districts of this region's millionaire cities. Here in over three dozen agglomerated cities, the population density soars to over 300 per acre and it is reported that residential districts in Tokyo, Hong Kong, Shanghai, and Calcutta have over 625 persons per acre. Many streets are so narrow and congested that only man-powered transportation vehicles can move with the crowds.

In contrast with the population densities just described for Asia, the average man-land ratio for the world is sixty persons per square mile.

Population associations · Most of the urban and rural dwellers live adjacent to or within a few miles of permanent flowing streams or permanently filled canals. With few exceptions, cities with populations of 100,000 or more are located adjacent to large rivers, and many of the smaller cities are located either adjacent to rivers, large or small, or lakes and reservoirs. The villages of the rural dwellers are also concentrated along the banks of rivers and canals.

To interpret the river-canal patterns of settlement of this region, many physical and cultural factors must be considered. People and their domestic animals obviously need water 365 days a year. About two-fifths of the region receives less than 20 inches of rainfall a year and evapotranspiration is high. The arid lands are concentrated in the west and central-interior parts of Asia. But an annual rainfall map can be misleading. In the monsoon lands of South Asia, Southeast Asia, and the interior of eastern China, the lands are arid for periods from four to eight months and in drought periods it can be from twelve to eighteen months or longer. By the end of the wet season when the annual monsoon rains approach the average or higher, rivers will have spread naturally or through canals over their flood plains; water tables are at or near the surface; and lakes, reservoirs, wet-weather swamps, ponds, wells, cisterns, and huge jars are brim full and overflowing. Near the end of the wet season, if one were to travel by air, starting near the mouth of a major river and following a zig-zag flight back and forth across the delta and flood plains, he would see vast sheets of water stretching for miles and miles. Jutting through this inland fresh water sea, one would see the tops of the natural levees, elevated roads, and mounds which are the sites of cities, villages, and farmsteads.

Then the rains stop rather abruptly, and the dry season begins. Daily run-off and evapotranspiration lowers the water; the fields become dry; rivers return to their channels and log rafts begin to float down the rivers. Quickly the crops are harvested, the rice is threshed and farm products are rushed to market by boat before the river flows drop too low. Now the tempo in the rice and saw mills, wood-working industries, oil pressing sheds, and other factories increases as raw materials from farm and forest come downstream into the larger settlements. Riverboats return upstream as often as time permits carrying products from the cities to the upper part of the watersheds and returning with additional loads of farm products. But the water levels drop quickly in rivers not regulated by dams; conse-quently, large-boat navigation ends abruptly.

By the end of the dry season, dry channels remain where small rivers and canals flowed. And the huge volumes of water in the large rivers have become so drastically reduced that in many places there are mere trickles, and the flows are insufficient to fill their own sandbar-clogged channels.

Water tables in the flood plains drop so low that numerous shallow wells, swamps, lakes, and ponds become dry. The parched earth contains gapping cracks which extend several feet deep. Trees and other biannual plants drop their leaves. Desiccating winds, blowing twenty-four hours sometimes in almost a gale, draw water and moisture from every nonliving and living thing. Both man and beast put up a desperate struggle to stay alive until the wet season starts again. When the wet season is late or the rains are drastically reduced in volume, drought, famine, disease, and death follow.

Wherever twentieth century technology is practiced and high dams constructed, great volumes of water are stored in secondary-stream reser-voirs and in long "river-lakes" in the primary rivers. The multiple use of this water for domestic and industrial use, navigation, and irrigation helps free the large cities from the vagaries of uncontrolled river flow. However, most rural dwellers are still dependent upon natural flow. As a result, population densities tend to decrease as distances from the large rivers and permanent canals increase, but not at a uniform rate.

Asia's teeming millions are also concentrated near the coastline, espe-cially on the deltas, also on coastal alluvial plains. The deltas, just like the flood plains adjacent to the rivers, are laced with distributaries and huge ditches (canals) which provide irrigation water, drainage, a waterway for small boats, domestic water, and some edible fish and plants. Also the deltas, like the flood plains, are covered with young alluvial soils which are less leached and which are somewhat enriched by the sediments deposited by the muddy flood waters. Moreover, the clay characteristics of the soil, coupled with plowing it while wet, help produce an impervious layer below the plowed ground of the rice fields. In this way diked and flooded rice fields are partially protected from loss of water by gravitational flow.

More than half of the 1.9 billion people living in this area are less than 500 miles from the coastline. However, small isolated areas of dense population are found on the interior of this region and are associated with well-watered intermontane basins and piedmont alluvial fans.

Since Asian civilizations are so entwined with rivers and their depositional landforms (deltas, flood plains, and alluvial fans), it is well to keep in mind that three of the longest rivers in the world are in this region. A counterbalancing fact should also be kept in mind: approximately four of the 10.5 million acres of this region are without drainage to the sea.

REALMS

With the exclusion of the Soviet Union, Asia is frequently divided into four realms: East Asia, Southeast Asia, South Asia, and Southwest Asia.

East Asia · A study of the many facets of geography indicates that East Asia not only ranks first among the four realms in many geographic elements, but also excels the three in some. With approximately 4.5 million square miles of land, this realm is nearly as large as the combined land areas of the Southeast, South, and Southwest realms (4.9 million square miles). In 1968, with a population of over 780 million, East Asia had about two-fifths of all the people living in the four realms.

Communist China is the largest and oldest country in this region and the second largest in the world. Only the Soviet Union is larger. By population, Communist China is the largest in the world. Within its vast territory are large and numerous deposits of minerals, some of which are unproven and some not yet developed. Among the nations, this country leads the world in the production of tungsten and antimony; ranks second in salt, and third in the production of coal, tin, graphite, and magnesite.

Japan has the largest and most numerous modern industrial complexes in Asia, the second highest percentage of people who live in cities (over 40 percent), and the best transportation system connecting the rural areas with the cities. The fact that Japan has the fastest passenger trains in the world is indicative of the efficiency with which it has adopted and improved upon western technology.

Within this realm, there are several political divisions, all with populations of over a million, namely China, Japan, South Korea, Taiwan, North Korea, Hong Kong, and Mongolia. Although Mongolia is over twice the size of the areas of Japan, North Korea, South Korea, Taiwan, and Hong Kong put together, it has about 1 million people in comparison with over 3 million in Hong Kong and 94 million in Japan. Japan's economy epitomizes the greatest development of garden agriculture on a limited base of level land and alluvial soil, while Mongolia epitomizes the extensive pastoral use of vast land expanses endowed only with meager amounts of water and vegetation. Whereas Mongolia has little evidence of twentieth century technology, Japan, with only meager physical resources, has built an efficient industrial-urban society which enables it to compete with western Europe and Anglo-America in manufacturing, international trade, and in the support of a dense population. Moreover, Japan has the benefit of the sea for fishing and trading, and Mongolia is landlocked.

In spite of the intensive industrial-urban-trade developments of relatively small areas such as Hong Kong, Tokyo–Yokohama, Kobe–Osaka–Kyoto, Shanghai, and Peking–Tienstien, most of the people in East Asia make a living from farming. Rice, the major food crop, occupies the greatest acreage and wherever possible is double-cropped, grown under irrigation, and heavily fertilized with animal and human manures and, in Japan, with commercial fertilizers. Both Japan and China have sufficient latitudinal spread that their northern territory is too cold and dry for rice production. In northern China wheat, millet, and *kao-liang* (grain sorghum) are the dominant crops. In spite of the increased coal production of China and the imports of coal and petroleum into the realm, wood and charcoal are still the major sources of cooking fuel.

Of these seven political areas only Taiwan and Hong Kong have been under the political control of a non-Asian country. In part because of geographical position and the stability of the political and cultural societies in East Asia, this realm primarily escaped European colonialism while most of the other three realms were occupied. Although this realm escaped European imperialism, in the past most of these countries have occupied or attempted to occupy the territory of the other.

Southeast Asia · Centrally located between the East Asian and South Asian realms and Australia, Southeast Asia is the most marine realm in this region. In gross area it is about the size of the United States, but approximately half of this realm is in seas. About half of the land area is in Indonesia and the Philippines. These are sometimes called Insular Southeast Asia because of the large number of islands in each and because neither has territory connected to the mainland. Even on the mainland in continental Southeast Asia, all of the countries are ocean oriented except Laos. Mountain ranges, horseshoe-shaped in pattern and opening to the sea, almost surround countries such as Burma, North Vietnam, and Thailand. In these mainland countries people and settlements are concentrated on the delta and flood plains of the major rivers and these rivers (often with trunk rail lines and highways built roughly parallel to them) are the primary transportation arteries. These arteries feed downstream the products from farm, forest, and mine to river-ocean ports located in the largest cities. Imports and exports flow through these metropolitan cities with necessities (such as salt) and manufactured goods moving upstream to the hinterlands. No railway or all-weather highway systems provide land connections over which might flow people, goods, and ideas among all the mainland countries of Burma, North Vietnam, South Vietnam, Laos, Cambodia, Thailand, Malaysia, and Singapore. The largest railroad network links only the last five countries, with peoples and goods flowing freely only between Thailand, Malaysia, and Singapore.

During the last century while Japan was adopting western technology and developing the largest and most efficient industrial complexes in Asia, the countries in this realm were invaded and brought under European colonialism. Economically the colonial lands were expected to provide raw materials and markets to the mother country. Little or no attempt was made to educate or be concerned with the needs of the peoples or in developing viable states. Rather, the goal was to keep these countries dependent on their conquerors. Although the Japanese invasion and occupation during World War II brought destruction, it also helped kindle the fires of independence.

This realm has less arable land than the other three, but approximately 75 percent of the working population is engaged in agriculture or the processing of its products and/or in fishing or forest exploitation. The ratio of arable land varies between 0.4 and 2.1 acres for each inhabitant. Laos and Cambodia with 2.1 and 1.7 arable acres per capita, respectively, are in a better food producing position than is China, which has only 0.5 of an acre per capita. The pressure of people on the land is about the same in Burma (1.1 arable acres per capita), Malaya and Thailand (1 acre each), and the Philippines (0.9 acre) as that of India where there is 0.9 of an acre of arable land per capita. However, Indonesia and Vietnam, with only 0.4 of an acre for each person, have greater population pressures on arable land than either India or China. Additional arable land could be made available through large-scale irrigation-drainage projects in most of the continental southeast Asian countries.

Grown primarily under irrigation, rice is both the principal food crop and agricultural export. Prior to World War II, Burma, Thailand, and South Vietnam were the three largest rice exporting areas in the world.

Although most of the arable land is in small holdings and farmed by its owner, the colonial powers introduced the plantation system. Rubber, sugar, both coconut and oil palms, and sisal are the primary plantation crops; quinine, kapok, abaca, spices, tobacco, and teak are also grown.

Besides producing about three-fifths of the world's tin, the realm also exports primarily to East Asia small but important quantities of petroleum, iron ore, chromite, and bauxite.

Most of the people live in villages; in North Vietnam, Thailand, Cambodia, and Indonesia over 85 percent of the people are rural. However, there are seven cities in this realm with over a million inhabitants. Each country here except Vietnam has a primate city (a city which is two or three or more times numerically greater than the second largest).

Culturally the region has a great diversity and interspersion of religions, languages and dialects, ethnic and national groups, architecture, and dress. In migrations from East Asia, South Asia, and Austro-Asia, intermarriage and isolation of numerous small areas have contributed to the diversity.

Some of the realm's unifying characteristics are its low per capita annual income, low educational attainments of its people, attitudes toward colonialism, paucity of industrial development, slow pace of economic and political development during the past century under colonialism, destruction of transportation facilities during World War II, problems of communistic penetration during the past two decades, and rising tide of individual expectations. Because of these and other factors most of the political governments of countries in this realm are unstable and/or nonviable.

South Asia · This irregularly shaped triangular area is sometimes called a subcontinent because to the northwest, north, and northeast it is bounded and partially penned off by high and rugged mountains from the rest of Eurasia. No railroads or all-weather highways cross the mountain barrier of the Himalayas and associated ranges to provide land access between South Asia and the other three realms to the west, north, and east. The southern part of this realm, with approximately one-half of its border, juts southward into the Indian Ocean.

The mountains have not only helped block the cold air masses which might otherwise have come in from the north, but throughout history have influenced the people here to migrate southward primarily by water into Southeast Asia, Southwest Asia, and eastern Africa rather than northward.

The six countries of India, Pakistan, Nepal, Ceylon, Bhutan, and Sikkim vary greatly in size and population. India contains about two-thirds of the territory and nine-tenths of the people. During the nineteenth and the early part of the twentieth centuries, Bhutan, Sikkim, and Nepal served as buffer areas between the British Indian Empire and Russia and China. However, since the dissolution of that empire in 1947 and the rejuvenation of Communist China following World War II, the latter country has not only engulfed Tibet, but border clashes between Communist China and India during the 1960's have almost led to war.

With between 5.5 and 6 million people this realm contains one of the three major concentrations of population in the world. More human beings live in East Asia than in South Asia, and, if the U.S.S.R. were included, more than are concentrated in Europe. But if the Soviet Union (U.S.S.R.) is excluded as a European country, then South Asia would have a greater population than all the European countries combined.

As in the other three realms, the population distribution here is very uneven with the heavy concentrations associated with well-watered plains and urban areas. The areas with the largest number of cities, villages, and well-water fields follow the east and west coasts of India, occupy the flood plains of the Ganges River, and are concentrated on the alluvial fans on the lower slopes of the Himalaya Mountains as far west as the Lahore area of Pakistan.

Most of the people are engaged in extensively farming small acreages. But farming techniques are antiquated, few hybrid seeds are used, insufficient amounts of fertilizers are available, yields are often low or uncertain, and many land owners are satisfied with almost a subsistence type of farming or at best a low standard of living. Without the benefits of twentieth century science and technology most of the people remain poor and underfed and are plagued with malnutrition and disease. In dry years sickness and famine stalk many parts of this realm.

It is difficult to get unified action to recognize and solve rural and urban problems here because of the highly fractionalized nature of the culture. The population is subdivided into numerous groups because of differences in language, religion, racial, and ethnic background.

Although India and Pakistan are in an early stage of shift from a rural farming to an urban industrial economy, the present cities are not yet able to provide adequate water, sewage, street, and lighting systems for the masses. Only the rich have adequate housing and large sections of the cities would be classified as slums by West European standards.

British colonialism brought more to this realm than French colonialism brought to French Indo-China. But the improvements which the British brought were offset by a population explosion. According to Professor John E. Brush, the population of India and Pakistan increased 58 percent during a period of seventy-nine years prior to 1951.

Southwest Asia · This realm provides a land bridge between the rest of Asia, Europe, and Africa. Air routes, waterways, and highways focus on this region. For the past 3,000 years, as major centers of civilization in this realm as well as in northern Africa and southern Europe grew and declined, Southwest Asia has been the site of relatively great movements of people. Either as individuals, groups, and/or armies, people from and beyond this realm have traveled in all directions along these major routes, taking goods, ideas, languages, and cultures from one geographic region to another. This realm is not only strategically important because of its central location in Africo-Eurasia, but also because it has the world's largest known petroleum reserves.

In part it is politically weak; with its twenty political units, it is the most partitioned realm in the entire region. Units vary in size from the largest country, Saudi Arabia, which is several times the size of Texas, to protectorates such as the Gaza Strip and Aden (each with 125 square miles of territory) and small independent sheikdoms such as Qatar which contains 45,000 square miles. Regardless of their size, these political units are neither economically nor politically viable or strong enough militarily to resist invasion and therefore be completely independent. They are constant pawns in the diplomatic world with their allegiance and resources coveted by the Soviet Union, United Kingdom, France, Communist China, and the United States.

Except for the one acre in nine which is arable, the rest of the area is occupied by deserts and mountains. With most of the people engaged in farming and living in villages, and with this realm ranking lowest among the four in total numbers of people and population density, cities are few in number and small in size when compared with urban areas in other Asian realms.

The physical environment has set harsh limits to future agricultural land development. Of the numerous facets of weather and climate, some of the most significant are the deficiency and unreliability of the rainfall, excessive summer heat, strong to gale winds in the form of dust storms, and both hot humid and hot dry desiccating winds which blow for short durations damaging crops, livestock, buildings, and human health; and torrential rains which produce unusually high or flash floods and often waterlog earthen buildings until they collapse. The realm has a limited amount of alluvial soil, desirable reservoir building sites, commercial forest products, and a small number of commercial minerals.

Although this realm was the cradle of Christianity and learning, both of which have had such a strong impact on Western civilizations, today two of its primary ubiquitous characteristics are the adherence of most of the people to Islam and the meager educational opportunities for the masses. At present the popular movements of Arabism, Pan-Arabism, and Pan-Islam indicate that peoples in this realm are giving more thought to common problems and unity.

GEOGRAPHY OF AN ASIAN COUNTRY

Each country in Asia has a distinct complex of physical and cultural geographic characteristics. Consequently, it is almost impossible to select one country from each realm, study it in detail and then generalize that other countries in the realm are similar. A thorough study of the geography of Communist China will not give one a deep understanding of Japan. Nor will such a study of the Japanese Islands result in the same understanding of the Philippine Islands or the Indonesian Archipelago. There are similarities in the geography of Thailand and Burma, but the differences here are as numerous if not more numerous than the similarities.

Some broad generalizations can be made. For example, rice, usually grown under irrigation, is the major food crop in all the countries in Southeast Asia and for most of the people in Asia. However, in Mongolia and parts of north and west China the physical environment is too cold and/or too dry for rice production.

It is usually impractical to study all countries in Asia in detail. The practice in precollege teaching has been to select a few of the largest and more important ones and study each in depth. Communist China, Japan, and India are three often selected for this purpose. If a class is to study the geography of a country in depth, it is imperative that the teacher have a good outline in mind. Without it, class discussions and individual and committee reports could digress too far and too long from the core of the subject.

Most geographers agree that the geography of a country may be divided at least into two large divisions — the physical and cultural (man-made) environments. Some of the major components of the physical environmental complex are the relative location (including accessibility), size, shape, and boundaries, landforms, climate (including weather), water bodies, soil, and natural resources (including native vegetation, native animal life, and commercial minerals). Some primary components of the man-made environment are population, houses and settlements (through the hierarchy from farmsteads and crossroad stores and services to the largest metropolitan areas), occupations, types of transportation, conservation, and recreation.

Some of the component parts just listed may be deleted and others rearranged; still others may be added to fit the philosophy of geography held by the instructor. With a definite outline the teacher can assign component parts to individuals or committees or the class as a whole for reports and discussion. In summarizing the study, students should relate the country to the realm in which it is located. Moreover, students should have an overall geographical perspective of the four major realms of Asia.

An alternative to selecting and studying a few countries in detail would be to study each realm and apply the same outline suggested for the study of a country.

20

Africa

For better or for worse the Old Africa is gone and the white race must face the new situation which they have themselves created.

JAN CHRISTIAN SMUTS

THE MAJOR OBJECTIVE in the teaching of regional geography may be said to be the presentation of concepts and relationships that will provide the student with an accurate, fundamental, and meaningful understanding of a particular region. In the teaching of a unit on Africa, this objective is perhaps more difficult to attain than it is for any other continental area of the world. Two major reasons account for this difficulty, but a skillful teacher should nevertheless be able to develop a unit that is informative, well balanced, and stimulating.

PROBLEMS OF TEACHING AFRICAN GEOGRAPHY

The primary problem in teaching African geography — unlike most other world areas — arises from the consequences of the unusual fascination that this continent holds for nearly all young people. Before the average child begins a formal study of Africa in school, his imagination has been gripped and excited by numerous descriptions, accounts, and other contacts with Africa which he has gained through television, movies, hearsay, and outside reading. By the time he enters fourth grade, he may have already accumulated a surprising store of knowledge about the continent, and in various degrees is acquainted with the Pyramids, gold and diamond mines, mysterious "casbahs," strange tribal customs, and many species of wild game. Unfortunately, much of his exposure to Africa has resulted in the acquisition of some very serious geographical distortions to which he may cling tenaciously because they have been repeated so often. These geographical distortions present the major obstacle to be overcome if the unit is to be taught successfully.

Distortions of the geography of Africa fall into two main groups: those which arise from overemphasizing spectacular aspects of the continent that are true and actually exist, but which are of limited significance when viewed against the continental background; and those which are outright fallacies and exaggerations.

Regarding the first group of distortions, the goal of the teacher should be the organization of a unit that provides a balanced survey of Africa which, by necessity, must relegate the spectacular aspects to their proper place and scope. Although the class will prefer to dwell on the spectacular and return to it frequently, this tendency should be minimized. On the other hand, it is almost impossible to discuss Africa in the classroom without reference to such bizarre and colorful topics as the consumption of cattle blood by a certain few tribes, passageways inside the Great Pyramids, and the habits of lions when stalking their prey. The teacher of a unit on Africa is in an excellent position to capitalize on the student's initial curiosity, and if he is careful to intersperse the spectacular topics with the less interesting, should be able to maintain a satisfactory level of student participation. This procedure may need to be varied according to the grade level of the class, but even in the fourth grade, the teacher should keep the problem of overemphasis upon spectacular topics in mind if the major objective is to be met.

The second group of distortions, consisting of various fallacies and exaggerations, requires nothing less than correction by the teacher. While misconceptions appear in all regional studies, they seem to abound in the study of Africa. Indeed, it is somewhat of a paradox that a continent attracting so much attention is at the same time the victim of so much misinformation. Some sample fourth-grade misconceptions are as follows:

1. All of Africa consists of steaming jungles that teem with wild game.
2. There are no cities in Africa — only huts in jungle clearings.
3. The black people are pagan, ignorant, and docile, but can be aroused to frenzies of wild dancing at the prospect of human sacrifice.
4. White people in Africa become either selfless missionary doctors or greedy thieves in search of jewelled idols.
5. In northern Africa, sultans, camel caravans, and harems are commonplace.

This list of misconceptions could be continued indefinitely, and there is no end in sight to the propagation of these and other fallacies by popular media, with the result that not only are children subject to confusion between fact and fancy, but teachers may be similarly misled. Nor is the plight of both teacher and student alleviated by the generally inadequate textbooks on Africa now in use. Despite these unfavorable odds, one of the major goals in the teaching of Africa must remain the elimination of false and exaggerated misconceptions which contribute to the retention of profound geographical distortions.

The second major problem encountered in the teaching of Africa is traceable to the relationship of American students to American Negroes and to African blacks. That this is a sensitive and delicate matter hardly needs to be said. It is sufficient to remark, perhaps, that the culture and history of the American Negro has diverged from that of the indigenous African to the extent that the two groups are no longer comparable in most respects. This point — that one group should not be confused with the other — ought to be made to the class at the very outset of the unit without any derogatory implications for either group. Further, it is well to portray Africans in a respectful and dignified manner, and the term "native" in its pejorative sense ought to be avoided whenever possible.

For the teacher, the replacement and correction of distortions about Africa that have long been entrenched in the student's mind may not seem to be an easy or pleasant task. The student may find the effect of giving up overly colorful and erroneous impressions progressively disillusioning. It is fortunate, then, that the study of the continent involves unique, rewarding, and challenging geographic concepts in which fact is considerably more interesting than fiction. If the teacher is able to present the basic concepts about Africa with confidence and enthusiasm, the problem of distortion and the sense of disillusionment should be overcome to a large degree. The remainder of this chapter is devoted to an outline of the major geographical concepts that might be stressed in a unit on Africa.

CONCEPTS

Concept of two Africas · Once the teacher has made reference, if he so desires, to the two conceptual problems noted above, the next point is to mention the division of the continent into its two main regions. Northern Africa, with its essentially white, Moslem, and Middle Eastern civilization, is culturally distinct from sub-Saharan Africa, homeland of the Negroid group. The frontier separating the two regions lies at the southern edge of the Sahara, but it should be noted in class that characteristics of each region have penetrated into the other over a long period of time and that the Sahara has not been so great a barrier to communication as is commonly thought. Because of the significant differences between the "two Africas," the teacher might find it advisable to focus on each one individually rather than risking weak and inaccurate generalizations concerning the entire continent.

African subregions · Having studied the concept of two Africas, the class is ready to divide the continent further into its subregions, that is,

North Africa, West Africa, Eastern Africa, Equatorial Africa, and Southern Africa. The process of subdividing will require students to become somewhat familiar with the names of each country and territory. The teacher should arrange to have available a recent map of Africa and should correct outdated maps in textbooks. In this regard, a responsibility of the teacher is to be aware of recent name changes, boundary revisions, and the status of various groupings of states in order to avoid confusion and personal embarrassment over map assignments.

African landforms · The chief concept to be stressed here is the plateau nature of much of the continent. Tilted higher in the south and east and lower in the north and west, the African plateau lacks great mountain ranges such as the Andes, Rockies, and Alps, and consists instead of a series of basins enclosed and separated by broad swells, with the larger basins being drained by five great rivers: the Niger, Congo, Nile, Zambezi, and Orange. Cutting through the plateau is the Rift Valley and its associated escarpments, lakes, and volcanic features.

The gross landform features of Africa are not difficult to grasp, but a basic explanation of the physiography of the continent must involve the fascinating and controversial hypothesis of Continental Drift.[1] Class discussion of this hypothesis can be undertaken as early as the fourth grade, and may lead to a variety of individual and group projects, particularly in the "reassembly" of continental areas into a supercontinent and the portrayal by cross section of the earth's crust.

African climates · When mapped according to the Köppen system of classification, African climates, with few exceptions, follow an orderly pattern whose logic should appeal to students. Because the Köppen zones are fairly broad in area and the continent is not encumbered by D or E zones, the pattern exhibits a simplicity that can be generally understood by children in the lower grades. Equally important, the pattern of climatic zones reveals a kind of symmetry at corresponding distances north and south of the equator, thereby permitting a study of the chief climatic control in Africa — latitude. The study of latitude leads, in turn, to an emphasis on earth-sun relations and the annual migration of the chief rain-producing mechanisms, the intertropical front (or convergence zone) and the belts of midlatitude cyclones. The final step in the appreciation of this relationship might focus on areas of double-maximum precipitation and on the general increase in the length of the dry season at increasing distances from the equator. There are, of course, so-called "anomalies" in Africa's climate, such as the cooler temperatures of the more elevated

---

[1] H. J. deBlij, *A Geography of Subsaharan Africa* (Chicago: Rand McNally, 1964), pp. 14–23.

plateau regions, the Highland (or H) climate of Ethiopia, and the dry areas of eastern Africa near the equator. A brief explanation of these anomalies should add to student understanding.

Some of the worst misconceptions about Africa pertain to its supposedly wretched climate. While this allusion may be true for certain areas, there are nevertheless very large regions having moderate temperatures and precipitation, and whose weather is in fact extremely pleasant. The teacher should point this out at length, and perhaps illustrate it by a comparison of temperatures recorded in African cities with July temperatures at home or elsewhere in the United States (Washington, D. C., for example). An effective method of comparison, and one which incidentally provides experience in graph construction, is for the students to prepare climographs. This can be done successfully as early as the fourth grade and will do much to replace geographical distortions.

Natural vegetation and soils · The close relationship between climate and vegetation may be utilized by the teacher as a means of reinforcing the study of either element in the landscape and as a means of dispelling gross misconceptions. Maps of climate and vegetation should serve as the principal tools, providing the student with insights into the relationship between the two and its expression in Africa. Audio-visual presentations will obviously enhance class discussion of vegetational patterns and such problems as conservation and soil erosion.

The teacher might stress the rather low proportion of Africa occupied by rainforest, a fact that becomes more meaningful in comparison with the rainforests of Latin America and the equatorial Far East. If feasible, distinctions could be made among the various climax forms of savanna and steppe vegetation, bearing in mind the concept of graduated transition zones.

The discussion of vegetation and soils might also encompass economic uses such as timber, grazing, and the gathering of nuts, fruits, resins, and gums. Mention should be made concerning the poverty of Africa's soils and their limiting effect on man's occupation of extensive areas. Here, too, the teacher should introduce the severe problems brought about by tsetse fly infestation.

Wild game · No unit on Africa is complete without an allocation of time for the subject of wild game. This part of the unit should result in considerable class participation and may eventuate into an excursion to the zoo.

A prevalent misconception concerning African fauna is that there are large numbers of animals spread widely over the continent. The task of the teacher is to negate this erroneous concept by noting the relationship of game habitats to climate and natural vegetation, and to go a step further in explaining that land competition between game and an increasing human population has led to the reduction or elimination of the former over vast areas within the last century. The teacher might introduce material about game reserves in Africa, and by extension place some emphasis on the need for game conservation throughout the world.

African peoples · The subject of Africa's peoples can be as interesting to the class as Africa's game. And as with game, there are long-held distortions that need to be replaced if the student is to gain a true perspective.

The rapidity of social change is perhaps the keynote in this part of the unit. Steadily increasing contact with the outside world is destroying the beliefs, customs, social structures, and traditions of the past. Passing also from the scene are odd and curious forms of behavior, dress, and human disfiguration that have characterized Africa in the eyes of the world for many years. Much remains of the old Africa, of course, but the teacher is obligated to mention the new — black people living in large cities and following urban occupations: doctors, engineers, clerks, bus drivers, and so forth. It would not be amiss to speak of this change as a social revolution, one which should transform the way of life of nearly all Africans within twenty or thirty years. Along with it goes a new dignity which makes the word *native* seem improper. There is also a strong preference for the term *African* instead of *Negro*. The pattern of social change is not uniform over the continent, which permits the teacher to note the geographical relationship between such change and historical-economic developments.

Certain other aspects of Africa's people concern varying population densities, rates of demographic change, health, education, the arts (music, dancing, story telling), religion, and standards of living. Another important aspect deals with the many kinds of ethnic groups and their location and relative numerical strengths.

Children's literature about Africa, much of which deals intimately with family life, may be of considerable value in the class. However, some children's books about African people are so dangerously misleading and unwittingly derogatory that the teacher should, if possible, prevent their use. Fortunately, children's books about Africa have become more accurate in recent years.

African history · The past of Africa may be conveniently subdivided into interesting periods upon which the class, or parts of it, may focus attention. The first of these periods involves anthropological data and theories relating to man's evolution and his earliest homesites and innovations. The second period concerns the history of Egypt, Kush, Ethiopia, and northern Africa, to which should be added the great kingdoms of the medieval western Sudan. Next comes the period of slavery, with its import for Americans, and then the fascinating period of individual exploration: Park, Caillie, Livingstone, Stanley, Speke, Baker, and others. The fifth period is that of European colonial rule on both sides of the Sahara, and the sixth is current in the political independence of most of the continent. A concept to be stressed in the historical survey is the contrast between the very old records of northern Africa and the very recent sense of history (100 to 500 years) in much of Africa south of the Sahara. By organizing the African past into these six periods, the teacher should more easily attain the desired goals.

African economy · Here again proper organization will facilitate class understanding. Economic activities may be broadly divided into agricultural, forestry, mining, manufacturing, and trade sectors. Traditionally, the economy has been depicted as one of subsistence agriculture embracing over 75 percent of the people. Actully, the full-scale subsistence farmer or nomad today constitutes only a small percentage of the rural population, most of which is engaged in a mixed cash-subsistence type of economy. European farms and plantations have lost much importance since 1960 in Algeria, Kenya, the Congo, and elsewhere, but this form of agriculture remains significant in South Africa, Rhodesia, and the two southern Portuguese territories. In describing agriculture, the teacher should underline the major cash crops of Africa and their chief areas of production.

The discussion of mining might involve the geological relationship between the landforms of Africa and the presence of a wide variety of minerals. Of particular interest to the students would be the mining of gold and diamonds, but other minerals, especially copper and petroleum, deserve mention. Specific information about manufacturing and internal trade need not require much time in class.

Essentially, Africa must be viewed as a source of raw materials and an importer of finished goods. Attention should be given to the industrial progress of South Africa and the United Arab Republic, and of rapid development in certain other favored areas. Development schemes and "dream" projects might be noted. An overall economic assessment of Africa, however, should not be too optimistic under present conditions. This assessment, incidentally, offers the teacher leeway to introduce the highly significant relationship between population growth and economic growth in percentage, or in per capita, terms.

African political development · The teacher's approach to political development will necessarily vary greatly according to the requirements of the class and depending upon events in Africa. Few guidelines can be provided here, other than the stressing of Africa's valuable products in world trade and its strategic location, particularly at Suez. Contemporary problems include Pan-Africanism of various kinds, inherited boundaries, tribal conflicts, racial segregation, unstable governments, revolts in Portuguese territories, the Rhodesian crisis, and tensions in Africa resulting from the rivalries among the great powers.

CONCLUSION

The concepts outlined above represent a topical or systematic approach to a regional subject. In the case of Africa, with its nearly fifty political units, this approach would seem to be preferable to a study, likely ending in confusion, of each of the units. The teacher, of course, may choose to focus on certain subregions or particular countries instead of attempting to cover the continent in all of its geographic aspects. In some situations, studies in depth of Nigeria, South Africa, Uganda, or the United Arab Republic, for example, might prove to be more fruitful than the continental approach. Studies of a few individual countries might also constitute a valuable supplement to the unit when there is sufficient time following the continental survey.

Perhaps the ultimate goal in teaching is not so much the imparting of specific information in this day of rapid change as it is to lay the groundwork that will bring about a desire on the part of the student to continue private study. Earlier in this chapter, the point was observed that most children first arrive at a study of Africa with much anticipation and with many distortions of fact and fancy which need correction or replacement. The teacher should be careful not to overemphasize his desire to dispel misconceptions, thus giving the impression that the main purpose of the unit is the negation of erroneous concepts. While it may be true that distortions form the major obstacle to a successful unit, the teacher might better subordinate a negative approach to a more positive attitude by which vital new information replaces the old. In this way, he should be able to accomplish the major teaching objective and, in addition, enhance the student's interest in further study.

21

Australia and the Pacific Islands

The distinctive character of the many Pacific island groups and the Pacific coast areas of the Australian and Asiatic continents derives as much, if not more, from the people living there as from the diversity of physical conditions. KENNETH B. CUMBERLAND

A BRIEF SURVEY OF Australia and the Pacific Islands provides the background for the development of projects and activities. Limitations of space made a selection of topics necessary. The islands exhibit wide variations in size, population, relief, origins, climate, and other characteristics. The topics chosen illustrate some of the geographic relationships.

AUSTRALIA AND NEW ZEALAND

From whatever direction these countries are approached, distance is still the major time factor. The north-south extent of New Zealand covers about 1,000 miles, the same as the airline distance between Los Angeles and Seattle. At its widest east-west distance on either island, it is less than 200 miles. A relief map shows the high mountainous backbone with glaciers on South Island. North Island has lower overall elevations with its own Yellowstone type of park. In many respects the climate, relief, land use, and crops are similar to Washington and Oregon coastal lands, and the country is naturally green. New Zealand to Australia is a three-day trip by ship, with over 1,000 miles of sea between them.

Australia ranks sixth in area among the world's nations. On a map showing rainfall, more than three-fourths of its area is marked by the colors of brown and tan because of lack of rainfall and high rates of evaporation. Maps show the peripheral distribution of relief, favorable climates, natural vegetation, and crops, and the patterns suggest the inference that population, too, will be peripheral in its distribution.

Australia is the industrial giant of the south and commands an amazingly recent rapid growth with more potential ahead. It still must use the vast open lands for grazing. It is busily locating petroleum and natural gas deposits along with metallic minerals. Its program of water conservation and development of dams for multiple uses — irrigation, domestic water supplies, hydropower, flash flood control, and recreation — continues to expand.

In New Zealand the number of cattle (6,700,000) and sheep (53,000,-000) have gained at a steady pace over the years. In Australia the toll taken by drought is suggested by the variations in some twenty-year periods from less than 100,000,000 sheep to over 170,000,000. From year to year a drop of millions may happen. Sheep show greater variation in numbers than do cattle, perhaps because sheep are in more marginal areas. Nevertheless, Australia continues to supply about 45 percent of the world's export wools. Cattle numbers vary around a half million from year to year, but are on the increase. Except for the volume of meat exports from Argentina, the two countries rank at the top.

Wheat continues to be the major grain crop of Australia. Over a forty-year period, production ranged from 117,600,000 bushels to 368,000,000 bushels per year. The yields are up one year and down the next, a possible reflection of variability of rainfall. In spite of this, Australia continues to rank fifth among nations in wheat exports.

ISLANDS OF THE PACIFIC REALM

The Pacific Islands are scattered over an awesome area of vast distances in an ocean of more than 63,000,000 square miles. This area is so large that if all of the land on the planet earth were placed into that ocean basin, the result would be one massive island.

The thousands of Pacific Islands extend from the Aleutian chain at 57° N to beyond 50° S latitude. Islands, islets, rocky detached pieces — some inhabited, others bare and unoccupied — and hundreds of coral reefs make up this vast realm. The latitudinal spread of 7,800 miles is far exceeded by the longitudinal spread. At 79° W longitude are the Juan Fernandez Islands off the coast of Chile, although some may say that 1,800 miles farther to the west Rapa Nui (Easter Island) at 109° W longitude marks the limit of the Pacific Islands. At 90° W, off Ecuador, are the Galapagos. Across the Pacific to the Philippines at 120° E are lone islands and island groups. Beyond 140° E lies most of Indonesia. At this equatorial location the distance from east to west across the Pacific is more than 13,000 miles, or more than halfway around the world.

Some of the islands are as large as a farm, or ranch, or county. The state of Hawaii is larger than Connecticut. The Fiji Islands have about the same area as New Jersey. The Solomons compare with Rhode Island. By far the greatest number of islands have areas measured in acres, but others are measured in square miles. Most island groups have a total of less than 1,000 square miles of land area. All of the islands, excluding the Philippines, Indonesia, New Guinea, and New Zealand, have a total land area of less than 50,000 square miles, or about the area of Louisiana.

When one considers the vast area of the Pacific Ocean, then the isolation of many island specks is obvious. Within island groups of the same political unit, a neighboring island may be within sight, but more often it is beyond the horizon which at sea level would be about 5 miles from the viewer.

POPULATION

Some ten years before Magellan cruised among the Pacific Islands, the Portuguese sighted New Guinea. In the 1500's exploring parties under the Portuguese, Spanish, and Dutch flags sailed about the Pacific. In the next century more expeditions arrived along with the Russians and English. In the 1700's the French and English were more active, and the Americans appeared near the close of that century. In the 1800's the British colonized Australia and New Zealand, and the French and Germans set up protectorates on other islands.

In the last years of the nineteenth century, Japan moved into some island groups. Following World War I, the former German colonies were placed under mandate of the League of Nations and were administered by Australia, New Zealand, Japan, and the United Kingdom. Following World War II, under the aegis of the United Nations, the United States, Australia, and New Zealand assumed trusteeships of former Japanese islands. In the last few years, the administration of some islands has been modified.

A few islands are owned outright by corporations operating coconut plantations, raising other tropical crops, developing mines, or other resources. The governing of a few islands is by local chieftains or hereditary rulers. However, the governing of most islands is controlled and regulated by the various countries who claim them as possessions or administer them as condominiums or trusteeships under the United Nations.

Three major native groups once dominated the tropical islands. Micronesia, the little islands, are located in the West Pacific beyond 180° longitude and north of the equator. The main groups are the Marianas, Carolines, Marshalls, Gilberts, and Ellice. Melanesia, the black islands, are also in the West Pacific but to the south of the equator and include the Solomons, Fiji, New Hebrides, New Caledonia, and others. Polynesia, many islands, are in the East Pacific to the north and south of the equator. They include Hawaii, Samoa, Tonga, Marquesas, and Society Islands. Other Polynesians are the native Maoris of New Zealand and the people of Easter and Pitcairn Islands. Apart from these three groups are the aborigines in the interior of Australia and the Indonesians who are predominantly Malayan.

Today there are few true native groups on the accessible parts of islands. The reasons for mixed races are numerous. Although interisland warfare had been common in earlier centuries, the present conditions can be attributed to the white man. During the last 400 years, discoverers, explorers, whalers, traders, slavers, missionaries, and exploiters came to the islands. Two world wars brought more rapid changes in recent decades. White man's diseases often decimated major parts of the population, as on the Marquesas. Then imported laborers from the Asiatic mainland added more variety. Movement of people between the islands has always been considerable. Plantation developments were possible only by bringing a workforce to such islands or groups as Flint, Palmyra, and the Carolines.

The population density like the areas of the islands varies from zero on islets and reefs, to islands settled by one, two, or three families. The density per square mile ranges from a few persons to over 270 on Guam and over 470 on the Ellice Islands. The largest islands do not necessarily have high population densities. Only thirteen persons per square mile occur in northeast New Guinea.

In Western Samoa are two islands. Savaii has seventy-nine villages on 703 square miles, with a population of over 19,000 (density twenty-seven per square mile). Upolu has 133 villages on 430 square miles with a population of over 40,000 (density ninety-three per square mile). These make interesting comparisons with sizes of counties and villages in the home state. Data for the political divisions of New Zealand and Australia are readily available.

NATURE OF THE ISLANDS

Elevations on some islands are only a few feet above sea level. Varying winds and tides may pull water over them until they are submerged or within a few feet of being flooded. On islands having a mountainous backbone or volcanic cores or cones, peaks and ranges rise to over 5,000 feet above sea level as on New Caledonia, Western Samoa, and Bougainville, and to 8,000 feet as on Guadalcanal and Tahiti. A few peaks rise to over 12,000 feet as on Hawaii and New Guinea. The very highest peaks are visible at sea from distances of 50 to 80 miles. Even the presence of low islands can often be detected by cloud formations which hover over them.

Within shallow tropical waters, where temperatures are suitable, corals build reefs, atolls, and barrier reefs which enclose lagoons associated with these formations. Often coral islands are built upon submerged mountain forms.

Earthquakes and volcanic activity on the ocean floor or around the continental fringes of the Pacific send messages throughout the realm by the tsunami. These huge tidal waves overwhelm low islands and shores of high islands. Damages can be catastrophic. Lava flows and eruptions in recent years have caused disaster areas in Hawaii and the Philippines.

Australia is a continent with sedimentary, igneous, and metamorphic rock formations. Vast plains in its interior are similar in origin to the interior central plains of the United States. Mountains, glaciers, deserts, grasslands, forests, minerals, and vast natural resources give further clues that physical emergence of Australia was not unlike other continents.

CLIMATE

Most Pacific Islands have one common climatic element, mild to hot temperatures throughout the year on the lowlands. Upland elevations, depending upon altitude and latitude, have mild to chilly temperatures in the season of low sun. At times, land and sea breezes help to move air about. Trade winds persist for some months alternating with the rainy monsoon. The spawning of typhoons in the western Pacific is frequent. The swirl of ocean currents is related, in part, to winds, but the movement continues regardless of season. Water temperatures influence local climates, their velocity affects fishing and handling of boats.

The distribution of rainfall is related to the winds, dry trades, and rainy monsoons. The amount varies from a few inches, 21 at Malden Island, to over 120 in parts of Fiji. Windward and leeward mountain slopes also make differences in amounts. Hilo, on the windward side of Hawaii, has 140 inches annually, but Honolulu, on the leeward side of Oahu, has only 21 inches.

The effectiveness of even small amounts of rainfall is lost in the quick drainage through coral sands and high rates of evaporation. Heavier rains on lava slopes erode soils which enrich the productivity of the lowlands.

Days and nights in equatorial latitudes are about equal in length. Hence the hours for cooling tend to make the night temperatures drop. It is often remarked, "Nighttime is winter in the tropics." During rainy seasons, humidity is high and almost unbearable by nonnatives. This is especially true in the western Pacific.

Pupils need to get the "feel" of climates other than those they have experienced. The making of hythergraphs, a wind rose, and sun paths will sharpen their observations of local phenomena and provide patterns for comparisons with faraway places.

TRANSPORTATION AND COMMUNICATION

On smaller islands, transportation is limited to paths and roads. Some larger and more populated islands may have highways and suitable motor roads. In some instances, roads and highways are the remnants of work done by World War II occupation forces.

Railroads are almost nonexistant except on larger islands in the far western Pacific. Short lines are used where mining operations require hauling ores to ports or loading docks. With the depletion of the resource, even these have been abandoned.

Local transportation between islands is by boat, ship, or plane. Some steamship lines have major ports of call at a few islands on or near shipping lanes. Some islands have local air service within their chain or with other island groups. Airfields on several of the strategically located islands serve major trans-Pacific airlines. Changes in the plane types have led to abandonment of some fields. A lone beacon light may be the only directional guide or landmark on uninhabited islands, as is the Amelia Earhart Beacon on Howland Island.

Radio stations operate on major islands. Local stations often serve a far-flung island chain. Those islands along main routes of trans-Pacific travel are equipped to serve both planes and ships. Many islands continue to be more or less isolated. A few are the anchor points for undersea cable lines reaching from Asia to Australia and to the mainland of North America.

PROJECTS AND ACTIVITIES

In presenting new projects, it is advisable to use local information and data whenever possible. Students will see their experiences graphically portrayed. This trial run is important. Students learn the techniques and have a basis for comparisons with other materials. The items about the Pacific realm provide materials for further individual work, group, or committee projects. The number participating depends upon the amount of information collected, time available, and the values to be gained by expanding the topics. Purposes common to every project are to provide useful experiences by visualization of facts, to gain some skill in use of media and tools, to discover some principles, factors, and problems, and to interpret and apply findings so as to gain a better understanding of faraway places.

In most instances the sources of information and materials about the Pacific Islands are not readily available. Therefore, a teacher planning to develop these projects will need to order special books and collect data and materials well in advance of the expected time of use. Information

about New Zealand and Australia appears in most textbooks and volumes
of statistical data.

Observations

All of the land mass of the earth makes but an island in the Pacific
Ocean. All of the smaller islands have a land area no larger than the State
of New York (or compare with home state). The total land area of the
large and small islands is about the size of Alaska or twice that of Texas.
If all of the small islands were in one mass, they would still be a speck in
the vast Pacific Ocean area.

Project: Use diagrams to convey distances in the Pacific area.

Materials: Atlas, wall maps, outline maps, other paper for charts.

Data: Use latitude and longitude to determine distances between islands
and mainlands. Refer to maps in atlas which show the mileages and
routes of shipping lanes, or airline distances between major ports.

Procedure: Make a grid pattern for the Pacific area, using a reasonable
scale of miles, or use outline maps. Pinpoint key places, sketch in shipping lanes, air routes, etc.

Set up problems that relate time and distance and type of travel. For
example, a freighter outbound from San Francisco departs January 5
for Suva, Fiji Islands. Its speed is about 15 miles per hour. Allowing
5 days for stops at other ports enroute, when will it arrive at Suva?
(4,867 miles in about 14 days.)

Application: Make comparisons with rocket flights in distance and time.
Compare distances and time for east-west travel across the United
States mainland; across the Atlantic; to ports in New Zealand and
Australia.

Areas and Distances

Project: Comparison of land and water areas by block diagram graph.

Materials: Graph paper with ten squares to 1 inch, and colored paper for
land areas.

Data: Pacific area 63,800,000 square miles, earth–land area 52,400,000
square miles. Total area of small islands in Pacific, 48,800 square miles.
Area of small islands and New Zealand, New Guinea, The Philippines,
585,000 square miles.

Procedure: Let the smallest square represent 48,000 square miles. Then
the 100 squares within the 1 square inch represent 4,800,000 square
miles. Solve the problem $63,800,000 \div 4,800,000$ — or thirteen of the
1-inch squares and thirty of the smallest squares. Arrange them to form
a square or rectangle without irregular pieces branching off the main
shape. This area represents the Pacific Ocean.

Solve the problem 52,400,000 ÷ 4,800,000 — or ten 1-inch squares and ninety-two of the smallest squares. Arrange into a shape similar to the one for the ocean. The area represents the land area of the earth.

On a piece of paper, mount the blue ocean area, on that mount the colored paper for land area, and then the smallest piece superimposed on that land for the islands.

Other variations may be worked out using the total area of all islands. Which state has about that same area? (Alaska.) Use the size of local farm, a ranch, a county, other states to compare with specific island groups: Fiji 7,005 square miles, Gilbert Islands 525 square miles. Data for islands may be found in an almanac.

Population distribution and density · Maps show distribution of population by means of symbols, the uniform size dot (one person per dot or one dot to represent 100 persons, etc.), by graduated dots, by balls (giving perspective and volume), by tints and shades of colors, and by pictorial figures. While the distribution may show density, in truth density is a ratio of persons per square mile.

To represent this fact, draw a square, an inch or more in size. Let it represent a square mile. The area of Pitcairn Island is 2 square miles, the population 150. What is the density per square mile? (75). If one dot represents one person, how many dots will be placed on that square mile? (75). Use dots of colored paper made by a hand punch. Paste them in a scatter pattern, avoiding rows and designs. This illustrates population density.

Another example is the largest Pacific Island, New Guinea, with an area of 317,000 square miles and population of 2,620,000. How many dots will be placed on an average square mile? (8). Of course, there will be villages with more people and isolated mountain and swamp areas with no persons just as it might be in the home state.

A third example is Hawaii. The island of Oahu has 589 square miles with a population of 353,000. What is the density per square mile? (about 600). But Honolulu alone has 294,200 people on only 84 square miles. What is the density in the Honolulu area? (3,502). It becomes apparent that the figure 600 persons per square mile is not realistic. One should find how many people live outside the Honolulu area. (58,800). What is the area of Oahu without Honolulu? (505 square miles). Now figure the density for Oahu. (116).

Let one square represent 1 square mile for Oahu and another represent Honolulu. With one dot per person, how many dots are there for Oahu? How many for Honolulu? Since the number for Honolulu is so large, let one dot represent ten persons. Now how many dots for Honolulu? (350). and for Oahu? (eleven or twelve). A look at a map of Oahu shows a few villages; hence one should scatter the eleven dots so a few will be closer together and the others farther apart.

Some observations of the charts show that small areas often have more population than larger areas. A capital city such as Honolulu has most of the population. Population densities are lower in rural than in city areas. Population is distributed unevenly over the land.

Comparisons should be made with places in the home state and with cities in New Zealand and Australia.

Relief models · Many of the attempts to make relief models result in distortion and misrepresentation. A reasonable facsimile is sufficient for pupils to understand some of the general aspects of structure of islands, their relief, and how these are related to water resources, drainage, soils, erosion, climatic conditions, and problems of harbors and navigation channels. Therefore, it is suggested that the models be just that — models — some average nonexistent island which represents a type.

Of the four types of islands in the Pacific realm, the low islands of coral are the most common. They often form on the submerged rims of old craters, called sea mounts or guyots. The following are examples of three coral island types:

1. Atolls: somewhat circular reefs of islands about a lagoon, as Midway, Wake, and Fanning. Kwajelein in the Marshalls has thirty islets along a reef. Its lagoon, 650 square miles, is the world's largest.

2. Barrier reefs: an almost continuous reef far offshore like a wall around a higher island mass, as Truk and Ponape in the Caroline Islands, and Bora Bora northwest of Tahiti.

3. Fringing reefs: form close to shorelines of islands. Examples are Tahiti and New Caledonia.

The fourth island type is volcanic in origin, most common in the West Pacific except for Hawaii and the Galapagos in the east.

A rough sketch should first be made of the type of island and its scale, features, shape, relief, and special aspects worked out. A sketch should be made on a piece of stiff cardboard or wall board no smaller than 5 by 5 inches. The sea areas should be colored blue with paper or paints. A reasonable ratio of miles for the lagoon and island sizes should be maintained; elevations are usually less than 100 feet above sea level. The land area may be built up with materials of salt-flour, detergent-flour, or *papier mâché*, and sand or pulverized limestone scattered on the moist surface. Maps may be studied to achieve a variety in shapes and arrangement of island and reefs. Compass direction and latitude and longitude lines should be indicated.

PROFILES OF RELIEF FEATURES

Profiles of relief models • Profiles of relief are easy to make but also suffer from the problem of exaggeration of elevation. Using a wall-size relief map of New Guinea, Hawaii, or Australia, one should place the edge of a long piece of paper (graph paper might be helpful) across the land mass so that contrasts in elevation will be along the edge of the paper. Wherever there is a change in color, one makes a tick on the edge of the paper and jots down the elevation for that contour interval. A line is then drawn about an inch under these data and the map scale transferred so one may know the distance covered by the profile.

On a length of graph paper some 5 inches wide and 15 or more inches in length, a base line is drawn. The linear scale is made to be two, three, or more times the interval used on the map and the pattern.

At the far right intervals are marked off along a vertical line to represent elevation by units of 1,000 or 2,000 feet per line. The unit depends upon the heights in the profile and the distance across the land mass. The smaller the unit, the worse will be the vertical distortion. Each elevation mark is transferred from the pattern to the proper mileage point on its correct elevation line. Lastly, the tick lines are joined to show the land surface. This should be shown with ups and downs, but the variations within a color layer must be controlled. At the color change, the exact elevation is known.

The profile may be colored gray or the color layers may be colored in as bands, each at its proper elevation range: green for sea level to 1,000 feet, yellow 1,000 to 2,000 feet, tan 2,000 to 5,000 feet, brown 5,000 to 10,000 feet, and dark brown or red for over 10,000 feet.

Comparisons can be made with home areas charted to the same scale. Relationships of relief to transportation, location of highways, size of cities, city patterns, and other items can be inferred, verified, and problems raised.

Hythergraph • The hythergraph is a change from the climatic graph with blue bars to show average monthly precipitation and a red line to show trend of average monthly temperatures. The hythergraph combines precipitation and temperature data. The chart shows the striking patterns with similarities, differences, and ranges of data.

Use quarter-inch graph paper 17 by 22 inches with a heavy blue line at one-inch intervals. Make a dot in the lower-left corner, two inches from the left and two inches from lower edge of the paper. Extend the dot vertically to within an inch of the top margin. To the left, one inch from the starting point, write —60° in the first heavy blue line, then an inch higher write —50°, and so on to 0°; continue on to 100°. Place the numbers as on a thermometer, bisecting the line, not in spaces above or below. Place a large T° or T (F°) at the top of the column.

Return to the starting point and extend the dot to the right by drawing a horizontal line. Below this line number every heavy blue vertical line to the right in sequence: 1, 2, 3, etc., so that it looks like a ruler or straight edge. The zero, of course, is the point marked by that dot at the far left. Place a large P″ to the left of the line.

The data consist of the usual average monthly precipitation and average monthly temperature. To locate the first point, use the data for the home region and place a finger on the temperature line at the left where the January reading belongs. Now find the point on the lower line for the January precipitation. Visually extend the temperature point to your right until it intersects the precipitation point which has also been extended visually upward. At this intersection point, place a dot and number it 1 for January. Continue this procedure until all 12 months have been charted and numbered. Connect the dots in proper sequence. The resulting pattern will be some sort of geometric figure showing precipitation and temperature relationships.

Since the chart is large enough for other stations, several can be charted. If some overlap, that only serves to show similarities. Keeping the numbers of the months visible gives information for comparisons and contrasts. The patterns might be colored to increase their visibility and carrying power.

As in any project, the completion of the device is not enough, A study of patterns and writing statements bring forth meaningful and understandable ideas which are more meaningful than when read from a textbook. The chart shows the possibilities of this device.

CONCLUSION

The brief summary of so vast an area must omit many interesting details, such as the coconut palm as the landmark of tropical islands, the characteristics of Melanesians, Micronesians, and Polynesians, and the unique fauna and flora of Australia. The items not mentioned provide opportunities for further reading and searching by the pupils.

Directions for making the projects are brief but the resourceful teacher and class will develop variations and additional features. Many of the activities can be adapted to different grade levels even though this was not stated. The projects need not be restricted to the Pacific areas.

The standards set by the teacher will affect the quality of group work, accuracy of facts used, the careful searching for understandings once the project is completed. Attention to details and the finished product need not be that of perfection, but it should be recognized for what it depicts and can enlighten as a learning tool.

PART V

Geographic methodology: the topical approach

IN SEVERAL HIGH SCHOOLS and some junior high schools somewhat specialized courses in geography, such as physical geography or economic geography, are offered for one or two semesters. Recently a few high schools have introduced courses called cultural geography or historical geography. In general, such classes study a topic on a specialized or world wide approach rather than on a regional base.

Four or five decades ago physical geography was an essential part of the curriculum of almost every high school. With the advent of general science the offering of physical geography rapidly decreased, and much of its subject matter was absorbed, with less depth, in the newer general science course. Today, however, with the introduction of the modern course in earth science, much more physical geography is being taught. Numerous supervisors and curriculum directors are beginning to agree about the value of such study.

> Physical geography makes a significant contribution to science in that it integrates or synthesizes seemingly detached portions of the physical environment into rational, orderly, meaningful patterns.[1]

Economic geography, the study that "has to do with similarities and differences from place to place in ways people make a living,"[2] is offered

---

[1] J. L. Guernsey and A. H. Doerr, *Physical Geography* (Great Neck, N. Y.: Barron's Educational Series, 1964), p. 3.

[2] R. E. Murphy, "The Fields of Economic Geography," in *American Geography: Inventory and Prospect* (Syracuse: Syracuse University Press, 1954), p. 243.

as a one-semester elective course in numerous secondary schools. Often study in this field is the only geography as such that many high school students have an opportunity to investigate. Usually the course considers some topic such as wheat growing, coal mining, or steel manufacturing from a world point of view.

In the four chapters that follow, each contributor states the aims and objectives of his particular field of study. Methods suggested for developing an interest in any of these areas of study — physical, economic, historical, cultural — and suggestions as to ways of presenting the subject may be adjusted by the teacher to suit his needs and ideas for either of the other topics. The study of geography from a topical point of view, then, is much like the study of regional geography in that the methods, objectives, and concepts can be applied to all branches of the subject.

22

Physical geography

*Whether man exists or not, the slow moving glaciers will smooth their
rough beds; the wind, bearing grains of sand, will sculpture the rocks
of the deserts; the waves of the sea will cause cliffs to crumble; and the
whole surface of the earth, raised or submerged, will show changes
due to the physical agents that have worked upon it. Such are the basal
facts which form the essential foundation of all "physical geography."*

JEAN BRUNHES

PHYSICAL GEOGRAPHY is one of the major topical divisions of geography. As such, physical geography emphasizes those areas of geographical investigation which examine the configuration of the earth's crust — landforms; the lower portions of the atmosphere — weather and climate; and the interactions of the solid earth and the atmosphere and their biota — soils and vegetation. In addition, physical geography is concerned with the earth as a member of the solar system; particularly with direct relationships between the earth and the sun.

Because an emphasis is presently being placed on earth science, especially in secondary school curricula, it is appropriate to distinguish between earth science and physical geography. Earth science, also called the earth sciences, is a broad area of interdisciplinary study of the physical earth; physical geography is an earth science just as is geology, astronomy, meteorology, oceanography, and hydrology.

> Technically there is no distinct discipline known as earth science. Rather, there are a number of fields of science which, in the evolution of specialization, have come to focus on particular aspects on the natural earth, its processes, and environment. Despite specialization, many common threads both in subject matter and method continue to bind the several fields together. The cementing agent is, of course, the earth itself.[1]

---

[1] Earth Science Curriculum Project, *Investigating the Earth: Teacher's Guide* (Boulder: Johnson Publishing Co., 1965).

Although many of the same topics are considered in courses in physical geography and earth science the objectives are somewhat different.

> A beginning point for physical geography continues to put the study of the distributions of forms and processes in the natural environment. Divided into some specialties, the field appears to encompass a broad array of major fields such as meteorology, oceanography, hydrology, geomorphology, pedology, and ecology, to each of which geography is suffixed. . . . Today, rather than emphasizing them, physical geography both draws from and makes common sense with these disciplines in an effort to describe the behavior of air, water, soil, and biota at the surface of the earth, and to explain the covariant distribution of diverse elements of the environment on a particular part of the earth's surface.[1]

Each of these areas of investigation is important to the geographer. The geographer, while interested in explaining the evolution of landforms, climate, etc., and wishing to classify and catalog these phenomena, is mainly concerned with accounting for the effects that these elements have on determining why one place on the earth is different from another. The objective of physical geography is to assist in answering the questions: What makes a place the way it is? Why is a place different from other places? And of what significance is a place to a man?

> Physical geography places particular stress upon the system relations among air, water, soil, and biota, upon their distribution into space and upon their relationship to man.[2]

Physical geography can provide only part of the answer. The inquiries of cultural geography and the other topical divisions of geography must complete the answer. Nonetheless it is usually to physical geography that one first turns, chiefly because it "sets the stage" upon which the cultural elements of geography evolve and develop. The physical environment has been referred to as the medium through which culture acts as an agent to produce the cultural landscape.

It would appear logical for the topic divisions of geography to be interpreted in the early phase of a student's geographic education. As a student progresses to a higher level of sophistication and intellectual capacity, physical geography may be developed as a separate independent discipline.

What central themes should be emphasized in the teaching of physical geography? How can these themes be effectively presented? The following central themes are proposed as those which would be of greatest

---

[1] Ad Hoc Committee on Geography, *The Science of Geography* (Washington: National Academy of Sciences – National Research Council, Publication 1277, 1965), p. 14.

[2] *Ibid.*

significance in geographic education on an elementary and secondary school level. The first five are probably best suited for use in the elementary grades; the latter three should be reserved for secondary levels. Methods of presenting these themes will vary with the intellectual capacity of the student. Each of the themes, however, should be constantly reintroduced and reinforced at all grade levels. The themes are as follows:

1. Scale.
2. The earth is a sphere.
3. The earth moves in a heliocentric solar system.
4. Energy flows from the sun to the earth.
5. The unequal quantity and irregular distribution of water and land areas on the earth.
6. A landform is a product of time and the antagonistic gradational and tectonic processes.
7. Soils are dynamic in nature, products of time, climate, mineral matter, and modification by organisms and man.
8. Vegetation has certain climatic and edaphic limitations; consequently vegetation, if undisturbed by man will reflect the natural environment.

In the following sections these themes are restated and expanded, and methods of presentation are suggested.

THEME 1: SCALE

Before any discussion of scale can be undertaken, the student must be able to measure, and he must be aware of the units used in measurement. He must also be able to plot these measurements at least two-dimensionally and therefore comprehend direction. Thus in the elementary grades especially it is advisable to start work on the concept of scale by first introducing measurement and direction.

The student of geography cannot see his subject — the earth — in its entirety. He cannot bring it, in its reality and totality, into the classroom or laboratory. Therefore whatever ideas or concepts he has of earth, or a part of the earth, are generally depicted in his mind as a mental image or constructed from this image in the form of a physical model. Perhaps on a more advanced level this image of the earth is described by mathematics and thus becomes a mathematical model. Regardless of the kind of model used, the plan of it — a map — must be constructed in terms of its size relationship to the real earth. Thus, the ratio of distances on the earth and on the model, or map, becomes of major significance. The teacher must be precise and must insist that the student be precise when comparisons between the earth and the map, or between the earth and the sun are made.

When utilizing maps and models, all teachers should use a certain caution where scale is concerned. The younger students particularly will have a tendency to associate relative sizes when viewing areas or objects in juxtaposition. For example, planetaria which illustrate only earth-moon-sun (and sometimes the planet Mercury) utilize spheres of disproportionate size; on some models the sun has a diameter which is less than twice that of the earth. The chief purpose of the planetarium is of course to illustrate earth movements; however, one should direct the attention of students to the inaccuracy of the scale of the several spheres. Three-dimensional maps or landform models frequently exaggerate the vertical scale so that mountains appear many times higher than they are in reality. Advanced students may easily comprehend vertical exaggeration of such models; beginners will only be awed by a mountain's great height or a valley's great depth.

Scale determines the degree of detail which may be presented on a map or a model. This concept should be presented to groups actually involved in map analysis. Methods of presenting concepts of scale should perhaps start only with simple verbal expressions (example: 1 inch on the map represents x number of miles on the earth's surface); however, at a junior high school level a representative fraction should be used (example: 1 : 24,000 or 1/24,000.

THEME 2: THE EARTH IS A SPHERE

The earth's sphericity, a basic concept, must be stressed for two important reasons. One, an understanding of this concept is essential for the study of earth-sun relationships and of weather and climate. Two, the earth's sphericity effects methods of location and measurement on the globe (latitude and longitude); a proper understanding of and ability to manipulate latitude and longitude is essential to map reading. The student is earthbound and can observe only a small part of the earth at any one time, thus it is perhaps best to begin the presentation of this theme by establishing the fact that the earth is a sphere. Proofs of the earth's sphericity should be offered to the student. These proofs may consist of such simple evidence as photographs taken from space to more sophisticated astronomical proofs such as the shape of a shadow cast by the earth upon the moon's surface during a lunar eclipse. When photographs from a satellite are used, these should be viewed and compared with the same surface areas of the globe. Other proofs which may be used include circumnavigation, near consistency of surface gravity, telescopic observations, differences in time, and actual measurement. At all times the globe should be placed before the student as it is the most desirable device available to assist in the illustration and comprehension of these proofs.

Once the shape of the earth has been established, the second step is to demonstrate the method of locating points on a spherical surface. The grid system formed by parallels and meridians may be introduced after latitude and longitude have been defined and explained. It is necessary here to introduce the sphere as a form upon which all points are like all other points — there is no top or bottom, no corners or edges. Following the establishment of these characteristics of a sphere, one must point to the rotation of the earth as establishing that this sphere is different from other spheres in that two points, the poles, may be distinguished from all other points. Now it becomes easy to explain the equator and its significance; the sequence is continued by an explanation of latitude.

For students in the seventh to twelfth grades, methods of determining latitude may be used to expand the concept of the spherical earth. Introductory geometry courses might be coordinated with physical geography units to demonstrate the principles of geometry for use in measurement of the earth's circumference and latitude positions.

Considerable attention must be given to measurements made on the earth's surface; to linear measurements of a specific or a real value such as miles and kilometers, and to angular, or relative measurements. Again it is essential to have a usable globe with a measuring tape scaled in miles or other real units. Angular measurements can be accomplished with the aid of a meridian ring or semimeridian ring and a great circle or equator ring. The slated globes make it possible for the teacher and students to draw parallels and meridians.

Effective presentation of the concept of the earth's sphericity will do much to eliminate many of the misnomers such as "top of the earth," "up" and "down" on the globe, and "bottom of the map." In addition, a major foundation will be established if map projections are to be considered. This concept, basic to the understanding of the physical environment, will then lead to the third and fourth themes; and should be considered as a keystone in the sequence of presenting them.

THEME 3: EARTH MOVEMENTS

Earth movements, both rotation and revolution, should be emphasized for two reasons: one, the understanding of these movements is essential to a proper understanding of seasons, time, and length of daylight-darkness periods; two, this theme naturally precedes the investigation of weather elements such as temperature, pressure, wind belts, and movements of air masses.

A careful preparation of illustrations and demonstrations is required in the presentation of this theme. A well-planned vocabulary, suitable for the grade level at which the concept is presented, is important. Again it should be stressed that movable three-dimensional models are desirable. The planetarium, although useful, allows the student to isolate himself from the earth. He may perceive the results of heliocentric motions thus oriented, but his chief objective should be to realize what happens on the earth. Consequently it is most important for the student to make observations and measurements over an extended period, such as a semester, to fully appreciate the results of heliocentric movements. A teacher might allow students who have made extensive observations to attempt to utilize these in developing an explanation of earth movements. Once an understanding has been achieved, one must go on to relate the heliocentric motion to shifts in sun altitude, changes in the length of daylight, and seasonal temperature changes.

THEME 4: THE FLOW OF SOLAR ENERGY

The preceding concepts establish the foundation for the examination of the flow of solar energy to the earth. The reception of solar energy by the earth's atmosphere and water-land surfaces is responsible for generating many meteorological and biological processes. Examination of these phenomena requires that four questions be discussed: How is solar energy received by the earth? What variations are caused by land-water surface differences? How do angles of the sun's rays (directness or indirectness) vary with latitude, location, and seasons? What effect does this have on the amount of energy received?

Since energy is transmitted from the sun to the earth and within the earth's atmosphere, the student must be made aware of the methods of heat transmission. Animated motion pictures are one of the best ways of accomplishing this objective. Laboratory demonstrations of convectional currents in closed air spaces or liquids and radiation in vacuum chambers are possible but are elaborate and beyond the means of most teachers. Variations of temperatures between marine and terrestrial environments may be well illustrated by use of temperature graphs for stations of similar latitudes but of varying distances from an ocean. Although elevations for all stations should be near sea level in the beginning, later presentations might easily illustrate the following influences on temperature: elevation, topographic forms (valleys and barriers to wind flow, etc.), and to cloud coverage.

The changing angle between the sun's rays and the surface of the earth during a 24-hour period is obvious to all; however, some difficulty arises when the student is introduced to shifting angles with the progress of seasons. A large slated metal globe and a projector (lantern slide for

35 mm) to represent the sun may be used in a darkened room. A small stick with a suction cup on one end or a slender straight bar magnet may be used to represent the zenith line (a line extending to a point directly above a point on the globe). If the zenith line is moved along the noon meridian of the sun (the meridian which faces directly toward the sun — the projector), it becomes obvious that a shift in latitude changes the directness (nearness of parallelism of light rays to the zenith line) of the sun's rays. The second step is to demonstrate that light rays (light energy) will be spread over a larger area when the sun's rays are close to the horizon. When the sun is higher in the sky and its rays are closer to being parallel to the zenith line, its light rays are concentrated over a smaller area.

THEME 5: DISTRIBUTION OF WATER AND LAND AREAS

Young students of geography tend to associate the landscapes viewed in their limited observations with all of the earth's surfaces. Thus it must be established early that most of the earth's surface is covered by water and that the remaining land areas are not evenly distributed in terms of a latitude-longitude grid. Generally this distribution of land and water influences climatic characteristics, soils, and vegetation. Herein lies one of the basic means of distinguishing the differences between the places where man lives.

Basic drills in measuring the area of land and water surfaces on the world map (an equal area projection is essential) are desirable. It is also important to examine the distribution of land areas on a latitude grid. Methods of accomplishing this may vary. One method utilizes a grid of squares superimposed over a world map so that a count of the squares covering land and those covering water may be compared, and a ratio formed. A possible simple solution is the manufacture of a world map (again it must be emphasized on an equal area projection) on a rigid material of uniform density such as plywood (¼ inch thick). Oceans and continents may be outlined and parallels (spaced regularly, say at a 10° or 15° interval) marked off. Then with a jig-saw the map may be cut along shorelines and parallels to form a jigsaw puzzle effect. The determination of areas of land and water surfaces could then be accomplished by weighing all of the land pieces and comparing them with the weight of the water pieces. A ratio thus established could be converted to area or percent of total area. Also one could determine area or percent of land or water which falls into certain latitude zones by weighing the pieces which are located within designated latitudes by the same method. Planimeters or other area measuring devices are also useful.

THEME 6: A LANDFORM

To the casual observer, or beginning student, a landform is an immobile object of permanency. However, analysis of the rocks found in the landform and the attitude, or structure of the rock, reveals that changes of a tectonic nature (earth building) have occurred. An examination of the landform's slopes and the pattern which they take further indicates modification of a gradational nature (earth leveling). Now it becomes apparent that tectonic processes operating in a spasmodic fashion within the interior of the earth are met and opposed at the surface of the earth's crust by gradational processes continually being generated on the earth's atmosphere. These antagonistic processes constantly change the surface of the earth.

The theme of landform change from opposing dynamic forces is a significant element if one is to present the broad concept that physical geographic phenomena are synergistic. Any imbalance in one element will produce reactions which result in change. A landform is always changing, but the change is slow by man's concepts of time.

Emphasis should then be placed on the evolution of landforms. The stream table is an excellent device to illustrate this theme. Several scientific supply companies have models, both static and dynamic, which may be used to illustrate landforms, their structures, and surface configuration. In addition, a number of motion pictures and filmstrips have been developed to illustrate these points. (A note of caution — motion pictures often distort the time scale.)

Lastly, a plea is made for utilization of this theme in the direction of landscape appreciation. Unfortunately, this is a little developed concept, but obviously one of tremendous significance in the increasing tempo of conservation education.

THEME 7: THE DYNAMIC NATURE OF SOILS

Soils are a resource of major importance to man; his wise or unwise use of them is of conservation significance. Soils are reflective of the elements of time and of the climatic environment in which they are formed. Consequently, a study of soils reveals the many important interrelations of a landscape.

Soils are at best a very complicated phenomenon for which there has been no satisfactory classification for the geographer. The soil scientist from the local office of the United States Department of Agriculture is an excellent source of information. He may be able to arrange a field trip for students, or he may visit the classroom bringing soil samples to discuss.

THEME 8: VEGETATION

This theme could be advanced coincidentally with that of dynamic soil. Vegetation in its original state and in a climax form represents an adjustment in the synergetic processes of climates, landforms, and soils. Since vegetation can readily be identified, it is often taken as a key indication of other factors, such as soil drainage, soil chemical constituents, altitude, and climate. Certain types of natural vegetation are of major resource value; hence this theme has importance for study in conservation. A study of the major characteristics of vegetation and their relationship to other physical factors aids in the distinction which may be made between areas.

Local field trips will often make it possible to observe vegetation differences between well drained and poorly drained areas; thin rocky soils and deep soils; shaded and well lighted slopes; valley bottom, slope, and upland areas. Exotic vegetation types can be well illustrated by way of film, slides, or printed photographs.

In the presentation of Themes 6 through 8, it is well to remember that the field is the natural laboratory for physical geographers and that students can be made aware of many environmental factors by encouraging their observation in the field. Field trips when well organized and carefully related to classroom topics are valuable learning experiences.

23

Economic Geography

*The problem of securing enough earth resources presents Americans
with a compelling choice: they must do something to insure a continuing
supply or take the consequences.* J. RUSSELL WHITAKER

Economic geography is concerned with the ways in which man
makes a living in the world. It covers the production of various commodities, their transportation, manufacture, distribution, and ultimate consumption. In the high school situation the terms commercial geography or the
geography of production may be alternated.

Economic geography brings data from related fields together to show
the relationships among these sets of data. For example, an ore is a substance from which a metal or other minerals can be obtained profitably.
The origin of the ore is studied by geologists; the extraction involves
engineering. Distribution of the ore calls for transportation; marketing
involves economics and other fields of knowledge. However, the relationships among location, difficulty of access, purity, problems of industry,
and marketing are geography. Economic geography is concerned with
assembling the pertinent data from specialized fields and showing the
interrelationships. For an agricultural product there are close relationships to the natural environment — weather and climate, soils, and other
aspects of the producing region which made it possible for that area to
grow a particular crop. There are equally significant relationships for all
products; for example, fisheries in the Canadian Arctic may not be important commercially because of distance from the present major consuming
centers, even though the local inhabitants may depend upon fishing for
part of their food supply and fishing activities help them survive.

The above may serve as a guide for the teaching content of the subject
in the secondary school. True, at the college level the field may be subdivided into agricultural geography, the geography of the raw materials
of manufacture, industrial or manufactural geography, marketing geog-

raphy, urban geography, and other specialties such as the geography of recreation.

Economic geography may be taught from several approaches. The two most usual ones are the regional and the systematic (or topical). The regional approach encompasses the economic activities and ways man makes a living in a geographic region or area of the earth. The region may be one delimited by relatively uniform natural and cultural conditions, and location, such as the Pampa of Argentina; it may be one of relatively uniform agricultural production such as the North German Plain, or one of broadly similar activities (the ways man makes a living) such as the manufactural belt of the northeastern United States. In fact, the regional approach even may be by political units (political regions) such as a state, a province, or a nation.

The topical or systematic approach is that of the study of a particular commodity in its worldwide setting — the world location of the steel industry, the growing of wheat, of cotton, or of coffee, or the world pattern of manufacturing. The relationships and reasons for the world patterns and locations are developed and discussed.

The teacher of economic geography, whether using the regional or systematic approach, must possess a good general knowledge of the world and its major subdivisions, must have atlases and globes, as well as wall maps, available in the room — a specialized geography room if possible. He should be enthusiastic about the subject, for here the pupil's knowledge of the world may be broadened.

The emphasis that is most desirable, and that will (or should) remain with the student is the regional diversity of the world and the regional diversity of his own country. All parts of the world do not produce the same commodities, whether the product is one from agriculture, from the forests, oceans or lakes, from a manufacturing plant, a mine, or from some other activity. The people of the world do not consume products in the same amount. Cultural differences are important; the foods in demand in some places are not eaten in others. The transport to market may use different forms or kinds of transportation. The fact that, hopefully, the student is familiar with his home region does not mean that other places are similar to his in their activities.

A POSSIBLE INTRODUCTION

The teacher can awaken interest at once and provide a preview of our complex dependence upon many places near and far by having the pupils make a list of what each has had for breakfast. Upon completion of the list the teacher will indicate that while the mothers have purchased the food at a store, this is only the final place of distribution. Where did the foods come from? What happened to them before they reached the store?

Let us say that the list included orange or apple juice, cocoa or milk, a hot cereal, toast with butter or margarine on it, and soft-boiled eggs. The world is "spread" before the students. Through discussion and questions and the use of maps and globes, the teacher can take the students from the tropics to the middle latitudes, and from faraway places to near. She can lead into processing and manufacture, to distribution, and skillfully provide a net of interlocking subdivisions of the field. The tropical products are the original raw material of cocoa, the cacao beans from West Africa or coastal Brazil, or the coconut oil from the Philippines that was used in the manufacture of the margarine. Explaining further, the cacao beans were processed with cane sugar — also from the tropics — and with some milk and additional sugar to produce the cocoa the student drank for breakfast. The coconut oil may have been mixed with other vegetable oils, such as home-produced soybean oil from the South or the Middle West or corn oil from Illinois for the churning of margarine. Continuing, the teacher can point out that the oranges may have been grown in Florida, Arizona, Texas, or California; the apples in the state of Washington; the wheat on the dry edges of the humid climates of the United States; the butter manufactured in the dairy regions of Wisconsin and Minnesota; and the grains in the cereal may have originated on the Great Plains or in the American Corn Belt. The eggs may have been produced by a nearby poultryman or may have been shipped to market from distant parts of the country.

Following this introductory "home dependence" upon places near and far, the students may be led to discuss examples of even more dependence that they may have. Complex settings may be introduced by the teacher. The people of the great cities of the world or of an area such as Great Britain live in a very complex setting; some use the resources of their immediate home area to make a living, but all draw upon resources from all over the world for their support and for their businesses. The support of the city, or of Great Britain, comes from distant places (most food) or from many worldwide areas (minerals, raw materials for manufacture). The markets to which they ship their finished products are in hundreds of places — near, far, and overseas. To receive food and raw materials, and to market surplus manufactured items, there must be commerce. Transportation by ship, railroad, truck, or airplane must be continuous. The stoppage of transportation will result in shortages in the food supply, closing of factories, loss of markets, and many other difficulties.

The teacher may introduce other examples, depending upon the home situation. They will be different for a small rural area, where the stopping of transport will result in the inability to market crops, than for a great city where food supplies may last for only a few days.

THE GENERAL BODY OF MATERIAL

The economic activity of a part of the world may be simple or may be highly complex. The simple economies of some primitive tribes are usually not stressed because of time, and the fact that they make little or no impact upon the modern areas of the world. If there is time a sample of a primitive economy may be introduced. Students are interested in these ways of making a living, but study of them should be limited.

Economic geographers, secondary teachers, and textbooks differ as to the approach to the subject in the modern world. Traditionally economic geography has been organized in a pattern that has proceeded from so-called simple production to the complex; this has meant that the basic agricultural products and the varied ways of making a living in the production of agricultural foods and raw materials have introduced the subject. The course then continues through the products (or regions) of forest production, the fisheries of the world, to the introduction of mining through the discussion of one of the sources of power (coal) for manufacturing. Other sources of power, the mineral raw materials, the transport of raw materials of all sorts to the factory have led into our complex manufactural scene of the present, for the factory and the manufacturing region depends upon materials from wide sources. As a result the world's landways, seaways, navigable waterways, and airways fit into the economic scene. Thus many units culminate in the study of modern manufacture, and the transportation of raw materials to the factory and of manufactured products to the market place.

The textbooks have given about equal emphasis to the primary products from the earth (those from agriculture, forestry, fishing, and mining), to the secondary or industrial and manufactured materials, and to commerce and transportation. Less to date has been published in the texts about tertiary activities, such as the serving of others (for example, doctors, lawyers, repairmen, doormen, etc.) or the recreational industry (providing recreation for others makes a living for many persons). These tertiary ways of making a living, particularly the service occupations, have been the fastest in growth in the United States recently.

CHANGED CONDITIONS

The teacher in the United States of today is confronted in many parts of the nation with students from cities and suburbs. More than two-thirds of the pupils are said to come from these urban settings. To these students agricultural production is almost like a foreign subject. The course may begin with agricultural products or regions and include a good worldwide introduction to "simple" rather than complex commodities, showing their close relationships to the environment. With this approach, the teacher may overcome the urban student's idea that farming does not affect him except in providing food for his table. It should be stressed and restressed that most agricultural products are raw materials for manufacturing, that the processing of food is one of the major sources of factory employment, and the job of the student's father may depend upon the flow of such materials to the factory in which he works. Many farm products are not foods and are only used as raw materials in manufacturing — wool, cotton, tobacco, flax for linen, hides and skins, etc. Two-thirds or more of all food crops are first processed in factories before they are shipped to the store: wheat–flour–bread; cattle and swine–meat-packing establishments; fruit juices–fruit concentrates; sugar cane and sugar beets–sugar refineries; vegetable oils (soybeans, peanuts, coconut, corn)–vegetable oil refineries; flaxseed–linseed oil mills; milk–cheese, butter, and powdered milk; and so on. Thus the urban student who is aware at first hand only of his immediate surroundings may be indoctrinated in the fact that people in agricultural occupations make it possible for his present existence both as to foods and to factory products, such as his clothing, shoes, and other necessities as well as some luxuries he enjoys.

The teacher may then ask about foods. What fresh fruit or vegetables did your mother prepare yesterday? Today the list may be surprisingly short. Thus a further impact of agriculture upon manufacturing is brought to the attention of the pupils. The canning and freezing of prepared foods has become a major manufacturing activity; the percentage of farm products that are consumed in fresh form — from farm to market — declines annually, and, today, except for lettuce and a few other items is negligible. And, even these "fresh foods" may have been transported to warehouses in which they have been wrapped, bagged, or packaged.

The changed conditions as to the location of population in the United States, and the dependence of the majority of the people upon activities other than agriculture, mining, fishing, or forestry are resulting in some courses "working backwards" — from the urban setting of factories, commerce, service occupations to the so-called basic primary activities. Possible ways of doing this in the classroom are discussed later.

TEACHING OF MANUFACTURING

All aspects of how or what to teach cannot be covered in a brief summary. What, however, should precede the ways of making a living in manufacturing? Power, by all means, as power is basic to industry. It is basic in agriculture, forestry, fishing, and in other activities too, but it is modern manufacturing that consumes the largest quantities of power. One of the major differences between the developed parts of the world and the underdeveloped or the undeveloped is that of the consumption of power.

The study of power results in a knowledge of the regional pattern of coal fields, oil fields, gas fields, and of waterpower resources in a region, state, or nation — indeed of the world. The present development of atomic power, which can be placed near the market by man, is included. As always, transportation enters the scene. Coal may be shipped by rail, barge, or ships to the place where it is to be burned in the power plant. Oil and gas are transported by pipeline, barge, ship, or rail. Power from water, generated at the dam, is shipped to homes and factories in the form of electricity, as is power from coal or oil-fired power plants. Thus modern industry actually receives the power as electrical energy; some forms of transportation, such as elevators, are powered by electricity. Because the student takes power in the form of electricity for granted, the teacher can ask the class to find out the source of the electrical energy in his community. The answers will be surprising and lead into good discussions; the inquiry will enhance the student's appreciation of this item to which he has given little previous thought. For example, for the area served by the Tennessee Valley Authority the students invariably answer that the power source is waterpower; actually nearly 80 percent of the TVA electricity is generated from coal. Many power plants of the southwest use oil as a fuel; in the northeast coal is the chief source of electrical power.

The teacher now can introduce other ingredients of manufacturing: the raw materials. Where do they originate? What is the source of the workers? Do they live in the city or do they commute to work? What about the capital for the enterprise — is the factory home-owned, or is it part of a large national organization? Why is the factory here? What does it produce? Where are the markets for this product? How are these markets reached? Although these questions may involve home industry (assuming there is such), they may be broadened in time to clusters of factories or to distant manufacturing regions, and to the reasons for industry of a certain type clustering together. The concept of the development of specialized manufacturing regions can be introduced. Eventually the world pattern of manufacturing and its regionalization will be clear.

The advent of the dominance of the urban and suburban student in the classroom is resulting in some courses being oriented in reverse order from the traditional — from the city and its factories, business districts, and commerce to the sources of the materials that make these activities possible. This may start with the factory and its sources of raw materials. The students or the teacher can find out the sources through interviews. For example, in a city of Tennessee a factory that produces flat glass for the automobile industry in Michigan obtains its glass sand from the western part of the state (although the factory is more than one hundred miles from the sand pits), its feldspar from the mountains of western North Carolina, the soda ash from Louisiana and Ohio, the salt cake from western Texas (near the New Mexico boundary), and uses natural gas for the fuel in the manufacture of the glass. The gas has been produced from gas wells in Louisiana and Texas and reaches the factory in pipelines. The electrical energy is produced in a nearby power plant that burns coal. The final product, automobile windshields and windows, is shipped to the automobile plants of Michigan and to other assembly plants in cartons and cases made in a wallboard factory some distance away. The amount and variety of transportation involved both in the assembly of the raw materials and the marketing of the final factory product are evident.

A steel mill on the shores of one of the Great Lakes obtains its iron ore by ship from the mines in the Lake Superior region, its coal and coke by rail from western Pennsylvania, eastern Ohio, and southern Illinois, its limestone by ship from quarries on the shore of Lake Huron, its manganese from overseas. These, and many other examples, lead the student to the area of primary production. The assembling, for manufacture, of agricultural raw materials may be equally diverse. A cheese factory in Wisconsin receives local milk, but the rennet that is used may come from the Netherlands, the coloring matter is from annetto seeds grown in Jamaica or Hawaii. A freezing plant packing "TV dinners" in a city of the central United States obtains beef from the meat-packing centers and from Guatemala, potatoes from Maine and Idaho, peas from Wisconsin, Minnesota, Washington, and Oregon, carrots from California, salt from the mines of Louisiana, aluminum dishes and foil from the aluminum plants of Tennessee, and paper containers from the paper mills of northern Wisconsin.

TERTIARY ACTIVITIES

The service activities are most evident in urban centers because of the concentration of population. The relationship is to people. Thousands make a living by serving others in professional capacities as doctors, lawyers, bankers, in insurance, and other similar occupations. They "sell" their special skills. Others sell their services as yardmen, doormen, street cleaners, window washers, workers in transportation, workers in filling stations, and in other ways. The dense urban populations and their equipment call for repairmen for radios, television sets, automobile mechanics, home repair, plumbers, and many others.

The teacher can use several devices and methods to stress the importance of the service occupations. Groups or committees of the class can compile lists of the professional and service activities from the headings in the yellow pages of the telephone book. The occupation of persons in the neighborhood can be listed. After an awareness of the importance of these people is attained, the pupils can be shown that thousands of others, such as workers in agriculture, in the food industries and in clothing and shoe factories, to name but a few, help supply some of the needs of the workers in services.

CONCLUSION

Economic geography can be so broad that the teacher will have to select some items for special emphasis. The subject can be adjusted to the needs of the kind of class and the background of its members. In all cases, no matter what the approach the students should gain an appreciation of the diversity of economic activities — the ways of making a living — and the regional diversity of these ways in the world. The course should emphasize the broad and basic principles of the subject and prepare the student for future understanding. The details may change with the years, for economic geography is a dynamic and constantly changing field of knowledge; the details of production or of other aspects can be looked up from year to year, but the broad principles remain. Finally, aspects of economic geography are in the daily news; it is a live and up-to-date subject and the teacher can relate it in the classroom study to daily events in the world.

24

Historical geography

Any study of past geography or of geographical change through time is historical geography, whether the study be involved with cultural, physical, or biotic phenomena and however limited it may be in topic or area. ANDREW H. CLARK

IT IS COMMONLY THOUGHT that geography is a contemporary discipline. History, in the common view, studies time and all past events; geography, present-day places. However, nothing can be further from the truth. Every place, every area, every region has its own past — its own contemporary geography. What, for example, was the town of Newark (New Jersey) like during the Revolutionary War (1775)? — at the time the Morris Canal was completed across the state (1831)? — during the days of Seth Boyden, the inventor (1870)? Why did the Virginians, Colonels George and Robert Poage, select the Ashland (Kentucky) site (1790) for their little settlement? What became of the community? How different was it in 1815? — in 1890? And what was Moscow (Idaho) like before and immediately after the Palouse was seeded in golden grain?

NATURE OF HISTORICAL GEOGRAPHY

The questions raised in the preceding paragraph provide clues for an understanding of the nature of historical geography. Historical geography is first and foremost an integral part of geography itself. It is primarily concerned with place. Its practitioners attempt to reconstruct the past geographies of particular sites or areas; they attempt to trace the changes that occur at particular places through time.

How does the historical geographer pursue his goals? What are the basic tools of his trade? By and large his data are historical. He delves into old land records, newspapers, census reports, and business and industrial directories. He reads local histories, letters, diaries, geological and geographical descriptions, and travelers' accounts of particular places. He consults old maps, gazetteers, and almanacs, and pores over old photo-graphs, paintings, and engravings. He searches the memory of living men for their knowledge of the local site and tramps over the ground himself in an effort to see what history has left for him to see.

His methods, however, are geographical. Carefully sifting and sorting his data — let us say for Newark after the turn of the nineteenth century — he begins, sometimes by actual reference, at other times by inference, to get a "picture" of the old town.

The "Shoemaker Map" (1806), for example, might serve him well as a starting point (Figure 24.1). It clearly depicts the Passaic River, the

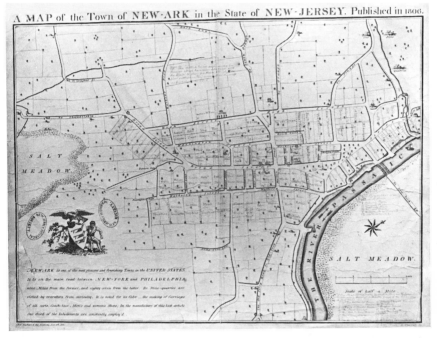

A MAP of the Town of NEW-ARK in the State of NEW-JERSEY. Published in 1806.

FIGURE 24.1   *The "Shoemaker Map" of Newark, New Jersey.* (By permission of The New Jersey Historical Society.)

so-called salt meadows, the street pattern, the position of the old home lots, the earlier locations of the Watering Place, the Burying Ground, the Training, Landing, and Market places. It shows the location of the stone quarries, the bridge over the river, and the roads to Philadelphia, New York, and the Oranges. And under the picture of the shoemaker at his lasts — in the lower left-hand corner of the map — the cartographer obliges with a description of the town:

Newark is one of the most pleasant towns in the United States. It is on the main road between New York and Philadelphia, nine Miles from the former, and eighty-seven from the latter. Its Stone quarries are visited by travellers from curiosity. It is noted for its Cider the making of carriages of all sorts Coach-lace Men's and women's Shoes. In the manufacture of this last article one third of the Inhabitants are constantly employed.[1]

An admirable beginning, but the study of the map must be conscientiously followed up. Every piece of historical and geographical datum must be examined and critically analyzed. Every piece of usable information must be fitted into the puzzle. The goal is to make as complete a picture as possible of the town of Newark at the turn of the nineteenth century.

But it is still only a beginning. The historical geographer must make yet another study (utilizing the same methods). He must get another glimpse or picture of the very same town twenty-five, thirty, or even fifty years later. And he must pursue his second study with the zeal of the first. His second picture must be equally complete, for the comparison of an area, a region, a community at two or more distinct dates forms an important basis for analysis in historical geography. In fact, such comparison may be historical geography's chief reason for being.

Comparisons through time serve well in documenting both geographical change and geographical persistence. How and why, for example, did Newark change? What happened, if anything, to the cider industry, and to the manufacture of carriages and shoes? What happened to the street pattern? Had yet another bridge been slung across the Passaic River? Was the town larger or smaller? And what features of the town did not change at all? What patterns, both physical and cultural, persisted, lasted with the town through the years? What old features persist to the present day?

IMPLICATIONS FOR THE SCHOOL PROGRAM

How can the methods of historical geography be adapted to teaching in the American school? How early in the school program can historical geography be introduced? How can important place, space, and time concepts, implicit in the teaching of historical geography, be placed in proper sequence in the schools? What do school-age youngsters know and understand of place, space, and time?

Primary grades · While youngsters in the first three grades find it impossible to handle true chronology, they certainly must not be frustrated in their efforts to dip into the past; they should be encouraged to do so.

---

[1] F. J. Urquhart, *A History of the City of Newark, New Jersey* (New York: Lewis Historical Publishing Co., 1913), p. 520.

A child will not learn the most intricate subtleties of most concepts, but he may be able to learn something about them. That his understanding may be incomplete is no cause for complaint and no justification for deferment. There is reason, however, for serious attention to be given to the level of meaning he has attained and for careful selection of experiences which will stimulate his continued growth.[1]

The local area may well serve as a geographical laboratory. With the aid of stimulating teachers students can learn much with the approach through historical geography about the changing landscape. A point of departure for such studies might well be the American Indians and their use of the local area. Differences in land utilization can be indicated by the coming of European settlers — by changing settlement patterns, means of subsistence, and forms of transportation. These can be shown graphically through the skillful use of models, pictures, and dioramas.

Still pictures (the flat opaque kind), including photographs, sketches, and paintings, are particularly effective for the tender years. They are easy to get and cheap to buy or reproduce. They can be handled easily by students at their seats or desks. They can be shown for particular dates — 1780, 1825, 1850, or for 1875, 1900, and 1925 — to depict the changing landscape. Special care, of course, must be taken with choice of site. If possible (it often is not) the site viewed should be identical or nearly identical for all selected dates. Still pictures of house types, roads, farms, fences, public buildings, skylines, and transportation forms are particularly useful.

How different a still picture of the downtown area of Newark appears in 1825 (Figure 24.2) when contrasted with the same area during the Civil War (Figure 24.3). How different the essentially rural Poage Settlement of 1815 from the site surrounded by iron furnaces in 1851. How different the old Tat-kin-mah, the "spotted deer's place" of the Nez Perce Indians, from the Moscow of 1889.

For best results in the transfer of learning, still picture showing must be followed up by other activities. In historical geography the early grade school teacher has many excellent opportunities. He can bring his parent-supervised students to the actual sites, walk over the actual ground seen in the pictures, point out or ask about what is old and what is new. He can arrange visits to the local museum, library, or historical society to view their occasional exhibits. In the classroom he can read — even at this elementary level — from the numerous contemporary or near contemporary accounts: Gordon's description of Newark in 1834; the account of Ashland in the *Ironton Journal* of September 7, 1854; the eye-witness

---

[1] O. L. Davis, Jr., "Children Can Learn Complex Concepts," *Educational Leadership*, *17* (1959), p. 174.

FIGURE 24.2   *Broad Street, south from Market about 1825.* (*From Frank J. Urquart,* A Short History of Newark, *Baker Printing Company, Newark, N.J., 1916.*)

FIGURE 24.3   *Northwest corner of Market and Broad Streets during Civil War times.* (*From Frank J. Urquart,* A Short History of Newark, *Baker Printing Company, Newark, N.J., 1916.*)

reports of Lieutenant I. I. Stevens (1855) or Father Cataldo, S.J. (1866) on the Tat-kin-mah site.

The teacher in Moscow might well begin with the Stevens account. On

June 21, 1855, he might explain that the lieutenant and his party made camp near the Nez Perce trail.

> . . . we reached the extensive kamas grounds of the Nez Perce. Here were six-hundred Nez Perce — men, women, and children — gathering the kamas with at least two thousand horses. So abundant is this valuable and nutritious root, that it requires simply four days labor for them to gather sufficient for their year's use. In 2¼ miles further we struck the great Nez Perce trail, coming from Lasswai, a much larger and more used trail than the one we had followed from Red Wolf's ground. . . .[1]

Continuing, the teacher might point out that eleven years after Stevens' visit (1866), Father Cataldo, on a trip from the Coeur d'Alene mission to Lewiston, reported on the Tat-kin-mah site: ". . . it was truly an immense Camas-prairie, where many hundreds of tepees, or Indian lodges were up, with several thousands of Indians of different tribes digging camas. . . ."[2]

The Nez Perce, Palouse, Umatilla, Yakima, Coeur d'Alene, Spokane, and others were all at Tat-kin-mah. The site was obviously a favorite camas gathering ground; it was also a far-famed site for recreation. The Nez Perce, for example, often climbed the Lewiston hill to Tat-kin-mah in summer to escape the heat in the Clearwater and Snake river valleys. There they romped and raced their horses.

But changes were in the offing. Settlers came to the shadows of the mountains. The Nez Perce defeat in 1877 brought many more settlers. By 1889 the Tat-kin-mah site, at various times known as Paradise Valley, or Hog's Heaven, and finally Moscow, was an entirely different place. Its main street already showed numerous signs of "civilization."

> Main Street, running north and south, was a long wagon road, which following the dictates of the seasons, was either a sea of mud or ankle deep in dust. Other streets, hardly more than lanes, veered off from Main Street at places and angles suiting the convenience of the villagers. The business establishments of the town, housed in one or two story frame structures, lined Main Street on either side. The bank presented the only suggestion of permanence. . . . It was of brick.[3]

Imagine the possibilities, at the lower elementary level, for the teacher of historical geography in Moscow. What is camas? Does it still grow in the Palouse or on Moscow Mountain? Where was the old Nez Perce trail? Did it go as far north as Spokane? Where did the Nez Perce get their horses? Why did they have so many of them? When was the winding

---

[1] *United States Executive Document 46*, Thirty-fifth Congress, Second Session, *18* (1858–1859), pp. 175–176.

[2] *Lewiston Morning Tribune*, April 22, 1928.

[3] P. Martin, "History of the University of Idaho" (unpublished, n.d.), p. 13. (Copy in the library, University of Idaho.)

road built up the mountain from Lewiston? Was Main Street really like that? For the teacher in Moscow, the possibilities are numerous.

Upper elementary and junior high school years • Pupils in the upper elementary grades (especially grades five and six) are already fairly well oriented in concepts of space and area. They have a fair grasp of distance and elevation. They are aware of local community time, life-cycle time, and personal time. Their grasp of chronology has developed somewhat, but is still far from mature.

Junior high school students, near masters of space and area concepts, vary considerably in understanding time and chronology.

> They can tell time, use the calendar, recall some specific date-events, use definite and indefinite time expressions, understand simple time lines, relate dates to their own experiences, arrange in sequence happenings that possess a common element, and interpret numerical chronology to some extent. They also have a background of information about how groups of people live today and how different communities and people have lived in the past. Twelve-year olds usually are interested in people who are not related directly to them, nor to their activities, nor even to the present. At the same time, it is true that the information possessed by seventh-graders is uneven and not logically arranged and that pupils have forgotten much that they have been taught. Time concepts, to become more significant, must be taught, and taught again.[1]

It must also be remembered that the intermediate graders are living through a period of accelerated growth. They have an increasing desire for self-direction. The junior high student is apt to seem boisterous, antagonistic, but he, too, aspires to greater independence and wants to participate in decision making.

The challenge posed by the inability of upper elementary and junior high school students to come to grips with true chronology and the problems fomented by individual growth are formidable indeed. Both can be met successfuly, however, through the teaching of historical geography.

Two dates, 1854 and 1877, not remotely separated in time, can be used in a problem-solving orientation; the data for one of the dates are known. Teachers in Ashland, Kentucky, for example, might well begin with the following quotation from the *Ironton Journal,* September 7, 1854:

> . . . We found everything going ahead, as fast as the most sanguine could desire. Some 30 or 35 good houses had already been erected, and were being erected, besides foundations laid for others; and this exclusive of the cabins and shanties, of which there was a large number.

---

[1] A.W. Spieseke, "Developing a Sense of Time and Chronology," in Helen McCracken Carpenter (ed.), *Skill Development in Social Studies* (Washington: Thirty-third Yearbook of the National Council of Social Studies, 1963), p. 187.

Before the close of the present season some 60 or 70 good houses will have been erected in Ashland, and probably 1,500,000 of bricks will have been laid up. Population is flocking in rapidly, much of it transient, however, laborers upon the railroad and other works, and within a mile or so of the landing it cannot at present be less than 600. It is now confidently believed that 15 miles of the railroad out from Ashland will be completed in a year from this fall. This will bring the iron of eight more furnaces. Everything about Ashland betokens an active present and a great future.[1]

Other sources, of course, can be used to produce a more complete picture of the 1854 site. But what of the unknown quantity? What of Ashland in 1877, 1890, or at the turn of the 20th century? What was it like? What had happened to its population, its streets, its dwellings and shanties? What had happened to the railroad? Where was it headed and why? What were the "other works" described in the quotation? How much of the community of 1854 was still in place in 1877 or 1890? What on the site was totally new?

With the teacher acting as guide and information source the students attempt to answer the questions. They dip into the past. They use every available resource to get a picture of the Ashland of 1877, 1890, or 1900. They are encouraged to use primary sources, real historical documents, perhaps, for the first time. An example is the map in Figure 24.4. By thus looking into the sources, the students learn to "taste" their history. They learn to apply the knowledge they have gained to the place.

What other possibilities are available for enhancement of learning in historical geography? What techniques can be best used?

Maps, still pictures, motion pictures, models, dioramas, time lines, and time charts are particularly useful in upper elementary and junior high school classes.

> . . . the complexity of the pictorial media which the students are called upon to interpret will increase with the grade levels. Conceivably, it may be necessary at each step of increasing abstractness for the teacher to supply questions to guide students in the interpretation of motion pictures, various kinds of still pictures, dioramas, and models.[2]

Why was the Ashland Coal and Iron Works located so close to the river? What buildings can you suggest for the Norton Iron Works? What do you suppose took place at the Park and Fair Grounds? Where does Bath Avenue end today?

---

[1] Reproduced from *A History of Ashland, Kentucky, 1786–1954* (Ashland: Ashland Centennial Committee, 1954), pp. 59–60. (Unpublished M.A. Thesis, 1954.)

[2] G. H. McCune and N. Pearson, "Interpreting Material Presented in Graphic Form," in Helen McCracken Carpenter (ed.), *Skill Development in Social Studies* (Washington: Thirty-third Yearbook of the National Council of Social Studies, 1963), p. 225.

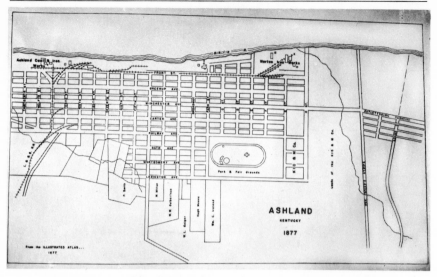

Figure 24.4   *Ashland Kentucky, 1877.* [*From* Illustrated Atlas of the Upper Ohio River and Valley from Pittsburgh Pennsylvania to Cincinnati Ohio (*Philadelphia: Titus, Simmons, and Titus, 1877.*)]

Time lines and time charts, often used by teachers of history, help students comprehend the chronological framework and overcome a vague time sense. When, for example, did the Poages first visit the country of the Big Sandy? When was the first horse-drawn streetcar pulled to Catlettsburg? When did William Deering discover iron on his Greenup County farm? When was the Ashland Iron Furnace completed and the Ashland Steel Company founded? When was Ashland named?

Historical geography in the high school program · Innovations planned in social studies curricula at the high school level provide opportunities for the possible inclusion of historical geography as a single semester elective course. The time is especially ripe for historical geography. For the first time, approximatetly at the sophomore year, students are able to deal with problems relating to place, space, and time with adult maturity. At this vital juncture (grades ten, eleven, or twelve) a course in the "Historical Geography of the United States,"[1] "The Historical Geography of Anglo-America," or on a selected region in North America might be offered to selected students.

Regional studies could be made on numerous themes: population and land utilization in the urban northeast, the rise and demise of cotton culture

---

[1] R. H. Brown, *Historical Geography of the United States* (New York: Harcourt, Brace and World, 1948).

in the changing south, cultural succession in the Great Plains, water use in the southwest and the like. The local area would again be used for research purposes. Students could work in the field and in the archives. The problem-solving orientation could now be used upon three or even four dates. Individual students might wish to delve into problems relating in space and time, to land occupance, settlement patterns, house types, water supply or even of man as an anthrogeomorphic agent. The research possibilities are limitless. They can be planned in accordance with students' interests and abilities.[1]

Aids employed for transfer of learning at the lower levels could also be used at the high school level. Only the degrees of complexity and abstractness would be different. The challenge is an extraordinary one; the rewards are most worthwhile.

CONCLUSION

Historical geography is an integral part of geography itself. It is concerned primarily with the reconstruction of the past geographies of particular sites or areas. The historical geographer is interested in problems relating to space, place, and time. He combines, therefore, historical data and geographical methodology in pursuing his goals. The methods of the historical geographer have value in school programs from the early years through the high school.

Its study can center students' attention on place during the tender years and furnish them with their first real notions of time. In later years its study can sharpen these notions, permit students to do research both indoors and outdoors and give them a better understanding of their local community or area. In high school the concepts and content of historical geography can be used to broaden the students' basic knowledge of the entire continent. Its study can serve to sharpen students' powers of observation and their ability to criticize, interpret, and analyze historical data in terms of place.[2]

The opportunities have been shown to be similar in Newark, Ashland, and Moscow. There are equal opportunities for school and teachers in Florida, Nebraska, and Arizona — for every city, town, and hamlet in America. Persistence and change, after all, are basic ingredients in the historical geography of every place. Schools and teachers need only take advantage of the opportunities.

---

[1] D. Jacobson, "The Role of Historical Geography in the American School," *The Journal of Geography, 64* (1965), p. 104.

[2] *Ibid.*, p. 105.

25

Cultural geography

No geography can properly be regarded as "Social" unless it draws its material from active study of men and women in their work and homes.

T. W. FREEMAN

CULTURE IS THE sum total of integrated learned behavior patterns which are characteristic of the members of a society and which are therefore not the result of biological inheritance; hence it is not genetically predetermined. Culture is wholly the result of social invention. It is transmitted and maintained solely through communication and learning. Culture is noninstinctive.

Cultural geography, unlike psychology and history, is a science that has nothing to do with individuals but only with human institutions or cultures. It may be defined as localization of ways of living. The subject may be approached by two methods: the study of the areal extension of individual culture traits, and the determination of culture complexes as areas.

Environmental response is the behavior of a given group under a given environment. Such behavior does not depend upon physical stimuli, nor on logical necessity, but on acquired habits, which are its culture. The group at any moment exercises options as to conduct which proceed from attitudes and skills which it has learned. An environmental response, therefore, is nothing more than a specific cultural option with regard to the habitat at a particular time. Habit or culture involves attitudes and preferences which have been invented or acquired.

We know that habitat must be referred to habit, that habit is the activated learning common to a group, and that it may be endlessly subject to change. The whole task of cultural geography, therefore, is nothing less than comparative study of areally localized cultures. Culture is the learned and conventionalized activity of a group that occupies an area. A culture trait or complex originates at a certain time in a particular locality. It gains acceptance, that is, is learned by a group, and is communicated outward, or diffuses until it encounters sufficient resistance, as from unsuitable physical conditions, from alternative traits, or from disparity of cultural level. These are processes involving time and not simply chronologic time, but especially those moments of culture history when the group possesses the energy of invention or the receptivity to acquire new ways.

Cultural geography is concerned not merely with the directly visible features, but also with the changes and processes of development that have produced the features. It follows, then, that cultural geography must employ an historical method. Since the shaping forces are constantly at work, the cultural landscape is not static but is continuously changing through time: the present is the fruit of the past and contains the seeds of the future.

No special value or emphasis is placed on either past or present methods, just as the geologist does not consider the Mesozoic more important than the Tertiary, or vice versa. Cultural geography is concerned with all of human time. Thus, it is necessary to examine all the evidence available to cultural geography. The explanation of many things in the landscape can be found only by digging among the roots of culture below the surface of the present level. The requirement of explanation alone is good enough reason for giving some attention to the past.

WHY TEACH CULTURE

Man's first experiences and relationships were social. They have been predominantly so since the beginning of time. From the simple culture of the primitive tribe to our modern complex world civilization, man's relationships to his fellow men have been the underlying theme of science, culture, religion, the family and other institutions, and the organization of society. It is the opinion of most educators that the social, economic, and political chaos that is rampant throughout the world today can be resolved into harmonious world fellowship only through international cooperation in teaching more effectively than ever before man's social and ethical responsibilities. The ultimate outcome must be cooperative with group planning and action, on a local, state, national, and world basis. This can be accomplished only through the development of wholesome character and social literacy (Figure 25.1).

Early civilizations were born in relative isolation. Most of the record of mankind is the story of provincialism in one form or another. Provincialism is the tendency of human society in one place to differ from that in other places, usually for reasons growing out of isolation. Civilization itself was largely a by-product of isolation. Egypt, Mesopotamia, Phoenicia, the Greek city-states, Crete, and other early civilizations were nurselings of isolation from the universal brutality and insecurity of a chaotic world of

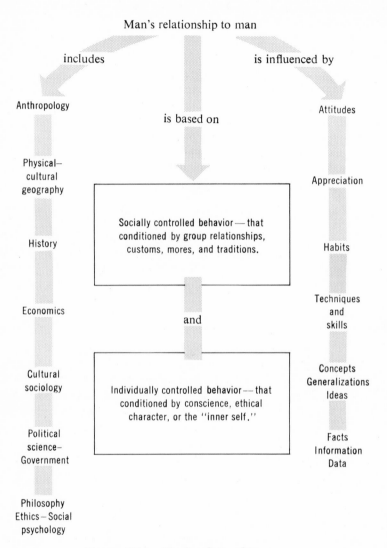

FIGURE 25.1   *Man's relationship to man.*

man and nature. Eventually civilization became strong enough to defend itself, to spread beyond its provincial limits of isolation, and to attempt the conquest and absorption of the barbaric outer world.

Recent civilizations have been based more upon accessibility, have ceased to be provincial and began to be world phenomena. The Macedonian Empire, the Roman Empire, the Chinese Empire, the Moslem domain, the realm of Genghis Khan, and still more recently the British Empire and Commonwealth, the American Federal Union, the German Greater Reich, and the Japanese Co-prosperity Sphere all represent world systems of culture actual or projected. This is a curious historical reversal of geographic relations: Early civilizations were cradled in isolated spots, whilst savagery dominated the openly accessible areas; modern civilizations are centered in the large areas of maximum accessibility, whereas isolated and remote areas today are veritable museums of backward or obsolescent cultures.

In the past no culture has ever become really worldwide. It was not even able to attempt to become worldwide. Geographic limitations doomed it to remain regional or provincial. No one could build a world road or highway. No one could build a world railway. At best a road or railway could be only transcontinental. No seaway is a world lane. Even the modern steamship cannot penetrate the "heartland of Eurasia."

The air and missile age, however, projects mankind into a three-dimensional era of world transportation, communication, and military assault. Even the solar system eventually may be within man's grasp, thus freeing him from his traditional earth-bound culture.

Under the impact of man's new technology in science, communication, and transportation, the world has been so reduced in size, when time is used as the standard of measure, that formerly remote lands and people are now our neighbors. Lack of knowledge and understanding of the various peoples of the world are the bases of fear and distrust which in turn lead to tensions and wars. Lack of knowledge concerning the peoples of the world is a serious matter in a democracy attempting to provide world leadership.

Peoples of the world knowing enough about each other may well be one of the long sought answers to the problem of war. The difficulty is to know enough. Obviously all cannot actually visit and become acquainted, desirable as that may be. The next best approach is to unlock storehouses of information represented by the various social science disciplines. Isolated bits of information as presented by the various studies now making up the curriculum may or may not be effective, depending upon each student's ability to transfer and relate that information to problem situations. One of the purposes of a course in cultural geography is to eliminate as much of the chance as possible. By focusing all of the various disciplines making up the social sciences on a people at one time, in an organized manner, the chances are far better that the student will know more about those people as they now are and about the forces causing them to be that way.

CULTURAL REGIONS

The human world can be divided into regions in several ways, for example, according to language, religion, or nationality. Another kind of differentiation can be made in terms of the predominant type of economic activity. Regions may be designated as farming areas, industrial belts, lumbering districts, hunting or fishing regions, and lands of livestock production. It is this type of differentiation that is most relevant to geography. Ultimately all men depend for their living on the utilization of natural resources, and it is by means of this utilization that humanity most directly affects the natural landscape and partly makes it over into a cultural landscape: man hunts the game, and game populations change; he gathers plants for food, and the vegetation is affected; he cuts down forests, plows up grasslands, tunnels into mountains, superimposes his structures on the surface of the land, and the face of the earth is transformed.

Firm lines cannot be drawn or exact boundaries given for any one culture area, but the following classification suggests at least one way of attempting to study the world through the medium of culture areas:

1. Latin (France, Belgium, Italy, Spain, Portugal, and large parts of Latin America).
2. Anglo-Saxon (Great Britain, the United States, Canada, Australia, New Zealand, and South Africa).
3. Germanic (Germany, Austria, the Netherlands, and Scandinavia).
4. Slavic (The U.S.S.R., Czechoslovakia, Poland, Bulgaria, Hungary, Yugoslavia, and other parts of Eastern Europe).
5. Oriental (China, Korea, Japan, and to some extent parts of Southeast Asia).
6. Indic (India, Ceylon, Burma, and to some extent parts of Southeast Asia).
7. Semitic (The Middle East, North Africa, a part of the U.S.S.R., Indonesia, and other countries where the Moslem faith is predominant)
8. African (Africa south of the Sahara).

A study of world cultures is intended, not only to develop a sensitivity to and an understanding of the peoples of the world, but to develop definite skills in social science. For this reason such a course requires the use of a wide variety of materials rather than a single text.

As a guide to the teacher in planning the development of a unit, the following problem areas relating to culture are suggested. No indication of sequence is attempted; each merely suggests an area of study of a people. These and other problems, or some entirely different approach, may be used in the study of each unit:

1. How group affairs are managed.
2. Mores, customs, manners.
3. How the culture is preserved and transmitted.
4. The position of men and women in the culture.
5. The needs satisfied by the environment; how it has been used and modified.
6. Development of natural resources and steps toward their wise use.
7. Controlling factors in economic life, such as industrialization, agriculture, distribution of goods and services, etc.
8. Controlling factors in social life, such as the size of the group, characteristics in terms of urban or rural.
9. Controlling political ideologies and their evolution.
10. Civilizations that preceded the present one, evidences and influences; age of present civilization.
11. Relations with other people and other countries.
12. The ways in which ideas are communicated, such as language, art forms, and dance.
13. Use of leisure time, such as literature, play, drama, athletics, entertainment.
14. Values established and emerging in the culture.

TYPICAL KNOWLEDGE AND UNDERSTANDING

1. All people belong to a culture or cultures and they tend to defend and perpetuate them.
2. Each culture has grown up within an environment and that environment has influenced the choices that have been made.
3. All culture is learned.
4. Culture is a matter of choices that people have made at a given time within a given environment.
5. Culture is constantly undergoing change.
6. It is possible to modify an environment but not change it completely.
7. Cultures of others may be sources of conflict or enrichment.
8. Where several cultures, steeped in tradition, come into competition conflicts are likely to follow.

9. The problems people of various cultures face are similar but the solutions may be different.

10. No modern culture is without contributions from other modern cultures as well as from their own heritage.

Typical Attitudes and Appreciation

1. Change is universal.
2. Difference is not unusual, peculiar, odd, or queer.
3. All parts of the world have become interdependent.
4. Agreement upon basic values makes group living possible.
5. Values are the highest goals of culture.
6. Personal responsibility, intellectual curiosity, and honesty in searching for the truth are possibilities within any culture.

Typical Skills and Abilities

1. Locating and using a wide variety of materials.
2. Problem solving.
3. Interpersonal and intergroup relationships.
4. Communication skills (Figure 25.2).

SOME SAMPLE CULTURE UNITS

Introduction: What Is Culture?

Overview: In order that students may develop a tolerance for other people and ways of doing things, they must understand that culture is learned. Each person is a part of a culture. Variations within a culture or among cultures are results of choices that have been made. The problems faced by various cultural groups may be the same or similar, but the solutions are the result of choices made at a given time within a given environment. Each person is a member of several groups and values vary from group to group, even within a culture. Successful group living depends largely upon agreement as to the common goals, or values. Wars result when cultural differences cannot be settled peacefully. This knowledge is necessary when people move about as much as they do in the United States, and individuals have as much say in national decisions as they do in America.

Students might begin this unit by listing customs and traditions of their school and comparing the list with known customs and traditions of other schools. There will be many differences. Then they might list superstitions that still carry some weight and find out how they began.

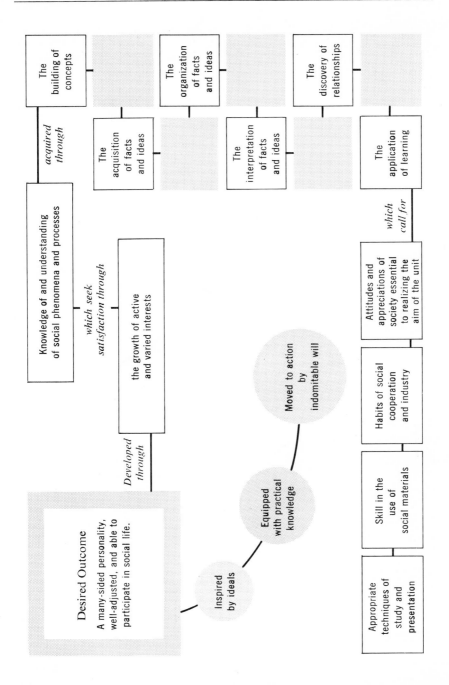

FIGURE 25.2 *Communication skills.*

PROBLEMS AND TOPICS	ACTIVITIES
1. Do we practice any ancient rituals?	Make a list of all the superstitions you can think of. Try and find out.
2. Are group controls necessary?	Discuss the necessity of rules and referees for games. Look up and report the history of democratic government.
	List the various groups to which you belong and then list the controls surrounding each group.
	Discuss what each of the above groups would be like if the controls were removed.
3. Did native civilizations disappear in America?	How they began.
	Locate all the places having Indian names in your state or region.
	Discuss in class the part the Indian has played in American life.

SOME ADDITIONAL PROBLEMS

1. Am I part of a culture?
2. How do cultures grow?
3. Upon what things do I place value?
4. What common values must a home, school, and community have to have successful group living?
5. How may culture be changed?
6. How do values in the various groups to which I belong vary?
7. In what ways am I part of a larger culture beyond my community?
8. What things in American life are a part of our culture?
9. Are any of the elements of our culture also found in the cultures of people of other countries?
10. What do people of all cultures have in common?
11. Why are peoples of the world different in some ways?

THE UNITED NATIONS: A CULMINATING UNIT

OVERVIEW: This unit is intended to be a review of the units previously studied and an overview of the work of the entire series of units. In it an attempt will be made to bring together the trends of thought, the modes of living, the historical and cultural development of the many peoples of the world with the idea of promoting better understanding among them. If this can be done, the main objective of a course in cultural geography will have been attained.

We have learned that different people live differently. Many things considered proper in one culture are found to be unheard of in others. Some cultural groups have described themselves as being "civilized," and yet we know that each culture considers itself to be satisfactory in furnishing a pattern of living for its people.

Some cultural groups look down upon others that do not have the same standards that they accept; they call such different peoples backward, primitive, or even uncivilized. Of course, whether or not one belongs to a "civilized" culture, depends upon his point of view. We may consider ourselves superior in ways of living, yet there are those who believe that we are queer because we have only one wife instead of many; because we give women a place of respect instead of making them slaves; because we wear clothes; because we cook our food; because we do not tolerate people of other races; because . . . and the list may be continued indefinitely.

Not only do we consider those who live differently peculiar, but we also feel definitely superior to them. Throughout the history of Western Civilization we find references to the "White Man's Burden" referring to the "duty" we have as a race to carry our culture to all other peoples of the world — whether they want it or not, simply because we consider it superior and therefore good for them.

After thousands of centuries of misunderstanding each other, the nations of the world are attempting to get together in an organization known as the United Nations for the purposes of making international relations easier and thereby insuring better living for all people regardless of their nationality, religion, race, or other conditions heretofore held as basically important differences in mankind.

Peaceful conditions cannot develop unless we begin to respect the other fellow for what he is, instead of what we think he ought to be. Surely, no group can meet in the assembly halls of the United Nations and conduct any worthwhile business if each considers himself superior to the other delegates and tries to impose his way of living, his standards of value, his religion, his politics, and his customs on everyone else. The main objectives of the United Nations must be to develop human understandings and tolerances so that the nations can live peacefully in a world which realizes the worth and dignity of human life. Let us try to determine the chance the United Nations has of developing a world of harmony and cooperation; let us observe the main points of friction so far encountered and see what progress is being made to solve them.

PROBLEMS AND TOPICS	ACTIVITIES
1. What national, racial, and/or cultural groups are found in the United Nations?	Secure a large map of the world and color the nations which are members of the United Nations.
	Show members of the class the national flags of these countries.
	Play phonograph records of music from as many of them as possible.
	Secure pictures of the peoples of these nations in their native costumes.
2. What are some of the international problems that have caused the nations to join together in an attempt to live peacefully with one another?	Prepare a talk for your classmates on outstanding differences in ways of living, in entertainment, in dress, and in methods of earning a living.
3. What were some of the important attempts to secure international peace before the United Nations was formed?	Prepare a discussion of the League of Nations. Bring out the reasons for its organization; the nations belonging; the reasons why it failed.
	Discover the major problems that have been considered by the United Nations since its formation. What has been the disposition of each of these?
	What do you consider to be the greatest weakness of the United Nations in its attempt to maintain world stability?
4. What can you and I do to promote world peace and understanding?	Do you think you could be happy living in another culture than ours? Prepare a discussion on why you could or could not be.
	What are some of the chief causes of intercultural misunderstanding?
	Make a list of the fine things you have discovered in your study of world cultures about at least five other cultures.
	Make a list of things you would not like about at least five other cultures and tell why you dislike them. Do you think you could overcome these dislikes? Explain how this might be done.

SOME ADDITIONAL PROBLEMS

1. What is the primary purpose of the United Nations?

2. What are the essential powers of the organization? Indicate its organization.

3. What are the essential functions of the United Nations?

4. Why were the major powers given a privileged position in the United Nations?

5. How effectively has the General Assembly been able to operate in the political field?

6. How effectively are the organization's economic and social functions being carried out?

7. How well has the Security Council functioned?

8. Why do we seem to need more than regional and collective defense arrangements for world peace?

9. What are some of the other plans being promoted, and that have been advocated in the past twenty years to attain the same objectives of the United Nations?

PART VI

Geography: its contribution to education

GEOGRAPHY AS A WHOLE is neither a science nor a social science; it is both. Curriculum directors and supervisors have long been bothered by the fact that geography cannot be put in one of the well-marked categories of subject matter. Because they look mostly at the physical factors — climate, soils, earth–sun relations, landforms — some school systems teach geography as a science; others may teach geography as a social science because the instructors think largely in terms of cultural factors — economic, political and historical. In spite of its location in the curriculum, geography is still a subject that deals with distributions, interrelationships, and change taking place between man and the earth on which he lives.

Geography can contribute much to the education of any youth, teenager, or adult as it brings together the various components of living. Man is a product of his total environment not some small part thereof. What each individual does may influence either directly or indirectly what every other individual on the face of the earth will do. Thus, every individual, regardless of age, size, color, or creed, is a part of the environment in which all mankind lives. Geography, therefore, with its where, what, and why attitude, can aid each person to understand his homeland, the homelands of his neighbors, and the constant changes taking place.

In many respects geography is the base on which numerous school programs stand; it is the foundation on which historical time, economic production, and social relationships have existed and will continue to exist. As such it is a part of much of the subject matter taught, but by the same token it takes much of its material from a variety of other subjects. Geography, then, gives the synthesis and analysis that are needed to bring a variety of ideas together and give them meaning.

26

Geography and its relation to the sciences

All branches of knowledge which have anything to tell us about the earth more or less hinge into or are connected with geography, or you may if you like, say they diverge from it as specialized departments of that general knowledge which it presents in its connection with the whole. JAMES BRYCE

THE CONTRIBUTIONS OF GEOGRAPHY to education derive from the structure of the discipline, its unique relation to other fields of study, and its method of approach to problems. The emphasis in this chapter will be upon the place of geography among the natural sciences (earth, physical, and biological) as distinguished from the social sciences. This limitation is not intended to depreciate the role of geography in the social sciences. Rather, it serves to call attention to an often misused and sometimes completely neglected power of the field of geography in education.

GEOGRAPHY AS A SCIENCE

In relation to the objective in Part IV — to examine the contribution of geography to education — the structure of the field as a science will be reviewed before examining its relations to other sciences. Through its concern with the natural and cultural aspects of the world habitat, geography is both a natural and a social science. "Geographers in general consider their field to be first and foremost a social science, but many value highly its bonds with the physical and biological sciences. Others emphasize its common spirit with the humanities."[1] In the public schools, teachers readily admit to the teaching of geography either as a separate subject or as a recognized component of the social studies. Less commonly it is

---

[1] J. O. M. Broek, *Geography, Its Scope and Spirit* (Columbus, Ohio: Charles E. Merrill, 1965), p. 3.

considered to be one of the contributing fields in general science. However, the study of the subject, particularly its physical side, has many
contributions to make to science education.

As a science geography is best defined by its approach to the body of
knowledge rather than by a particular category of knowledge. Its approach
is integrative and spatial. Its concern is with relationships among cultural
and physical factors and distributions of those factors, singly and in combination, through space and time. It selects and interprets the significance
of facts in terms of their relation to other facts. It affords opportunities for
analysis of observed facts and the formulation of generalizations. Equally,
it provides for the construction of hypotheses and their testing in many
and varied situations. If applicability of the methods of science is the
criterion, geography qualifies as a science.

Geography thus conceived is very different from when it was considered
as a vehicle for recording observations by explorers and was taught as a
catalog of facts about places. It has become "a way of looking at the
earth, not an inventory of its contents."[1] But the viewpoint of science itself
has changed. Science is no longer thought of as

> . . . a highly organized body of collected knowledge as viewed by spe-
> cialists, but . . . as a study, as a way of coming to understand why things
> happen as they do, what man can do with natural resources, what we can
> use to live by, how we can be more intelligent about living so that we are
> not deluded as often or as easily, so that we can predict . . . in terms of
> causes and effect, and plan and act accordingly.[2]

Geographers can subscribe to this point of view.

Geography employs techniques of scientific investigation in its attempt
to advance knowledge of human cultures and the natural environment.
These techniques are shared with other sciences, but geography directs
them toward the goal of understanding relationships among the cultural
and natural elements and ultimately between man and his environment.
Basic among the techniques of science is observation. Observations of
natural and cultural phenomena are the foundation of geographic knowledge. Organized description, often aided by cartographic, photographic,
and statistical techniques, serves to record observed data. Classification
affords an orderly arrangement of observed facts as well as a language for
communication. Thus, we observe, describe, and classify. Indispensable
as these operations are, they do not of themselves constitute the whole of
a science of geography any more than plant identification and classification
make up a science of botany or the periodical table is the science of

---

[1] Broek, *op. cit.*, p. 72.

[2] L. Zirbes, "Thoughts on the Education of Science Teachers for Today's Schools,"
Science Education, vol. 42 (1958), p. 283.

chemistry. A science goes beyond mere classification to seek laws, to examine relationships, to develop and verify explanations, and to reveal the magnitude of man's ignorance when laws, relationships, or explanations are not forthcoming. By means of analytical and comparative techniques and the procedures of inductive or deductive reasoning, one searches for conclusions which will facilitate forecasts of events involving similar combinations of factors. This is all that can be asked of any science. It is what must be asked of geography as a science and be sought in the teaching of geography.

The view from the ivory tower is sometimes obscured by the problems of educating school children. From infancy onwards students can learn to observe, describe, and classify, and they can be taught to improve their competence in each. Both teacher and learner encounter difficulties in developing the ability to analyze, reason, and explain. However, this is where the principal contribution of geography as a science begins. If geography is not merely a collection of classified facts, neither is it a set of unsupported generalizations. Properly taught, geography trains students in critical thinking, in the evaluation of the significance of facts, in the organization of ideas, and in the application of the methods of science.

Because of its concern with both man and his natural environment, geography shares much common ground with both the natural and the social sciences. It draws widely but selectively upon the stores of knowledge as well as the basic concepts of other fields. The ultimate objective of geography is not the study of a single category of natural or cultural phenomena, but the investigation of all characteristics of man and place which bear upon man's interrelations with place. This approach in no way excludes the treatment of particular relationships among cultural and natural factors by any of the systematic sciences. The geologist can legitimately claim a bridge to economics in the study of economic geology; the botanist has clear interests in such sciences as meteorology, geology, pedology, or hydrology in the study of plant ecology; the archaeologist must venture into geology on the one hand or anthropology on the other to interpret prehistory. What geography seeks is an understanding of the composite man-land relations at a place or in a region, the differences from place to place, the changes through time, and the interactions among places or regions. In this sense geography is an integrating science of place.

Thus defined the task is formidable. For how can one comprehend all facets of area and culture and formulate sound generalizations? Like other sciences, geography has to be subdivided into manageable parts. A detailed study of any one of the parts leads inevitably to specialization. Specialized investigation of geographic relationships may be likened to the solution of a jigsaw puzzle. By turning one piece of the puzzle slowly and testing it in relation to other pieces, one is able to achieve a fit. A detailed analysis of landforms, for example, is an appropriate part of the geographic study of a region, for one cannot interpret the significance of land forms in the natural environment of man without understanding the landforms themselves. Similarly, the facts of location, climate, water, soils, vegetation, and mineral resources are needed to complete the picture of the natural environment.

To return to the analogy, one need not proceed entirely at random. Just as the pattern of the puzzle lends valuable clues to selection, and the shapes of the pieces considerably reduce the possibilities for matching its elements, so in the study of geography one seeks the broad patterns as they are represented by combinations of the constituent elements. The pattern may emerge from the arrangement of a great number of elements, or it may be outlined in advance as an hypothesis and tested to determine whether it will actually accommodate observed facts. In either case, the "overriding problem" of geographic science is a fuller "understanding of the vast system on the earth's surface comprising man and the natural environment."[1] In contrast to the systematic microsciences which probe such puzzles as the structure of matter and energy, the origin and nature of life, or the basis of thought, geography organizes the facts of space, time, matter, and life around the theme of man in his natural setting. Geography is a macroscience. Whereas the microsciences seek an understanding of things in ever greater detail, geography strives toward an integrated view of the whole. Its techniques, therefore, frequently involve reducing the scales of space and time rather than enlarging them. S. W. Wooldridge has stated, ". . . geographical method is an antidote to the vice of exclusively analytical thinking."[2]

GEOGRAPHY AND THE NATURAL SCIENCES

The subdivisions of geography with the closest relations to the natural sciences are those that make up physical geography. They are more than a mere collection of systematic sciences. Their unity arises from their common objective — to understand the earth as the home of man; thus unified, the whole is greater than the sum of its parts. "Physical geography steps across the boundary of any earth science if there is material on the other side needed for the understanding of place."[3] It may be useful to remind ourselves that arbitrary divisions of knowledge into separate fields

---

[1] Ad Hoc Committee on Geography, *The Science of Geography* (Washington, D. C.: National Academy of Sciences, National Research Council, 1965), p. 1.

[2] *The Geographer as Scientist* (London: Thomas Nelson, 1956), p. 30.

[3] L. Kennamer, Jr., "The Place of Physical Geography in the Curriculum," in Preston E. James (ed.), *New Viewpoints in Geography* (Washington: National Council for the Social Studies, 1959), p. 213.

are products of human ingenuity, conceived for purposes of convenience. Physical geography attempts to regather fragmented knowledge around the concept of unity in the natural environment by focusing attention on the composite of elements that give character to place. It does not purport to integrate subject matter disciplines, each with its own approach to knowledge; rather it integrates facts and concepts in a spatial context.

The commonly recognized branches of physical geography are geomorphology (sometimes equated with physiography), climatology, soil geography, biogeography, and hydrology. Less well defined branches are the geography of oceans, mineral geography, and geodesy. Each of the subdivisions of physical geography is a connecting bridge to the natural sciences. Each employs scientific techniques. Each holds concepts involving areal distributions, spatial interactions, and succession through time. Inevitably the question arises, why cannot the facts of the physical environment be accepted as observed, leaving the task of explanation to the appropriate related fields? On a philosophical plane the question is hardly germane. Geography is concerned with the *why* of things as well as the *what* and *where,* and the physical geography of the earth can be studied in its own terms and for its own sake.[1] On more practical grounds geographers have had to engage in the search for explanations of more or less isolated physical phenomena in order to provide the type of information needed in the solution of problems that are more central to their field. There is a grave danger that axiomatic acceptance of landforms, climate, or other elements of the physical environment may lead to misinterpretation of their relations among one another and to man. Human "response to the environment cannot be evaluated definitively in the absence of accurate, detailed knowledge of the environment itself."[2] Wherever man is involved as an agent of change, genetic studies are firmly rooted in the center of geographic science.

A brief examination of the major subdivisions of physical geography will indicate their scope and their relative position between the core of geography and the array of systematic sciences that deal with particular groups of natural phenomena. Geomorphology, the study of landforms, shares the facts and concepts of geology, especially those that treat the surface of the land. It has been called "the historical geography of the physical landscape."[3] Its explanations lead in the direction of historical geology, stratigraphy, and geological processes. Its interpretations in terms of man converge with cultural geography in the examination of regions,

---

[1] J. Leighly, "What Has Happened to Physical Geography?" *Annals Association of American Geographers,* vol. 45 (1955), p. 309.

[2] Ad Hoc Committee on Geography, *op. cit.,* p. 22.

[3] S. W. Wooldridge and W. G. East, *The Spirit and Purpose of Geography* (London: Hutchinson's University Library, 1951), p. 90.

where we recognize the increasing role of man in altering the land surface.

Climatology lies on the frontier between meteorology and geography. On the side of meteorology it delves into the processes of the atmosphere that produce weather and the resulting climate. In the direction of geography it is concerned with the distribution of climatic factors in space and in time and their relationship to man's activities. Its scope includes those activities that modify climates, if only on a microscale. Thus, physical climatology is intimately related to meteorology whereas regional climatology is nearer the central theme of geography. But the former is no less useful in the solution of geographic problems. Applied climatology implies many connections in such special subfields as bioclimatology, agroclimatology, or industrial climatology. Studies of climatic fluctuations bear directly upon the concepts of change and succession both in cultural and physical geography.

Biogeography links the distribution and ecology of plants and animals with physical geography on the one hand and biology on the other. Although in its widest sense biogeography would include human geography, in practice it is usually confined to the study of plant and animal geography.[1]

Biogeography merges into applied aspects of forestry, agrostology, agronomy, pathology, and conservation. Cultural effects on the natural environment are perhaps more evident in biogeography than in other branches of physical geography, for it is comparatively easy to observe and map the results of deforestation or the grazing and plowing of grasslands. Indeed, it has become increasingly difficult to identify "natural" plant communities that are unaltered by man, and many wild animal species have undergone changes in both numbers and extent of habitat. The significance of succession with changing ecological relationships is a dominant theme of biogeography.

Soil geography obviously connects physical geography with soil science or pedology. The soil geographer seeks patterns of distribution as well as relationships between soils and other factors, both cultural and natural. The pedologist's major interests are origin and composition. In its applied phases soil science enters into such fields as agronomy, ecology, and engineering. Like biogeography, soil geography has a concern with man as an agent of change and with change as a factor in a dynamic natural environment.

Hydrology deals mainly with the waters of the continents. Hydrologists have partitioned their field into special studies of ground water (geohydrology), rivers (potamology), lakes (limnology), and ice (cryology) and

---

[1] Wooldridge and East, *op. cit.*, p. 57.

have called upon meteorology and climatology for aid in understanding the hydrologic cycle. Almost every science has direct or indirect interests in water. Viewed as a resource, water is an especially pertinent topic for geography. The regional approach, for example, has proven highly effective in the investigation and management of water resources over entire river basins.

Although there is no justification for the restriction of geography to the study of land areas, few geographers have pursued the study of oceans either as a topical or as a regional specialty. Nor have oceanographers widely adopted the geographic point of view.[1] Physical geography gives some attention to waves, currents, tides, and the effect of oceans on the terrestrial heat and moisture balances, but a distinctive field of "oceanographic geography" has not been established. However, oceans as sources of water, food, and mineral supplies are becoming increasingly important subjects of geographic study.

Mineral geography is treated more often in the context of economic geography than as a branch of physical geography. Mineral deposits "play little or no role in any integration in which man is not included, for they are 'resources' only for man. . . . Hence, it seems peculiarly arbitrary that in many texts the discussion of mineral industries and mineral deposits should be separated."[2] If a field of mineral geography exists even theoretically within physical geography, its position is in need of clearer definition.

Geodesy deals with determination of earth shape and size as well as measurements and location on earth. It draws upon astronomy and mathematics, and contributes much to the techniques of cartography. Some geographers designate certain aspects of geodesy and astronomy as mathematical geography.

In summary, each of these subfields represents a link between one or more of the systematic sciences and the study of the physical environment as the home of man. Taken together they generate a formidably complex mosaic of concepts and interrelationships. As science reveals new knowledge, and as human societies change, the degree of complexity increases.

The "big" picture does not become less important simply because it becomes more complicated. If a liberal education involves anything, it must certainly involve an attempt to understand man and the world in which he

[1] C. J. Burke, "The Geographic Study of Oceans," in Preston E. James and Clarence F. Jones (eds.), *American Geography: Inventory and Prospect* (Syracuse: Syracuse University Press, 1954), p. 411.

[2] Richard Hartshorne, *Perspective on the Nature of Geography* (Chicago: Rand McNally, 1959), p. 76.

lives. Physical geography as a part of geography should contribute to this understanding.[1]

GEOGRAPHY IN THE SCIENCE CURRICULUM

In the early years of this century physical geography and geology were regular offerings in the high schools, but biology, chemistry, physics, and general science (the latter sometimes including small portions of geology and physical geography) later came to dominate the secondary school science curriculum. In the colleges combined departments of geography and geology were common, and a few have maintained this close association. As geography underwent a marked shift in emphasis to the study of man it was merged into, or in many instances submerged in, the social studies at the public school level. Ironically, at the same time, social scientists began to appreciate the physical bases of geography as something "associated with their subjects of study, yet generally beyond their competence to treat."[2] The result has been a recognition of geography as an earth science by historians, anthropologists, or economists but as a social science by natural scientists. It is probably not far from the mark to state that today as much physical geography is taught, however inadequately, in the social studies as in so-called earth science or general science. There has been an unfortunate tendency to equate earth science with geology. Consequently a great deal of subject matter, certain useful concepts, and alternative points of view have been lacking.

During the last decade encouraging developments in geography and earth science programs for the secondary schools have occurred. The High School Geography Project has been concerned with the development of teaching units for geography as a separate subject. The units treat conceptual themes and incorporate problem solving approaches to a wide range of subject matter. They signal a trend away from the dispersal of geographic learning among units in earth science and social studies in a manner that has, in the past, virtually destroyed the basic spatial framework of geography.

In the Earth Science Curriculum Project groups of specialists from the fields of astronomy, geology, geophysics, hydrology, meteorology, oceanography, and physical geography have been engaged in preparation of teaching materials for the high school level. It is expected that earth science will become an increasingly important part of science programs

---

[1] W. D. Pattison, "The Four Traditions of Geography," *The Journal of Geography,* vol. 63 (1964), p. 215.

[2] M. G. Wolman, "Physical Geography in the Liberal Arts," *Geography in Undergraduate Liberal Education* (Washington: Association of American Geographers, 1965), p. 54.

in the high schools of the nation. The earth sciences, if given balanced treatment, afford an exposure to areas of knowledge and approaches to science that have been long neglected. Physical geography can assume important responsibilities in achieving a better balance among both the kinds of subject matter and the concepts introduced.

THE CONTRIBUTIONS OF GEOGRAPHY

The contributions that any branch of science can make to education arise from the subject matter selected for study, the methods of study employed, and the conceptual framework established by the science. As previously described, geography shares a vast body of knowledge (subject matter) with a number of systematic sciences. The facts of location, areal distribution, spatial interactions, and temporal succession of phenomena may be treated in the contexts of various sciences. For example, the geodesist can bring mathematical precision to location; the distribution of soils is of concern to the pedologist; interregional movements of air masses claim the attention of the meteorologist; and changes in vegetation associations invite examination by the botanist. The major contribution that geography makes to education for better understanding of natural phenomena comes from its unified approach to those phenomena. It thus augments the teaching of the concept of unity in nature. It dramatizes the concept of place as part of a continuum in space and of the present as part of a continuum in time. It gives relevance to the here and now, a relevance based not only on the interrelations of natural phenomena but also on interactions between physical and cultural systems. Accordingly, one should not expect the contributions of geography to education in the natural sciences to be entirely divorced from those it makes to social science education, or, for that matter, to the humanities.

This does not mean that geography is a reconstruction of the ideas of other sciences. Geography assumes primary responsibility for teaching the fundamental spatial concepts of location, scale, and direction which are necessary to provide orientation. Questions of size, shape, and relative location cannot be ignored in any study involving the earth's surface. The objectives and tools of geography fit it especially well for treatment of these basic matters.

The concept of areal differentiation is likewise solidly implanted in the fabric of geography. No place has physical (or cultural) characteristics exactly like those of any other place. How much simpler, and how unexciting, geography would be if all places were alike. And how much more challenging other sciences become when the concept of areal differentiation is introduced. There is, however, a corollary concept: Physical and cultural elements exhibit similarities in different parts of the earth's surface, revealing a measure or order in their areal distribution. It is possible, for example, to group climatic, pedologic, or biotic phenomena into recurring world patterns and to treat areal associations of interconnected natural processes in the framework of ecosystems. "The actual pattern of ecosystems, however, is a compromise between the principle of regularity and the principle of irregularity."[1] Every educated person should have at his command a set of valid generalizations concerning the spatial arrangement of things on earth. This necessitates an understanding of concepts regarding land and water masses, landforms, climate, and natural resources — the physical bases of geography.

But geography's contributions to an understanding of the physical environment range far beyond compilation of static distribution patterns and the respective explanations. Geography treats also the relations among areas, or spatial interaction. The transport of vast amounts of moisture and energy by air masses; precipitation and runoff to the oceans; the work of water, wind, and ice in degradation and deposition; and the migration of plant and animal species are examples of processes involving spatial interaction. These and other natural processes of their kind are of first order importance in the study of physical geography. When man and his works are brought on the scene the drama of interchange across regional boundaries begins to take on its full meaning. Yet, one very important member of the conceptual framework remains. It is the concept of time.

Considered in its narrower, utilitarian sense of measurement and arbitrary determination, the concept of time can best be taught in the framework of physical geography, where it overlaps related concepts of earth measurement and earth motion, and where the ideal tools for its understanding — maps and globes — are at hand. A broader concept of time encompasses the succession of events in the constant process of change. In this sense time is one of the dimensions of geography. It is a dimension that intersects the space dimension at any place which we may choose for study. The geography of a place at a given time cannot be fully understood without knowledge of the changes of the past any more than it can be comprehended without knowledge of its areal relations with other places. Above all, the goal of scientific prediction cannot be attained without reference to events leading up to the present.

In addition to its major contributions to understanding of scientific concepts geography, when properly taught, affords training in a number of skills and intellectual processes. The reader will immediately think of map reading and the interpretation of symbols; and map making is one of the

---

[1] P. E. James, "A Conceptual Structure for Geography," *The Journal of Geography,* vol. 64 (1965), p. 293.

avenues to effective map reading. The student who has actually made a useful map has thereby engaged in observation, selection, interpretation, and the recording of data. If he has mapped data gained by field observation, so much the better for his training in a basic scientific skill. Outdoors is the obvious laboratory for certain kinds of geographic observation and experimentation, and the opportunities for problem solving in a setting of reality should not be bypassed. To the teacher who is accustomed to thinking of geography as a social study it may come as a surprise to learn that a good indoor geography laboratory is a scientific laboratory; that maps, globes, and relief models are scientific apparatus; and that the possibilities for demonstration and experimentation are innumerable, ranging from simple rain gauges or sundials to stream tables or models to simulate the effect of the earth's rotation.[1]

Written or graphic description, classification, and statistical manipulation are other skills of geography that lead in the direction of problem solving, the keystone of intellectual skills. Problem solving involves formulating the problem, suggesting hypotheses, gathering evidence, drawing conclusions, and checking conclusions. It calls upon skills in observation, interpretation, experimentation, critical thinking, and inductive or deductive reasoning. This is scientific method, in geography as in other disciplines. More than a set of formalized steps to be climbed in a lockstep order, it is an approach to inquiry.

The part geography can play in education for a scientific attitude is not confined to small scale problems nor to isolated skills. Such worldwide and complex problems as population growth, depletion of natural resources, or changes of climate are clearly within the purview of the subject, although they rightly demand the attention of many other branches of science. Research on complicated problems involving interrelated phenomena requires collaboration. Likewise, education for a scientific attitude toward problem solving calls for a concerted effort.

---

[1] For other examples see:

H. H. Flierl, "A Movable Date Line Chart," *The Journal of Geography*, vol. 62 (1963), pp. 175–177; L. Macomber, "Suggestions on Preparing a Movable Date Line Chart," *The Journal of Geography*, vol. 63 (1964), pp. 222–223.

R. M. Harris, *The Rand McNally Handbook of Map and Globe Usage* (Chicago: Rand McNally, 1959).

R. L. Ives, "Navigating with the Kamal," *The Journal of Geography*, vol. 60 (1961), pp. 268–273.

D. H. Lokke, "Teaching Clouds and Weather by Using a Shadow Box," *The Journal of Geography*, vol. 61 (1962), pp. 169–170.

B. L. Wills, "Coffee Can Aneroid Barometer," *The Journal of Geography*, vol. 59 (1960), pp. 421–423.

W. F. Wood, "The Dot Planimeter, a New Way to Measure Map Area," *The Professional Geographer*, vol. 6 (1954), pp. 12–14.

GEOGRAPHY AND THE OBJECTIVES OF SCIENCE EDUCATION

The objectives of science education offer a yardstick for testing the contributions of geography to education in the sciences. Does the study of geography lead toward the wider goals of science education? There have been many lists of objectives to guide teachers of science.[1] Although they may differ in details and organization, all have a common set of elements, usually incorporating desired gains in information, attitudes, habits, skills, and abilities. They can be summarized as follows:

1. To develop understanding of facts relating to space, time, energy, matter, and life.
2. To develop understanding of the concepts and principles of science.
3. To develop skills in observation, description, classification, interpretation, and experimentation.
4. To develop the ability to formulate and solve problems.
5. To develop an appreciation of man's environment in all its aspects.
6. To develop appreciation of the objectives of science and the work of scientists.
7. To develop vocational and avocational interests in science.

Insofar as geography may be regarded as an earth science, its educational objectives are remarkably compatible with those listed above. Those who view geography as a social science would, understandably, wish to focus more attention on cultural themes. In any case, the study of geography (or any other branch of science) is by no means qualified to achieve all these objectives completely and on its own. It makes significant contributions to each through the kinds of phenomena it treats, the concepts it espouses, and the techniques it employs. Its concern for spatial distributions, integrative viewpoints, and the significance of the natural environment to man place it in a unique position to complement the systematic sciences in their search for a better understanding of the earth.

The objectives of science education, and more particularly the objectives of geographic education, cannot be gained by a single exposure at some arbitrary grade level nor in a scattering through earth science and social studies units. To make a useful and lasting contribution to education, geography must be presented over a span of years as a "sequential development of increasingly difficult concepts,"[2] proceeding from the

---

[1] For a summary of several statements of objectives for science teaching see: E. D. Heiss *et al., Modern Science Teaching* (New York: Macmillan, 1950), pp. 26–29. See also: J. F. Newport, "Are Science Objectives Changing?" *School Science and Mathematics,* vol. 65 (1965), pp. 359–362; S. I. Boulos, "A New Look on the Goals of Teaching Science," *Science Education,* vol. 48 (1964), pp. 195–199.

[2] N. V. Scarfe, "Sequential Development of Increasingly Difficult Concepts Through the High Schools," *The Journal of Geography,* vol. 60 (1961), pp. 351–357.

known to the unknown, from the concrete to the abstract, from the empirical-inductive to the theoretical-deductive. Moreover, if the full potential contribution of geography to the educational program is to be realized, its concepts will have to be presented in their own right, combining both the physical and cultural aspects of geography in the study of earth *and* man. The total study of geography "as a way of looking at things" cannot be carved up and integrated piecemeal into other sciences without sacrificing the powerful and realistic integrating force that *is* geography. Geographers do not have to engage in soul-searching questions regarding the role of their science in human affairs. They can state a priori interest in and concern for the cultural implications of all natural phenomena as well as the implications to nature of changing culture.

27

Geography and its relation to the social sciences

Cultural traditions, domestic problems, and intellectual leadership have affected the nature of each social science and altered the emphasis, and thus the division of tasks, between the fields. We can, therefore, define each social science only by its core, not by fixing exact boundaries.

JAN O. M. BROEK

MANY GEOGRAPHERS BELIEVE that any comprehensive definition of geography includes some emphasis upon relationships between the physical environment — climate, landforms, water bodies, soils, minerals, plants, and animals — and man and his activities. Among man's many activities are those associated with his fundamental occupations, his material needs, and his political, social, and spiritual requirements.

Geography shows a definite influence upon man's efforts in meeting these requirements, but other disciplines, including the field of social science, just as surely make some contribution. Consequently, the teacher who examines today's world carefully will find that several subjects are related to and interrelated with world problems resulting from man's work upon the earth. In studying these relationships and interrelationships the teacher may discover geography involved with economics, history, political science, sociology, or all of them and more in a given local, national, or international situation.

The main purpose of this chapter is to examine a few national and international problems and to show how geography and the social sciences are interrelated in the various aspects of such situations. Each problem will be described in some detail and analyzed to point out the specific contribution associated with each discipline.

Only four national and international problems have been chosen for description and analysis, although their number is legion. The four include three short articles published in the local newspaper and written primarily to emphasize the place of geography in current events. They are "Sugar and Revolution in Hispaniola," "Gold Problems of the United States and South Africa," and "Climate: A Factor in Racial Unrest." "The Location of Delhi," was prepared for a class to demonstrate the relationships geography has to the social sciences.

SUGAR AND REVOLUTION IN HISPANIOLA[1]

The island of Hispaniola, which now includes the two countries of Haiti and the Dominican Republic, was the favorite isle of Columbus, and is one of many islands of the West Indies. For several decades in the latter part of the fifteenth and early portion of the sixteenth centuries, Hispaniola was the center of a growing Spanish empire. Here, Columbus founded the city of Santo Domingo, the present capital of the Dominican Republic; here his son Diego built a palace fortress where many famous Spaniards were stationed before they moved on to new discoveries and conquests. Cortes passed through archways of the fortress before he started on the journey to conquer Mexico; Balboa moved out from Santo Domingo towards the discovery of the Pacific; and Pizarro stopped at Hispaniola enroute to the subjugation of the Peruvian Incas.

It is doubtful, however, that Columbus, or any of the other well-known explorers mentioned above, would be happy with conditions in the island today; for the eastern two-thirds, the Dominican Republic, has been rocked with revolution; and the western third, Haiti, is far from either economic or political stability. Many causes have been suggested for past and present unrest; many may be responsible; but it may be worthwhile to comment briefly upon one that has received less publicity than others; and also upon a few other facts concerning the island and its people.

Dominican Republic · The Dominican Republic contains an area of 18,704 square miles, a little more than twice the size of Massachusetts; and the population of about 3,400,000 is approximately two-thirds that of the same state. These people live in a tropical country made up of three major east-west trending mountain ranges, the Cordillera Septentrional, the Cordillera Central, and the Sierra de Bahoruco. Among these mountain groups and along the coasts are valley and coastal plains trending in the same general direction as that of the highlands. One of the famous valleys is La Vega Real (The Royal Meadow), a lowland named by Columbus centuries ago. It is still known by that name today.

On the Vega Real and other Dominican plains, farmers grow several tropical crops, one of the most important of which is sugar. Sugar cane grows best in frost free temperatures averaging 70°F. or more and on locations with an average annual rainfall of 50 inches or higher; or with water supplied by irrigation. The Dominican physical environment qualifies well in

---

[1] E. B. Shaw, "Sugar and Revolution in Hispaniola." (By permission of the *Worcester Telegram*, Worcester, Mass., May 14, 1965.)

both climatic and topographic requirements for large scale sugar production; and it is the dominance of sugar in the Dominican Republic economy that was one of the important causes for the 1965 political instability. One may ask, how can this be?

For many years prior to 1965, sugar accounted for as much as half or more of the value of the Dominican Republic exports; and fluctuations in the price of that commodity were drastic between 1963 and 1965. In the former year, when world sugar supplies were low and shortages were feared, wholesale sugar prices rose in New York to a forty-three-year high of $12.60 per hundred pounds Caribbean port basis. But on May 6, 1965, the New York sugar market had declined to a price of $2.35 a hundred pounds F.O.B. Santo Domingo. The difference in the two figures is more than 10 cents a pound.

Price differences like the above can play havoc with the value of a country's gross national product; with profits of the farmers and the manufacturing plants; and with wages of their workers and others directly or indirectly dependent upon the country's most important export. All this makes for serious dissatisfaction among both employers and wage earners who are likely to blame the government for their economic trouble. What follows may be a revolution, such as that which began April 24, 1965. Of course, sugar was not the only cause responsible for the 1965 revolution; but geographers and others believe it to be one of the most important causes.

Haiti · Nearly two centuries ago, sugar was indirectly responsible for a revolution in the western third of Hispaniola, now Haiti, whose physical geography is quite similar to that of the Dominican Republic. In 1795, when Spain ceded western Hispaniola to France, the 30,000 white settlers held nearly 500,000 Negroes in slavery working on their sugar plantations. At that time sugar was a very valuable crop and much in demand in western Europe. Consequently, many European nations were anxious to own sugar producing colonies in the West Indies.

However, in western Hispaniola, the imbalance between white plantation owners and Negro sugar plantation workers of about fifteen to one made conditions ripe for a successful slave revolution. And in 1804, after rebellious Negroes had either killed their former white masters, or driven them out of the country, Haiti became the second American nation to break its ties with Europe, and the first Negro Republic in the world.

The question is sometimes asked why present-day Haitian population is almost entirely Negro, whereas the Dominican Republic on the same island and with the same general physical environment has as many whites, about 15 percent of the total population, as Negroes — there are also about 70 percent mulattoes. The difference in eighteenth-century land use on eastern and western parts of Hispaniola gives a large part of the answer.

Although some Negro slaves were used on the few colonial plantations in eastern Hispaniola, most of the land was utilized for grazing; and the number of Negroes was only a fraction of those employed on the western one-third of the island. In 1795, there were 70,000 whites in the eastern two-thirds of the isle and only 30,000 blacks. In Haiti, on the contrary, sugar plantations made large profits for French plantation owners who directed and controlled hundreds of thousands of Negro slaves recently imported from Africa. Thus, sugar not only was indirectly responsible for the Haitian revolution already mentioned, but also indirectly responsible for the racial character of the Haitian population.

The early nineteenth century revolution in Haiti and the more recent one in the Dominican Republic are only two of several occurring in the unsettled political history of the Caribbean in which sugar has played an important role. What the West Indies and all of Latin America need is to bring more diversity into the national economy; and to remove the heavy emphasis upon the production and export of only one or two major commodities.

Analysis of relationships · "Sugar and Revolution in Hispaniola" may be classified either with economic geography or political geography. Both are phases of human geography, which together with physical geography make up major divisions of the subject.

If one looks back at the opening paragraph in the chapter one will note that the definition for geography includes an emphasis upon relationships between the physical environment and man's characteristics and activities. Such a relationship is stressed in the paragraph describing the landforms and climate of the Dominican Republic and their suitability for raising sugar cane, a tropical crop. However, when the writer completes the description of this relationship and describes the great range of sugar prices between 1963 and 1965, he is drawing from the field of economics as it relates to his main story; for money and price are two important topics in any survey course in economics.

As the story proceeds, and the great drop in sugar prices becomes one of several causes of revolution, the description takes on a political tone, and shows some relationship to a topic in the field of political science. Thus the material on the Dominican Republic not only includes stress upon geography, but also geographic relationships with political science and economics; and there is also emphasis upon history in the two introductory paragraphs of the article.

History, economics, and political science also contribute to the geographic story of the early nineteenth century sugar revolution in Haiti; and a relationship to another discipline in the field of social science has been added — sociology. Although some geographers believe that geography working through climate and other features of the physical environment may influence racial differences and that some races are better adapted to hot, wet, lowland climates than others, the subject of race probably receives far more stress in sociology than it does in geography. At any rate race should be emphasized in teaching the geography of Haiti.

GOLD PROBLEMS OF THE UNITED STATES AND SOUTH AFRICA[1]

The United States and the Republic of South Africa are two countries well known for their gold; but problems of the two nations associated with the glittering metal are far different. In South Africa, the major difficulties are involved in the mining of a steadily increasing amount of gold, whereas the United States is worried about the depletion of a formerly much larger supply. Much has been written in the United States about the decline in the gold stocks of Fort Knox, but far less about increasing gold production in the Republic of South Africa.

In 1955, the United States gold supply had an approximate value of $22 billion, figured at the rate of the United States controlled gold price of $35.00 a troy ounce. During the week of March 15, 1965, the supply totaled only about $14½ billion, the lowest figure since 1938, or for more than a quarter of a century. What has caused this serious drop of approximately one-third of our Fort Knox hoard? The answer lies in the chronically unfavorable balance of international payments — foreign aid, both military and economic; the maintenance of thousands of military personnel overseas; the spending by millions of United States tourists in foreign countries — all these and other international payments have lowered our gold balance in spite of the favorable balance of our normal international trade. Moreover, our production of gold mined mainly in ten western states, Alaska, Arizona, California, Colorado, Montana, Nevada, New Mexico, South Dakota, Utah, and Washington is not nearly large enough to make up the deficit in international payments. In 1964, United States production, valued at slightly over $50 million, was the lowest peacetime output in more than a century and less than 3 percent of total world production. Over half of this small percentage, 51 percent, is recovered from gold ores found in the mother lode; 13 percent from placers (dredging from alluvial deposits); and 36 percent is a by-product of base metal ores, primarily copper.

Finally, our policy of buying and selling gold at $35.00 an ounce and maintaining free convertibility of dollars into gold at that price has accelerated American gold depletion. For example, several of the Common Market countries, especially France, a country that owes us billions of First and Second World War debts, have taken advantage of this situation and have exchanged millions of their surplus dollars for gold.

Gold in South Africa · In South Africa, better known for its racial apartheid policy than for its gold, the position of that metal is far different from that in the United States. In 1964, South Africa mined about 70 percent of the total world production, worth more than a billion dollars. This figure is over twenty times that annually produced in the United States.

The basis for such leadership came about eighty years ago when a part-

---

[1] E. B. Shaw, "Two Nations' Gold." (By permission of the *Worcester Telegram,* Worcester, Mass., March 27, 1965.)

time prospector stumbled onto the world's richest gold seam on a South African ranch near Lanlaagte, about five miles distant from present-day Johannesburg. Legend has it that the ranch owner's name was Witwater; and since the 1880's Witwatersrand, as the gold field is called, has been the source of 90 percent of all the country's gold. This eighty-year production of about 750 million ounces would bring about 25 billion dollars at today's gold prices, nearly twice the value of the Fort Knox 1965 supply.

Only a small portion of the Witwatersrand gold bearing rocks, laid down about a half billion years ago in an inland sea, now appear at the surface; and for many years the South African gold miners have descended to great depths as they follow the geological dip of the gold seam thousands of feet into the earth. In fact, several of today's mines go down 10,000 feet or more, some of the deepest mines on earth, where rock temperatures reach over 100°F. Here in order to protect miners from phthisis and silicosis, cooled and moistened air is forced into the area where the men are working.

Low-grade ore is another serious problem which South African gold producers face; but scientists discovered the cyanide process of separating metal from the rocks by a chemical reaction. This invention made valuable large amounts of Rand ore which were previously considered worthless. To give an idea of what is meant by low-grade ore, recently 0.2005 of an ounce of gold was recovered from each ton of ore.

Finally, labor has long been a serious problem. One of the earliest attempts to solve the difficulty prior to 1900 was the use of demobilized European soldiers, but this proved unsuccessful. In 1904, Chinese labor was introduced on a three-year indentured system. Although more than 50,000 Chinese were employed at one time, they were all repatriated by 1910. Since then Negro workers have been recruited and now make up a large percent of the mining labor. In 1961, South African mines employed a total of about 50,000 Europeans and over 400,000 non-Europeans, most of them Negroes.

Outlook for the future • What is the future of gold in these two countries? The answer lies in several variables for both nations. In the United States pressures from the government are slowing foreign investments and loans by United States corporations and banks. A strong drive is on to increase exports over imports. Foreign aid has been cut; and the limit of American tourist purchases in foreign lands without penalty has been lowered. These changes may help restore some of the Fort Knox gold; but United States bankers say that a real build up will not occur until there is a rise in United States interest rates.

In South Africa, gold production is likely to increase until 1970 at least, considering the planned expansion in several of the newer mines, and the activating of mines now in the developmental stage. After that date, increases may depend upon several factors, among which are the following: (1) the cost of mining has increased and represents an enormous outlay for each new mine. For example, between 1957 and 1963 more than 100 million dollars were spent on one mine before an average of 200,000 tons of

ore a month could be brought to the surface. (2) Even to bore an explora-
tory hole to depths of 10,000 feet or more costs at least $100,000; and many
millions have been spent during the past decade on unsuccessful exploration. (3) Finally, the national and international pressures on a government
supporting the apartheid racial policy between about 3 million Whites and
approximately 14 million Colored are always explosive; and should a political revolution take place, gold mining investments could be confiscated, and
production under an unstable political regime might decline significantly.
Thus the future of gold supply in South Africa, like that in the United
States, is uncertain. But reasons for this uncertainty in the two countries
are entirely different.

Analysis of relationships · Shortly after the above article was published, an economics professor at Assumption College asked if there was
any geography in the article. Although it was agreed that the story showed
many relationships to economics, the writer also insisted that the emphasis was upon geography as well as upon economics, and that the study
belonged in the field of economic geography.

As to the geography included, it was pointed out that locations of the
gold mining areas in both the United States and South Africa were given
and that location is one of the most important factors of the geographical
environment. In fact, one geography instructor has always stressed that
he could give a definition of geography in less than ten words: "Geography
is a study of the attributes of place." The ways in which man mines gold
in both South Africa and the United States were either mentioned or
described geographically. Each of the methods of producing gold in the
United States — from the mother lode, from placers, and from by-products
of mining other metals — is related to the ways in which the gold occurs
in the earth. In short, there is a relationship between man's activity of
mining gold and the physical environment in which the metal occurs. In
South Africa, emphasis was placed upon the great depth at which the gold
is found and on the adjustments that man makes in reaching and surfacing
the ore; and also on the necessity of maintaining healthful conditions while
engaged in these activities in order to avoid contracting serious diseases.
Note how closely these examples of relationships between man's activities
and the physical environment conform to the definition of geography.

Of course the gold story leans heavily upon relationships between geography and economics. There are economic relationships in the labor problems; costs of mining and processing the ore; methods of obtaining finances
to establish mining corporations; the imbalance of international payments
as it affects United States gold supply; and the maintenance of a stable
gold price and dollar convertibility into gold.

Relationships to other disciplines in the social science field besides
economics are less evident, but a few are included. It can be argued that

topics of international payments, maintenance of a stable national price for gold, and the convertibility privilege of foreign dollars into gold all belong in the field of political science as well as in economics. Moreover, South Africa's apartheid policy is a matter of national control and consequently that study also belongs to political science. The article includes relationships between the physical environment and man, between geography and economics, and between geography and political science.

THE LOCATION OF DELHI

Many geographic conditions associated with the location of Delhi made it a good place for the capital long used by the early conquerors of India. The following study is concerned mainly with a brief examination of these conditions and with showing their relationships to activities of the armies invading India from the dry lands to the northwest.

Delhi is located at 28° 54′ N and 77° 13′ E, on the right bank of the Jumna river, a tributary of the Ganges. This location is near the western end of the Ganges Lowland where it approaches the eastern terminus of the Indus Plain. Its latitude is similar to that of New Orleans, Cairo, or Shanghai.

The Ganges Lowland, on which Delhi is located, is the seat of an ancient civilization. With alluvial soil, subtropical temperatures, and an adequate rainfall for most crop agriculture, the physical environment favors sedentary farming — a type of farming which has supported a dense population for centuries. The Indus Plain to the west has soil and temperature conditions favoring a settled agriculture, but the rainfall is not as much or as dependable as that of the Ganges area; and until irrigation developments took place in the nineteenth century, this plain was not utilized as it is at present.

The invasion route of the early conquerors moving into the Ganges Lowland from the northwest was along what might be called a corridor, comprising in part the northern portion of the present-day Punjab. To the north of the corridor were the high Himalayas; and to the south were the Thar Desert and a complex of lower mountains and plateaus. To reach this corridor from the Iranian upland, the invaders usually followed two natural passageways — the one over the lofty but narrow spine of the Hindu Kush, down the Kabul Valley and over the Khyber Pass to the crossing of the Indus a little beyond Peshawar; the other through Herat and Kandahar around the ends of the Sulaiman and Kirthar ranges through the Bolan Pass. The two passes just mentioned converge on the Punjab, which lies north of the Thar Desert and south of the Himalayas. These two natural routes to the Upper Indus and Ganges valleys were used by the invading armies of India's Moslem conquerors; and here in the Punjab entrance to the Ganges Valley stands Delhi, the many-times capital of India.

One might say that Delhi lies at the Ganges Plain end of a corridor extending northwest-southeast from the Iran Plateau to the Ganges Valley. The Indian section of the passageway is made up, for the most part, of the northern fringe of the Indus Plain, a relatively fertile and habitable area. This part of the corridor favored rather than repelled the early invaders of India, for it gave them food and water as they moved east to the more productive Ganges Valley. The fact that the region was one on which an invading army could live as it passed through was of vital importance in early days.

The invaders chose the Delhi location many times for their capital for other reasons too. At this point the conquerors were at the edge of the fertile Ganges storehouse where they could get an abundance of supplies; they were near enough to the dry Iran Plateau homeland where they could recruit armies when needed; and proximity to the rich Ganges Valley made it easy for them to collect tribute and taxes from the people they had conquered.

It should be noted that no capital of the Moslem invaders was farther east than Agra which served as the invaders' administrative center for several years. Possibly this city, a little over 100 miles southeast of Delhi, was too far advanced into the Ganges storehouse, too far away from the homeland recruiting grounds. Moreover, for twenty years, the capital was at Lahore, some 250 miles to the northwest of Delhi. The fact that it was located here but once, and for such a short time, suggests that it may have been too far away from the Ganges storehouse. The area around Delhi, in short, seems to have been at the right location between the main storehouse and the homeland recruiting grounds of the Moslem invaders.

Still other factors were important in the early choice of Delhi for a capital. The position on the navigable Jumna (boats at that time could go from Delhi to Calcutta) not only gave opportunity for water transport into the heart of the conquered peoples, but it also gave the invaders a site near an adequate water supply — a fact of considerable importance to these people from the dry lands of the northwest. The right bank location also offered superior advantages to that of the left. It saved a river crossing, a fact of no small importance; furthermore, the right bank of the Jumna at Delhi occupies higher ground than the left, a situation obviously more favorable in a plains location.

Not only was Delhi strategically located for the Islam rulers, but the British also chose the same location when they moved the capital from Calcutta to Delhi in 1912. In 1947, it became the government center for modern India, with the administration offices in a western-style section known as New Delhi. Its nodal location near many of the major regions of India is still vital, for this gives an obvious advantage to the business of government. With the coming of rail transport, Delhi's central location has favored the area as a focus for an important railway net, which connects with all major Indian provinces. Moreover, the distance from Delhi to the three major Indian ports, Calcutta, Bombay, and Madras, favors no one of them seriously over the others.

Finally, in any study of the choice of Delhi as a capital by the Islam invaders, attention should be called to the influence of these early invasions upon present unfriendly relations between India and Pakistan. Part of the cause for Indian hatred of Pakistan is associated with the knowledge of the cruelty, bloodshed, and slaughter of Indians during the Moslem control centuries ago. Indians have read this history carefully; and the mistreatment of their ancestors by the followers of Mohammed has left a legacy of hate so evident in the Kashmir fighting in 1965.

Analysis of relationships · The preceding short study contains many relationships between the physical environment on the one hand and activities of the invaders on the other. Causes for invasion, not even mentioned, involve limited food producing potential of Asia's southwestern dry lands located within striking distance of the more humid section of the Indian subcontinent. The topographic corridor, through which the invaders passed to the Ganges storehouse, gave them a maximum security from serious attack; there were high mountains to the north and a parched desert on the south. Moreover, the invaders could live off the land, at least off the eastern part of the corridor, when they moved east toward the Ganges Valley.

Again, numerous relationships are cited in the choice of Delhi for a capital. Among these are location on high land along the bank of the Jumna river, with adequate water supply. This situation was at an ideal distance from both the home recruiting grounds and the Indians who paid tribute and taxes to their conquerors. Other relationships could be added.

One may ask, what about geographic relationships with other disciplines in the field of social science? Invasion of India by Moslem armies began as early as the eleventh century when Mahmud of Ghazni started his conquest of India. In doing this he robbed and destroyed Hindu temples, put thousands of Indians to the sword, and raised pyramids of skulls taken from the people he called infidels. Even the Mogul Dynasty, which ruled India for two centuries and with Delhi as its capital for much of the time, had its Hindu baiters. For example Baber, who conquered the Indians in 1526, raised a hideous pile of over 50,000 Hindu skulls, imposed enormous taxes, and forced many to swear religious allegiance to Mohammed.

All the action briefly described in "The Location of Delhi" occurred long ago and rightly belongs in the field of history as well as geography.

Some say that the article is an example of historical geography with relationships between geography and history; or it may be classified as political geography, since, as Derwent Whittlesey aptly remarked, "the roots of political geography are buried deep in history." Still others may point to relationships associated with the events described in the preceding study and the modern friction between Moslem Pakistan and Hindu India. Considered from this standpoint, the article may be related to current events and world affairs, two relatively new disciplines belonging to the field of social science. Thus there is good evidence that "The Location of Delhi" may be related to history, political science, current events, and world affairs — all belonging to the social sciences.

CLIMATE: A FACTOR IN RACIAL UNREST[1]

How could a humid subtropical climate and a Connecticut Yankee contribute to racial problems in the United States? Some may doubt that they had anything to do with the late 1960 riots, but geography and history suggest that they did.

The humid subtropical climate of the southern United States has been an important geographic factor in the encouragement of cotton farming in that region for more than a century. The South's long summers provide a growing season of at least 200 days, with relatively high temperatures and freedom from frost. There is well distributed rainfall averaging 40 inches or more annually, an amount of moisture more than adequate for the cotton plant to mature properly. However, even with these favorable growth conditions, cotton needed help from a Connecticut Yankee to assure its long domination of southern agriculture.

Why? Because removing seeds by hand from the cotton fiber was an extremely time-consuming job. The cost of labor, even slave labor, was too great for export of the fiber to the European market. Until the Connecticut Yankee applied his genius to the cotton-seed separation problem, rice and tobacco remained the leading export crops of the South. In fact, cotton growing and cotton export really began to expand in 1793 when Eli Whitney invented the cotton gin. This Connecticut machine made seed separation easy and southern agriculture profitable. Moreover, about the same time that Whitney produced the cotton gin, Northwest Europe was improving textile machinery and demanding more exported cotton from the humid subtropical South.

Associated with the commercial demand for the fiber and the consequent expansion of cotton farming, was the rapid increase in the use of West African Negro slaves purchased by southern planters. More laborers were needed to plant, weed, and pick cotton. Many southern ports, especially Charleston and Savannah, became import cities for the slave traffic.

---

[1] E. B. Shaw, "Climate: A Factor in Racial Unrest." (By permission of the *Worcester Telegram*, Worcester, Mass., April 17, 1968.)

White plantation owners, most of them descendants of North Europeans who lived in a cool temperate climate, were adverse to hard labor in the hot, humid, southern summers. Negroes, coming from a hot, humid African climate quite similar to the humid subtropical southern summers, could adjust more easily to hard work in the cotton fields than could the whites of North European ancestry. Even before the expansion of cotton farming in the South, slaves were used on the rice and tobacco coastal plantations of the southern colonies. But the Whitney invention made cotton more profitable than tobacco and rice and increased the use of African slaves significantly.

Areal spread of cotton · Territorial expansion of the United States also extended cotton farming and slavery from the Atlantic coastal fringe far into the interior of the continent. The Louisiana Purchase and the consequent opening of the fertile flood plains along the Mississippi River accelerated the western movement of cotton growing by settlers; so did the separation of Texas from Mexico, and the later annexation of the Lone Star state to the Union. It is true that cotton's westward movement was slowed by Indian uprisings in western Georgia, Alabama, and Mississippi, but these delays were only temporary. In short, by the time of the Civil War, only a little over a half century after the invention of the cotton gin, cotton and slavery dominated southern agriculture from the Atlantic Seaboard to western Texas.

The Civil War · The difference between northern and southern viewpoint on slavery was one of several causes of the Civil War. During that conflict, Lincoln's Emancipation Proclamation legally freed the Negroes, but it never gave them full rights of citizenship. For decades, most of them remained economic slaves to the plantation system of the South. Thus legal freedom without economic liberty may have deepened the already significant racial problem.

Two conditions unrelated to climate were important in the large-scale migration of Negroes from the South: (1) mechanization of the southern cotton plantations and (2) better job opportunities in the urban North during World War II.

Summer riots · If climate influenced the expansion of cotton growing and increased importation of Negro slaves, it also influenced the riots of the descendants of former slaves. Over and over again in the late 1960's the American people read or heard dire predictions about long hot summers. These unpleasant seasons encouraged Negroes to swarm out of their ghettos to engage in burning, lotting, and shooting. Those seeking to control the riots prayed for rain — a climate factor which can slow riots and help put out the fires.

Thus climate remained a geographic factor in racial problems even in the late 1960's. However, the geographer would be the first to admit that climate is not the major cause of our racial difficulties; that major cause is the refusal of many people to accept all men as brothers, whether their skin is white, black, yellow, brown, or any combination of shades.

Analysis of relationships · Surely all geographers will agree that climate is one of the most important elements of the geographic environment. In the preceding study, the author describes the climate of the Old Cotton Belt of slavery days and the relationships between climate and cotton growing. He contrasts the climate of the South with that of northern Europe and compares the former with that of West Africa, the homeland of Negro slaves brought to the South. The areal spread of cotton growing is discussed, a description that brings in the geographical factor of location. And finally, a geographic touch is added by showing relationships between hot summers and Negro riots.

However, the study is not all pure geography. It is necessary to add history to show the influence of Eli Whitney upon the expansion of cotton growing and slavery. Economics becomes significant with the mention of exports and profits. The area of political science is touched in comments on the Louisiana Purchase, the annexation of Texas, and the Emancipation Proclamation.

Finally, in the title of the article the author mentions a subject important in sociology and psychology, "Racial Unrest." Again in the final paragraph he admits that it is necessary to call on other disciplines in the social sciences before any answer can be given to the subject of racial problems in the United States. Thus, throughout the study, relationships are evident between geography on the one hand, and several of the social sciences on the other — history, economics, political science, sociology, and psychology.

CONCLUSION

Possibly some will disagree with the author's belief in the importance of geographic relationships stressed in the opening paragraph of the chapter. If so, this is not surprising; for there is always a difference of opinion — sometimes expressed violently — in a democratic society. More than thirty years ago, there was little definite agreement among geographers upon a comprehensive definition of their subject. In the September 1934 issue of *The Journal of Geography* A. E. Parkins gave the results of a poll he had taken among his colleagues and called his study "The Geography of American Geographers." Nearly three dozen definitions were cited; those showing considerable similarity were classified into four or five groups.

In spite of these and present differences about a geographic definition, the study of geographical relationships lies at the heart of the subject. The good teacher will stress such an approach, especially in the elementary grades. The ability to stress such relationships properly will depend to a considerable degree upon the educational background of the instructor. This background should include survey courses in the physical sciences such as geology, climatology, botany, and soils as well as similar surveys in the social sciences such as history, economics, political science, psychology, sociology, and anthropology. Obviously all of us do not have the opportunity to acquire such a rich scholastic background when we first start teaching geography. Thus, if a teacher has been unable to include these courses in his early collegiate training, he can improve his teaching greatly by reading survey texts on his own. Whatever the way used to obtain this background, the teacher will find it extremely useful in presenting a well rounded approach to geography — a subject whose many aspects provide clear relationships to both physical and social sciences.

28

Geography in the space age

Come, my friends, 'tis not too late to seek a newer world.

ALFRED, LORD TENNYSON

D O WE, AS TEACHERS, realize that probably most of our students will be living during at least a part of the twenty-first century? Are we preparing these students to live and participate in the activities of this rapidly changing world? Has the curriculum of our schools been adjusted to take these factors into account, or is it still in the same condition it was ten or twenty years ago? The boys and girls, young men and young women, in our schools and colleges today must be educated for life in a constantly and rapidly changing society, "for life in a global society, for life in an affluent society, for an age that has urgent need for all its human resources, for life in an urban society, for an age in which survival depends on man's ability to learn to live with his fellow man, and for an age of increasing pressures to reform."[1]

It is absolutely essential that we, as teachers, fully realize that everywhere, every day the world changes. In ages past the change was not so rapid as today, but occurred just as assuredly and as definitely. People in all parts of the globe are reaching for that which they believe will make life more worth living, that which will give greater happiness. "They want something that will give them a greater sense of personal worth, more freedom, more recognition. Today the entire world is in a great revolution, for not only are the patterns of the past being broken up, but there is also a never ending struggle to find new ones for the future."[2]

---

[1] W. B. Ragan and J. D. McAulay, *Social Studies for Today's Children* (New York: Appleton-Century-Crofts, 1964), pp. 52–53.

[2] J. W. Morris, "An Age of Reality," *The Southwestern Social Science Quarterly, 46* (1965), p. 1.

GEOGRAPHIC ILLITERACY

Too much geographic illiteracy exists today in the United States in spite of the fact that this nation is involved in various types of activities on all parts of the earth. Some few years ago Dr. John W. Studebaker, when he was Commissioner of Education, pointed out this circumstance to the American public.[1] Since that date many newspapers, large and small (*Spokesman Review* of Spokane, *Press Enterprise* of Riverside, *Tulsa Tribune, Post-Intelligencer* of Seattle, *Washington Post, New York Times, Christian Science Monitor,* and others) have carried editorials and articles pointing up the need for better geographic education. Important magazines such as *Time, Life, Newsweek, Saturday Evening Post,* and the *Saturday Review* have published similar information, but not much has been done to improve the situation.

In some states it is possible for a teacher to secure an elementary certificate, or even a secondary school social studies certificate, without taking a course in modern geography. These poorly qualified teachers undoubtedly do the best they can, but too often they teach what was taught them by some previous grade school teacher who was also unprepared. In many instances, the teacher may ignore the subject since he knows very little about it and does not understand the importance of geography or the concepts that should be developed. This lack of understanding can easily make geography so boring that the pupil, in spite of his love for maps and his natural curiosity about the rest of the world and its peoples, soon loses interest in the subject.

Frequently the chief source of information available to the student is from out-of-date textbooks and old, worn out maps. As stated in Chapter 8, the making of a text is a long and difficult task. Sometimes parts of texts are obsolete before they come from the press. Teachers, then, must be constantly aware of changes in production, shifts in economies, activities of peoples, transformations of landscapes, and other physical and cultural situations. Much effort must be spent in keeping abreast of the times.

It is extremely difficult for most persons to replace ideas that have been "drilled" into them and to change their ways of thinking about certain regions or facts. For example, where is the American Cotton Belt? Is north up and south down? What is the top of the earth? What direction is at the top of the map? Why do many persons object when you state a river flows north?

The ideas most people have about the Cotton Belt are based upon what they learned about the South when studying the Civil War in a history class. The things they studied were true for the Civil War period and for

---

[1] P. Bacon, "Exit Sad Lament, Enter Golden Age," *The Journal of Geography,* vol. 65 (1966), pp. 252–253.

some time thereafter, but are they true today? It is still true that much cotton is grown in the Old South, but the modern Cotton Belt is in western Texas, Arizona, and southern California. Life in these places is a direct contrast to that of either the Old or New South. By keeping his information up-to-date the teacher can correct a common mistake and show the importance of the concept of change.

Up and down certainly have no relationship to direction. Too often people talk about going up north or down south. What do they do when they go east or west? A simple example of word meaning can correct this mistake which is made in some elementary texts. For example, if one travels northeast from Oklahoma City to Chicago he travels both up and down, but in Chicago he is down from Oklahoma City since the elevation of Chicago is less than that of Oklahoma City. In a like manner if he travels southwest to Mexico City the end result is up since the elevation of Mexico City is greater than that of Oklahoma City. Thus, up and down relate to nearness to the center of the earth, not direction. The Nile River, like every other river that flows north, is flowing down. Thus, the applied study of a few simple words can bring meaning and understanding to the concepts of direction and elevation.

How many times have you heard the statement that the top of the map is north? How many times have you read statements stating that the North Pole is at the top of the earth? As was carefully pointed out in Chapter 5, any single direction or several different directions may be at the top of the map. Most maps of North America will have west, north, and east all at the top. Look at the globe when it is placed with its axis correctly tilted 23½° toward the plane of its orbit. The Arctic Circle, not the North Pole, would be at the top if there is a top to a sphere. Since the earth rotates, this "top" would have to be a constantly changing location. If the students understand the concepts of "globalism" and "round earth on flat paper" such mistakes will not be made.

Many other simple and more complex situations dealing with climates, environmentalism, and distribution can be pointed out. Preston James has frequently discussed incorrect statements and word usage.

> Geographers for at least a hundred years have been pointing out that the highest temperatures ever recorded at the earth's surface, and also the lowest ones, are both in the temperate zones. The only truly temperate climates occur in the tropics.[1]

Another statement by James is as follows:

> Yet social studies classes in 1958 were taught that the world is divided

[1] P. E. James, "New Viewpoints in Geography," in Roy A. Price (ed.), *New Viewpoints in the Social Sciences* (Washington: National Council for the Social Studies, 1958), p. 53.

into just those zones of climate (torrid, temperate, frigid) first suggested some four centuries before Christ and proved to be inadequate 13 centuries after Christ. No modern discussion of world geography would mention these zones except as a part of the history of geography.[1]

In spite of the fact that these mistakes were pointed out almost a decade ago, one can still find the terms used in some recently published elementary and junior high school textbooks as well as a recent book discussing the teaching of the social studies.

During the past few years organizations such as the National Council for Geographic Education, Association of American Geographers, and National Council for the Social Studies along with several interested individuals, foundations, and papers have been working to combat geographic illiteracy. The federal government has recognized the problem with the establishment of NDEA institutes and fellowships. Much, however, remains to be done. Special attention must be given to teacher certification requirements, curriculum development, the training of more teachers for the elementary and secondary fields, and the improvement of textbooks. Also, the geographer needs to get his material before the public in such manner that no doubt is left in the mind of the layman about its practical application to world problems.

NEED FOR GEOGRAPHIC LITERACY

Geography can and should make an essential contribution to the education of American citizens. If properly taught, geography can help individuals to visualize more accurately world conditions so that they will be better able to evaluate world political and social problems. The subject presents a distinct point of view and brings natural science into the study of human affairs. Geography evaluates man's use of the earth. Should it not then be one of the chief concerns in the teaching of geography to make certain that the pupils "understand geography as a study of living things — of people who live and landscapes that actually exist."[2] In teaching such as this it will be necessary for the teacher to keep in mind that geography is constantly changing. As G. H. T. Kimble states it, "Geography isn't what it used to be."[3]

One of the prime purposes of geography, then, is to bring out the often crucial problems that men must solve if they are to live in growing numbers and at a higher standard of living on the earth, which now seems very

---

[1] P. E. James, *op. cit.*, p. 53.

[2] G. H. Gopsil, *The Teaching of Geography* (New York: Macmillan, 1956), p. 8.

[3] "Expanding Horizons in Our Shrinking World," in Lynn White (ed.), *Frontiers of Knowledge* (New York: Harper and Row, 1956), p. 116–131.

small to us. It is now possible to go round the world, not like Jules Verne's hero in 80 days, but in less than 80 hours by regular airlines, or in just a little more than 80 minutes as the astronauts in their space satellites have done.

The geography that is taught in today's schools should be a study of the modern world with its numerous complications. It must be a course that is alive, a course that deals with peoples and their problems in the inter-relationships that exist between them and their physical and cultural environment. Some basic geographic factors about the people of the world which might be studied are the following:[1]

1.   Most of the people of the world are nonwhite, the term white here referring to color, not race.

2.   Fifty-six out of every 100 persons in the world live in Asia, in fact one person out of every four in the world is Chinese.

3.   Most of the people of the world live in villages. It has been estimated that there are more than half a million villages in India and more than a million in China. Here is where basic changes in the life of these people must take place, probably starting with the water supply at the village well. Even in the United States more people now live in incorporated villages, towns, and cities than in rural areas.

4.   Over half of the people of the world live in what is known as "extended families," that is, married sons and their families live under the same roof as the parents or grandparents, or in compounds.

5.   Most of the people of the world are fishermen or farmers or both. To understand these people one must know something about subsistence agriculture throughout the world as well as have an understanding of the laws that govern the land use of the country.

6.   Most of the people of the world speak a language other than English. Language is often a problem within a nation as well as among nations. India has fourteen major languages with written literature dating back for centuries. Ghana with only five million persons has as least five major languages. The problem of communication is enormous.

7.   Most of the people of the world are extremely poor. A great majority live on an income of less than $100.00 per person per year. One of the most important factors to bear in mind about the world today is the disparity of income.

8.   Most of the people of the world are ill-fed, ill-housed, ill-clad, illiterate, and simply ill. These conditions are largely consequences of poverty that may result from a combination of geographic as well as economic factors.

It makes little difference if such items are studied as a part of a regional or political setting, or from a topical point of view, they should give the student a broad understanding of how specific human complexes are

---

[1] L. S. Kenworthy, *Guide to Social Studies Teaching* (Belmont: Wadsworth, 1962), pp. 17–18.

related to specific natural environmental complexes; how various types of human items are related to a given type of natural environmental complex in all the parts of the world wherein this type of natural environmental complex is dominant; how a given type of human adjustment is related to the varied natural environmental complexes in all the parts of the world wherein this human activity pattern is an identifying element; and how specific human complexes are related to the natural environmental complexes of regions outside the area wherein the adjustment is made. A study of geography should encourage students to think well of other people and to try to understand the way in which they react to difficulties. However, when the students study how men react toward each other the world over, the picture is indeed a gloomy one. Instead of sensible relationships, men fight, put up tariff barriers, discriminate, and develop prejudices. Certainly the historians will agree that much history is a long and sorry story of man's inhumanity to man. It was not strange, therefore, that the old League of Nations put geography as the first and most important study in the school for the development of the ideals for which it stood. It is not surprising that the United Nations through its agency UNESCO set up its first international seminar (in Montreal) for the study of geography as a means of developing international understanding. They believed that a proper understanding of other lands and the peoples living in them should develop tolerance, sympathy, and good will and promote the cause of peace. The fact that the great resources of the world are unequally distributed over the world means that men must trade to exchange goods and services if the welfare of mankind is to be maintained. International trade depends upon peace and good will, and again geography is right in the middle of such a study.

What then should be the place of geography in the modern curriculum? The social studies in the schools must consist of separate subjects — geography, history, government — and not the integrated mixture.

> If the key to knowledge and understanding lies in the structure of a given field of learning, then learning in geography will take place only when children learn to think in terms of the basic concepts of geography and to think as a practitioner of that discipline thinks. These objectives cannot be achieved so long as isolated facts having geographic significance are taught only as they are related to historic events.[1]

When each subject is taught as an individual discipline it can place the emphasis where it belongs. Each can use the other as background or reference material as needed. To say that one can teach the history of the

---

[1] C. F. Kohn, "Basic Concepts of Geography and Their Development," in Edwin Fenton (ed.), *Teaching the New Social Studies in Secondary Schools* (New York: Holt, Rinehart & Winston, 1966), p. 408.

United States by teaching its geography is just as incorrect as it is to say that you can teach the geography of this country as a by-product of the history class.

Let us use the Oregon Trail as another example of the differences in the historical and geographical points of view. The history teacher will use some geography, but not the geography of today. He must take his students backward into time, to present the people and their problems as they were long ago, and somehow cause the students to visualize the cultural and physical environment as it was at the time of the westward migrations. Certainly the geography of the Oregon Trail country in the 1840's was very different from what it is today. There were no paved highways — only dirt trails; no automobiles or airplanes — only wagons or carts pulled by oxen, poor teams, or human beings; no telephones, telegraph, radio, or television — only passing carriers who might take a communication back to the nearest town; no large fields of wheat or great ranches — only mile after mile of grasslands with possible large herds of buffalo or semi-desert lands with few signs of life; no cities or towns with industries, commerce, and culture — only a distant Indian camp or an isolated small fort. The history teacher actually is using historical geography only to help explain some of the difficulties encountered by the users of the Oregon Trail as the people of that time played their part in the westward expansion of the nation. The student studying the geography of the United States will be concerned with current land utilization. Why are ranches and large farms common? Why is irrigation so important? Why did towns and cities develop where they did? What influences do the landforms, climate, soils, and native vegetation have upon the cultural activities of the area and, above all, how has man adjusted the natural environment to his activities? Thus we see that the two subjects can supplement, but cannot replace, one another.

CONCLUSION

Certainly in this day of intercontinental missiles, astronauts, and in the not too distant future, interplanetary rockets, no one will deny the importance of knowing the modern peoples and places of our own planet. The United States has had a very fortunate history in large measure because of its very fortunate geography. During most of the years of its existence as a nation the people have had room for the expansion of a growing population, natural resources to supply this population, and intelligence enough to improve their situation through research, inventions, and an increasing use of inanimate energy. Through most of this period the nation has not had to depend upon other nations for the raw materials needed. Today, however, the people of the United States find themselves in a different geographical situation. This nation, like all the other nations of the world, is now in an interdependent rather than in an independent situation. The population continues to increase, but no large areas of suitable unclaimed land remain for expansion. The nation must use its land more intensively as many nations have been doing for centuries. Supplies of natural resources are being rapidly exhausted, so rapidly in fact that the government is stockpiling many from foreign sources in case of an emergency. Research and inventions have advanced to the point that certain items not available in this country must be imported if the United States is to continue to progress.

Considering these factors, it is indeed time that geography be placed in the curriculum in its correct perspective. Should not the teacher be especially concerned that the boys and girls in the United States understand the peoples in other countries? Can any subject achieve more in this aim than geography when geography is properly taught?

Index

Foucault pendulum, 118
Fractional scale, 61
France, 235
French Guiana, 203
Fuchs, Sir Vivian, 8

Ganges lowland, 322
Gary, Indiana, 190
Gaza Strip, 235
Geiger counter, 118
Generalizations 25, 26, 131, 134, 137, 169
Geodesy, 307
Geographic association, 10
Geographic publications, sources of 10–11
Geographic skills, 23–24, 292
Geographic societies, 9–10
Geography,
  as a science, 301–304
  objectives of, 312
Geomorphology, 30, 260, 305
Geoperipheral areas, 162
Germanic cultural area, 290
Globe, 35, 36, 37–51, 118, 129, 153, 266, 270, 310
  axial mounting of, 39, 43
  cradle mounting of, 39, 40, 42
  horizon ring of, 39, 42, 49
  physical, 38
  relief, 39
  slated, 39
Gold problems, 318–321
  analysis of, 320–321
  in South Africa, 318–319
  outlook for, 319–320
Goode, J. Paul, 11
Graphic scale, 61–62
Graphs, 147, 185
Great American Desert, 105
Great Britain, 61
Great circle, 40, 41, 43, 45, 47
Great Plains, 94, 270
Greenland, 187
Greenwich, 45, 50
Grid, 57
Group reports, 149–164
  ad hoc, 152–154
  continuing, 157–163
  techniques, 151–152
  utilization of, 150–151
  limitations of, 151
  values of, 150
Guayana, 203

Haiti, 316–317
Hall, Mary, 106
Harris, Chauncy D., 10
Hedin, Sven, 8
Hemisphere, 41–42
Heraclitus, 33
Herodotus, 5
Hettner, Alfred, 12
Hibbing, Minnesota, 145

Hindu Kush, 327
Hipparchus, 4
Hispaniola, 315–317
  and Dominican Republic, 315–316
  and Haiti, 316–317
  relationships in, 317
  sugar and revolution in, 315–316
Historical geography, 88, 257, 276–285
  conclusions from, 285
  implications of, 278–285
    for high school, 284–285
    for primary grades, 278–282
    for upper elementary grades, 282–284
  nature of, 276–278
History, 168, 317
Home community, 177, 179, 183–186
  and materials, 184–185
  and exchange of information, 185–186
  field trips in, 183–184
  and maps, 185
  pictorial and graphic information about, 185
  resource persons in, 185
  service projects in, 186
  surveys of, 184
Hong Kong, 228, 231
Horizon ring, 39, 41, 42, 49
Human ecology, 3
Human factors, 181
Human geography, 13
Human resources, 155
Humanities, 168
Hydrology, 305, 306–307
Hypsometric maps, 63
Hythergraph, 254

Ibn Batuta, 6
Ibn Haukal, 6
Idrisi; see Edrisi
Illinois, 173–175
Incas, 17
Inclination, 44
India, 91, 94, 228, 233, 324
Indic cultural regions, 290
Indo-Andean countries, 203
Indonesia, 231, 233
Informal evaluation, 138–139
Instructional aids,
  audio-visual, 112–128
  globe, 37–51
  maps, 52–65
  outdoor laboratory, 66–83
  pictures, 84–103
  textbooks, 104–111
Integrating science, 303
International Geographical Union, 10
Interrupted projection, 54
Intrazonal soils, 27

Iron ore, 190
  Mesabi district 141, 143, 145, 147
Isostatic imbalance, 30
Italy, 32

James, Preston E., 23
Japan, 228, 230, 231
Jefferson, Mark, 105
Jerusalem, 6
Julius Caesar 5, 52

Kabul valley, 322
Kamchatka, 61
Kant, Immanuel, 11, 20
  organizing principles of, 21
Kenya, 243
Key West, Florida, 190
Khyber Pass, 322
Kilometer, 41, 76
Klute, Fritz, 13
Korea, 231
Kosmos, 13
Kramer, Gerhard, 10
  mercator projection, 53
Kublai Khan, 6

Laboratory, 311
  A-V-T, 112–127
Lake Michigan, 190
Land and water distribution, 265
Land hemisphere, 42
Landform model, 118
Landforms, 29–31, 180, 266
  African, 240
  Anglo-American, 189
  gross relief features of, in U.S.S.R., 215–219
  and home community, 180
  and man-land relationships of Europe, 208
  and nature of the islands, 248–249
Landscape morphology, 3
Larksville, Pennsylvania, 145
Latin America, 162, 194–204
  and Central America and West Indies, 201–202
  and materials for developing understandings, 198–199
  objectives of, 194–197
  and South America, 203
  and suggested teaching procedures, 199–201
Latin cultural region, 290
Latitude, 40, 56, 57, 75, 262
Lesson plan, 129
Livingston, David, 8
Locations, 108, 166, 180
Locus, 45
Longitude, 40, 56, 57, 75, 266

and landforms, 266
pictures of, 94–98
scale of, 261–262
and vegetation, 267
Physical globe, 38
Physical map, 55, 154
Physical science, 301
Physical setting, 154–155
Pictorial information, 185
Picture scales, 91–94
Pictures; see Still pictures;
Moving pictures
Piedmont cities, 190
Pittsburgh, Pennsylvania,
190
Pittston, Pennsylvania, 145
Pliny the Elder, 5
Polar projection, 53
Political resources, 183
Political science, 317
Polynesia, 247
Pomponius Mela, 5
Pope Innocent IV, 6
Population,
of Asia, 227–230
characteristics of, 155
distribution and density
of, 158–159
growth of, 157–158
and Pacific Islands, 247–
248, 252
resources of, 159
and Soviet Union, 222–
223
world increase in, 158
Population associations,
in Asia, 228–230
Portland, Oregon, 191
Portolani sailing charts, 7
Possibilism, 14
Postlethwaite, S.N., 112
Power resources, 190
Preview,
of films, 85
Prime meridian, 57, 61
Problem approach, 167–170,
210
critical analysis in, 168–
169
and European geography,
210
hypotheses for, 168
pertinent information for,
167–168
solution of, 169–170
Problems,
for elementary classes,
170–171
and questions, 135–136
for secondary classes,
171–172
of teaching African
geography, 237–239
Process-centered objectives,
133
Ptolemy, Claudius 4, 6

Pythagorean school, 4
Pytheas, 5

Quebec, Canada, 191
Questions,
and problems, 135–136

Raisz, Erwin, 64
Ratzel, Frederich, 13
Real-life situations, 179
Réclus, Elisée, 13
Recreation,
in Anglo-America, 190
Rectification, 39, 43
Reference materials, 109–
111
Regional science, 3, 206, 208
Regional approach, 166–167
to Africa, 237–244
to Anglo-America, 187–
193
to Asia, 227–236
to Australia and Pacific
Islands, 245–255
to Europe, 205–213
to home community, 177–
186
to Latin America, 194–204
to Soviet Union, 214–226
Relief features,
of U.S.S.R., 215–219
mountains, 219
objectives in teaching
about, 215–216
plains, 216–218
upland areas, 218–219
Relief globe, 39
Relief models, 253–254
Resource persons, 185, 211
Rhodesia, 243
Rhumb line, 41
Richmond, Virginia, 190
Rio de Janeiro, Brazil, 153,
196
Riots,
summer, 325–326
Ritter, Karl, 11–13
Rocky Mountain Front, 190
Roger II, 6
Rome, Italy, 41
Royal Geographic Society, 10

St. Lawrence Valley, 191
Salt Lake Oasis, 190
San Diego, California, 191
San Francisco, California,
191
Bay area, 191
Santa Fe Trail, 191
Sauer, Carl O., 105
Scale; see Map scale
Scarfe, Neville V., 1, 24
Seattle, Washington, 41, 191
Seasons, 79–81, 263–264
Semitic cultural region, 290
Sequence of units,

for study of Europe, 207
Seven-year plan, 224
Shanghai, China, 228, 231,
322
Shape, 180
Shoemaker Map, 277
Silent filmstrip, 89
Singapore, 232
Single-concept loop, 88, 117,
118
Size, 180
Skills; see Geographic skills
Slated globe, 39
Slavic cultural region, 290
Slides,
35-mm, 89, 113, 116
preparation of, 121–124
Small circle, 45
Smith, J. Russell, 105
Social science, 18, 168, 301,
314–327
Société de Géographie de
Paris, 9
Socrates, 66
Soil, 26–27, 32, 181, 266,
305
Solar energy, 264–265
Solar time, 50
Solstice, 49, 79
summer, 79
winter, 79
Sorre, Max, 13
Sound filmstrip, 89
Sound track, 85
South Africa, 243, 318–319
South America, 54, 196, 203
suggested ideas for study
of, 203
South Asia, 228, 233–234
Ceylon, 233
India, 233
Nepal, 233
Pakistan, 233, 234
Southeast Asia, 228, 231–233
Cambodia, 232, 233
Indonesia, 231, 233
Laos, 231, 232
Malaysia, 232
Philippines, 231
Thailand, 232, 233
Vietnam, 232, 233
Southern hemisphere, 42
Southwest Asia, 234–235
Aden, 235
Qatar, 235
Saudi Arabia, 235
Soviet Union, 106, 214–226,
231, 234, 235
climate of, 219–221
economy of, 223
nationality in, 222
population of, 223
relief features of, 215–219
spatial concepts of, 214–
215
and transportation, 226